EX
LIBRIS

January 1990·New York, NY

Dear Reader,

It's Silhouette Books' tenth anniversary, and what better way to celebrate than to toast you, our readers. Thank you for your support these past ten years, for your invaluable feedback on what *you* feel is important in a romance novel, and for taking the time to bring home romance—Silhouette Romance.

We've got many special events planned for 1990, and our ongoing DIAMOND JUBILEE series is just one of them. To symbolize the timelessness of love, as well as the modern gift of the tenth anniversary, we're presenting readers with a DIAMOND JUBILEE Silhouette Romance title each month, penned by one of your favorite authors. And that's not all!

This *Diamond Jubilee Collection* that you're now holding in your hands is another part of our anniversary. This treasury contains three classic stories by authors who debuted in the Silhouette Romance line. Now, ten years later, their work can be enjoyed in all the Silhouette Books lines: Silhouette Romance, Silhouette Desire, Silhouette Special Edition and Silhouette Intimate Moments.

Wild Lady, Circumstantial Evidence and *Island on the Hill* were some of the first titles we published, and they helped to define the Silhouette Books tradition. And each month since we began in 1980, we've striven to bring you the best that romance has to offer—stories by authors who time and time again bring home the magic of love. We hope that you enjoy this book and all of the stories to come. Happy 1990!

Sincerely,

The Editors at Silhouette Books

DIAMOND JUBILEE COLLECTION

ANN MAJOR

ANNETTE BROADRICK

DIXIE BROWNING

DJC

Published by Silhouette Books New York

America's Publisher of Contemporary Romance

ISBN 0-373-83219-2

Printed in the U.S.A.

CONTENTS

To Nancy Jackson—for her enthusiastic and very expert help with this project

ANN MAJOR,
a native Texan, creates powerful tales that are filled with passion and intense emotion. During her career, this bestselling author has written over twenty stories for Silhouette Books. Ann Major was one of the premier authors to be published in the Silhouette Desire line, and readers have always loved her compelling, evocative stories. She lists traveling and playing the piano—especially work by the romantic composer Chopin—among her many interests.

Her upcoming books for Silhouette include: *Scandal's Child* (April 1990's *Man of the Month*, Silhouette Desire #564), "Santa's Special Miracle" (*Silhouette Christmas Stories 1990*), and *The Goodbye Child* (a *Man of the Month* book for 1991, Silhouette Desire).

"I feel that the best romantic literature is filled with love, humor and warmth, as well as with romance and adventure. It has been wonderful to be with Silhouette Books and write the kind of stories I love to read."

—Ann Major

Chapter One

The black-haired, black-eyed beauty smiled mockingly in the foot-high photograph on the society page of the *Corpus Christi Chat* beneath the sensational headline, "Oilman's Daughter Stranded at Altar." With trembling fingers, Kit gripped the paper even more tightly as she critically studied her own picture for a second time.

How had she managed that picture—the radiant smile, the sparkling eyes? The photograph depicted a young girl glowing with expectation at the prospect of marriage. Had she ever really been that girl?

She skimmed the article beneath. "Kit Jackson, daughter of wealthy South Texas oil operator, Howard Jackson, waited in vain last night for her bridegroom, Rodney Starr, to make his appearance..."

Oh! The paper made it sound so tragic! Everyone who read the article would think Rodney had deliberately stood her up! They would think that she herself was heartbroken! But it wasn't like that...

"If they only knew how relieved I really am," she said half-aloud. "If they only knew..."

"Relief!" Surely it was the sweetest word in the English language just as it was the sweetest sensation she'd felt for a long time.

She remembered the long months of tension that had preceded the events of last night. Her family and his pressuring them both into their decision. Once she'd agreed to marry him, plans for the grand, society wedding had been like an avalanche sweeping Rodney and her along. Neither of them had known how to stop things. Lavish parties, gifts, balls.... Occasionally across a crowded ballroom she'd caught an almost desperate look in Rodney's eyes, and surely he'd seen the same look in hers. She'd wanted to call the wedding off; she'd come close to doing it many times. But once the marriage plans had been set in motion, she'd lacked the courage.

Newspaper articles covering their engagement had made it sound like a fairytale marriage—the handsome heir to the Starr cattle and ranching fortune marrying the wealthy Jackson beauty.

She had never loved Rodney in the way a wife should love the man she planned to marry, although she was very fond of him. She had only drifted into a relationship with him on the rebound because of her devastating romance with the one man she'd truly loved.

Black print blurred and the paper fell from her hands to rest beside her untouched breakfast tray. The breeze gusting up from the bay caught its edges and they fluttered. She arose, clutching the wrought-iron railing that laced her balcony overlooking the grounds.

Beneath her billowed nine hundred yards of gaily-striped yellow and white canvas, the party tent the caterers had rented from some local outfit her father said was owned and run by a "brash young upstart" who'd insisted on being paid in advance for his rental, even from the Jacksons. As if the Jacksons were no better or worse than anyone else. She saw the rented tiki torches, the tables, chairs, the unused bandstand—everything set up with such care for the reception that had never been.

Last night came back to her. If she lived to be a hundred, Kit would never be able to forget it.

She'd dressed carefully—to be appropriately beautiful on her wedding day. She'd been swathed from head to toe in designer lace that scratched her flesh everywhere it touched. She'd been imprisoned in that stuffy dressing room with her mother, who mildly nervous at first had become frantic an hour later when there was still no Rodney. Kit, however, had had just the opposite reaction. When she was informed that Rodney was late, she'd felt the first glimmer of hope. Then when that first hour had passed without his coming, she'd decided that even if he did arrive she would have to summon her own courage and call the wedding off no matter how she disappointed and humiliated her mother and father before their society friends.

Two tortuous hours passed before Rodney called. By that time the hum in the sanctuary had grown to a deafening buzz. Kit's mother took the call in the minister's office and returned with the news she'd delivered with false brightness.

"Don't worry, *mi querida*..." Anitra Jackson had begun, lapsing, because she was nervous, into her native language, Spanish.

"Where's Rodney? What happened?" Kit blurted.

"There's been a little accident...a car wreck... Rodney's in the hospital...nothing serious...whiplash . . . He'll stay overnight in the hospital for observation . . ."

Kit's first concern had been for Rodney. What if he were really seriously injured? Her mother had at last managed to reassure her that his injuries were only minor. Relief had swamped her like a joyous flood, but she'd managed to conceal her true feelings from her mother. Dear Mother, she'd been so anxious that the wedding take place. Arabella Starr, Rodney's mother, was her dearest friend; a wedding linking their two families her fond dream.

"But, *querida*, we do have a problem of our own to face. The church is filled with wedding guests! What do we tell them?"

Kit had managed calmly. "The truth, Mother. I'll make the announcements to them now."

She'd stood before a thousand guests in the hushed sanctuary and somehow with legs weak from relief that she'd thought would buckle and send her sprawling—designer gown and all—but with a clear, sure voice, she'd told the crowd why Rodney hadn't come. Whiplash! She'd felt their skepticism, their pity for her. But she'd been too wild with joy to care. Let them think the worst of her! She was free! Never again would she allow herself to be swept along by the dictates of others. She'd put too many people to trouble as a result.

She flinched, sagging against the iron railing. She gazed beneath without really seeing the turquoise pool, the glossy red tiles of the cabana roof, the acres of sloping greenery, and beyond that the concrete sea wall and the glistening bay.

Suddenly she was shivering in spite of the blazing Texas sun. She moved restlessly inside her room and threw herself across the bed. The three-carat, emerald-cut diamond caught the sunlight and flashed its blue-white fire against the sprigged wallpaper. She remembered the day Rodney had slipped the ring on her finger. If only she'd refused it. How much simpler everything would have been.

How could she ever leave this room and face everyone who had worked so hard preparing for this wedding. Her parents, the Starrs, their friends.... All their time, effort, and money down the drain. She felt she'd used them all because she'd been too immature to stand up for herself.

Well, that would never, never happen again! It had only happened this time because of...of Ted. She swallowed something that was hard and painful at the thought of *him*.

Yes, it went back five years ago to him. She'd been a young and vulnerable eighteen, a college freshman in Austin when she'd fallen wildly in love with a man almost ten years her senior—Ted. He was in his last year of law school on the GI bill.

She'd loved him blindly until the last night she'd spent in his arms. The memory of that night was still vividly, horribly etched in her mind. Saxophone music had filled his small apartment with its husky sound. Ted had wrapped her so closely in his arms he'd seemed almost a part of herself. He'd drawn her down onto his studio couch, and she'd arched wantonly toward him because his kisses had filled her with a longing she'd never known before. But when his hands had gone to the zipper at the back of her dress, she'd suddenly realized she had to stop him. Sex was a physical and spiritual commitment she believed then and believed now she owed only to her husband. She'd run from his apartment, from him.... He had not tried to stop her. When she'd reached the safety of her dorm room, her telephone was ringing, but she'd been too badly shaken to answer it.

Later that night when she'd recovered herself, she'd realized how foolishly immature her actions must have seemed to him. She'd tried to call him on the telephone to explain, but when she'd called, he hadn't answered.

Kit would never forget the velvet-soft tones of Letitia's voice, purring sweetly when she answered Ted's phone, "He's in bed. Are you really sure you want me to disturb him?"

Kit had choked out some reply. Letitia was a girl Ted had dated briefly before he'd met Kit. Knowing that Ted had turned to Letitia after her own abrupt departure had hurt Kit deeply. She'd felt used...cheated.... She'd realized then that any woman could satisfy his needs—it didn't matter who. She had been no more than a conquest. This realization made her decide never to see him again. No matter how much she suffered, she was better off without such a man—however attractive he was, however impossible he was to forget. And she had not forgotten him!

She had refused Ted's calls. After all, what explanation could there have been for his behavior? Eventually she'd begun seeing Rodney, an old friend from her childhood. They'd drifted into a courtship. When they'd both graduated their families and friends couldn't understand why they weren't anxious to marry.

She'd allowed herself to believe that Rodney would make a good husband. After all they came from the same kind of backgrounds. He was very good with children. She'd almost convinced herself that they could achieve a happy family life together.

Last night when he hadn't shown up, she'd realized fully how wrong she'd been. She'd never wanted marriage to him any more than he had wanted marriage to her. They had had a comfortable friendship—that was all.

Ted...funny...even after five years it still hurt to think of him. She knew he lived in Corpus now although she'd never sought him out. It seemed odd to her suddenly that she hadn't run into him somewhere. Corpus wasn't really that large a town. Still, she had been away at college most of those years, and he was married to Letitia. Perhaps, after all, it wasn't so odd.

Why was she thinking of *him* again? Of the possibility of seeing him again? Long, sooty lashes squeezed tightly shut against her flawless, olive skin. If only she could shut him out of her mind and heart as easily as she could shut her eyes. But she couldn't. A vision that was all too real of him appeared before her. He was holding her tightly to him. Copper highlights glinted in his dark auburn hair. His blue eyes sparkled with love and tender desire for her. He bent his face to hers, his mouth claiming hers in a slow, deliberate kiss. She sighed heavily and opened her slanting dark eyes. Wistfully, she brushed her soft lips with a fingertip. She could still remember how wonderful his lips had felt. She wasn't over him. How could she have considered marrying Rodney when, incredibly, she still cared for Ted?

A fierce banging at her bedroom door disrupted the painful memory and equally painful realization.

Kit knew it must be her father, for no one else made that kind of noise this early in the morning in the house. Before she could answer, he let himself in.

He was as distinguished looking as always, dressed in immaculate, stiffly creased white slacks and a navy T-shirt open at the throat. Yachting attire. The race! She'd forgotten it entirely. But he hadn't.

He tucked his silver winged hair beneath a navy colored captain's hat—the final touch so that he looked what he was this morning—the debonair yachtsman. His gray eyes were on her—assessing.

"How're you feeling today?" He saw the pages of the newspaper on the thick pile of blue carpet—pages the wind had blown inside. He was bending over and retrieving the scattered pages. For a long moment his eyes lingered with a certain pride on her picture. "Guess I shouldn't have to ask." She was thankful there was no trace of sympathy in his voice. At least she wouldn't have to pretend with him.

"I'm doing all right."

Her answer caught him by surprise and he stared at her intently. "I can see that. I never did think Rodney was the right man for you in spite of the fact his father's an old friend of mine. Not much to the boy though, if you take away his ranch, thoroughbreds, those Santa Gertrudis, and that fancy car he drives."

"Daddy, if you thought that, why didn't you ever say..."

"It's not my place to make your decisions anymore, Kitten. You're old enough to make your own mistakes. Goodness knows I've made enough of my own to know how easy they are to make."

"Oh, Daddy..." She threw her arms around him. "I should have known you'd understand."

Slightly embarrassed by her show of affection: "I guess Rodney's sudden hospitalization means he won't crew for me today in the regatta." Howard Jackson spoke in a gruff, matter-of-fact voice as if the race were the really important thing.

"I suppose not." She smiled ruefully. "Can you imagine anything more unromantic than a bridegroom agreeing to crew for his father-in-law on the first day of his marriage? I should have refused to marry him for that reason alone!"

"I don't know why you didn't!" her father quipped. "It would have saved us all a great deal of trouble."

"Yes, I know," she said softly, guiltily.

"There... there... I was only kidding. The important thing is that you're out of it in time."

"I... I caused a disaster. All the money..."

"Disaster! Hardly! I know it all seems momentous right now, Kitten. And your mother did work herself up into quite a state." His fingers were parting her thick straight hair. "But life goes on. When you're as old as I am, you'll find out sometimes the crisis that seems to spell disaster is really a blessing in disguise. And sometimes we learn more from our mistakes than we ever would if we did everything right."

"I can't see how last night was a blessing when it could have so easily been avoided if I'd..."

"Well, you're not Mrs. Rodney Starr for one thing." He arose fingering his watch, his mind on the race once more. "The start's at ten. I came here to ask you to go with me. Your mother's down with one of her headaches. Last night was too much for her. Kitten, why don't you get dressed and come with me? Come on. I really need you. That brash young skipper of *Wild Lady* is going to give me a run for my money on this one. If I don't beat him today, he'll be the first in the series."

"*Wild Lady*." The name pulsated in her brain. It was the nickname Ted had called her five years ago... before Rodney... Here she was thinking of *him* again. And again she pushed the unhappy memory from her mind.

Her father was at the door, anxious suddenly to be gone. "Well, you coming?"

"No! I couldn't possibly face all those people down there."

"Kitten, what is it you think you have to live down? They gave a few parties for you and had fun doing it. Real friends want what's best for you, and they'll accept what happened without passing judgment. Besides we can return all the gifts. And if a few people are critical of you—I wouldn't care too much what they think because they will have proved they're not genuine friends anyway."

"I can't help it. I feel so guilty to have caused everyone so much trouble when I should have known all along I wasn't doing the right thing."

"Suit yourself!" He glanced down at his watch impatiently. He gave her one last look before he opened the door. Then she heard the door slam, the faint, rapid padding of his boat shoes as he descended the stairs, and later the distant purr of his car in the drive.

Kit sat up amidst the tangle of sheets and regretted for an instant her decision to stay behind. She felt lonely now that he was gone. At least the excitement of the race would have gotten her mind off everything for a while. Still, if she'd gone, she would have had to face everyone. And she wasn't ready.

She was rising from the bed. Once more her eyes drifted out the doors that opened onto her balcony to the grounds and she saw the pool. She would go for a swim...and a sunbath...a long languid sunbath that would bake away all her miseries. She pulled on her tan bikini—it exactly matched the color of her olive skin. She stepped into her floor-length, see-through lace cover-up so that she was covered from neck to ankle in cream-colored froth and because of her flesh-toned swim suit, it seemed as though she were nude beneath it.

She grabbed a velour bathsheet from her bathroom and as she did, she glanced into the mirror at her face.

The delicate oval was undeniably lovely. Soft brows slanted above large, thickly fringed dark eyes, eyes so dark they appeared almost black. Her nose was straight and delicately boned, her lips full and temptingly soft.

She dabbed at her face with a wet washcloth. Then she brushed her raven-black hair until it shone like silk. As she did she heard the buzz of the doorbell downstairs.

Ignoring the buzz—insistent now—she ran the brush through her shoulder-length hair one last time and put on some lipstick. Again she heard the buzz. She remembered her mother's headache. It was Sunday, the maid Maria's day off. Kit decided to answer the door on her way to the pool.

The buzz was a continual blare throughout the house as she descended the spiral stairs and crossed the gleaming stretch of saltillo tile to stop before the ornate black curve of wrought-iron gates that led to the foyer.

"For heaven's sake!" She felt unusually irritable as the sound persisted and she struggled with the gate. "Whoever's out there must be leaning on the doorbell!"

At last she managed to open the gate, and her bare feet were sinking into the thick pile of the Oriental throw rug in front of the door. All was silence as she peered through the peep hole. No one was there.

She opened the door and looked out. Still no one. Nothing to greet her but the balmy warmth of the new day, the first day of summer, pouring through the half-opened door.

Cautiously she stepped out of the house, and in the distance where the drive curved, she saw a yellow van with bold black lettering on it spelling out, "Bradley's Rental Center."

Bradley! The name should have sounded some sort of alarm, but because she was intent on telling off whomever had been ringing the bell, it didn't.

The doors at the back of the van were open, and she saw beneath them thrust widely apart two darkly tanned, muscled legs that wore ragged boat shoes. The man who belonged to those legs and shoes was rummaging furiously through the van.

She thought of her mother's headache, and the violent pain noise could cause her. Briskly Kit walked in the direction of the van. She'd tell him a thing or two—about standing on a doorbell at eight o'clock on a Sunday morning with her mother ill with a migraine.

The man was still hidden from her view by the door of his truck when she began imperiously, "Is there something I can do for you?"

From the depths of the van she heard a deep, masculine voice that sounded vaguely familiar. "I was stopping off on my way down to my boat to check on that tent y'all rented. Want to check the tension on the poles...the tie downs...make sure it's secure for the day. The weather forecast said the wind's building."

She cut him off. "Well, next time when you come to the house you should use the servants' entrance around back instead of the front door."

As if in response to her words something dropped with a resounding clatter inside the van, and the man swore under his breath.

She continued. "My mother's ill this morning...and I didn't appreciate the way you kept buzzing."

A large brown hand gripping the door of the van came slowly into view. And then the man stepped back from the van and out of its shadow—into the brilliant sunlight.

"Kit! Thought I might catch a glimpse of the—how did the paper put it...the stranded bride—when I came by this morning."

Her mind registered first the sarcasm and then the anger in his voice.

Kit's fingers—trembling—were at her lips. Her face had paled to the color of cream lace at her throat. She took a faltering step backwards. It couldn't be! It couldn't be! But it was! *It was he!* Ted Bradley!

He towered over her—all arrogant six feet, four inches of him. He was older, of course, and a little heavier than he'd been—more muscular, more powerful. There were lines at the corners of his lips and beneath his cobalt blue eyes and between his dark brows that hadn't been there five years ago. His skin was bronzed, his auburn hair streaked gold from the sun. He was as handsome as always—even more handsome than she remembered.

Just looking at him—and she was aching all over.

She saw that he was dressed to sail, but unlike her father he wore cut-off jeans and a blue T-shirt with the name of his boat, *Wild Lady*, lettered across it in white.

Things her father had said were coming back to her. The rental outfit was owned by a "brash young upstart that wouldn't give an inch." Her father was tied for first place with the "brash young skipper of *Wild Lady*." She should have known! Why hadn't she guessed?

Brash! In certain moods the word perfectly fitted the Ted Bradley she remembered. And she thought, "He's in such a mood now."

His mouth was curling in contempt as he stared down at her. She'd ordered him to the servants' entrance. Oh, why had she done that? He'd always had such a complex about money anyway. Her father's money had intimidated him right from the first. Lines between his eyes deepened as his brows drew together. His eyes were fastened on her face for one long shattering moment, and it seemed to Kit that Time stopped. Everything—Rodney, the horror of the wedding that hadn't been, what other people thought—no longer mattered.

She watched Ted draw a deep breath as if he sought to curb whatever emotion was surging through him. He balled his hands into fists and jammed them into the pockets of his cut-offs.

Then his eyes slid from her face down her throat, over her slim body tantalizingly veiled by the lace the wind was swirling around her. Once more he lifted his gaze to hers, and for an instant she thought she saw hurt in his dark-blue eyes. Then he smiled—insolently.

"So...I'm still not good enough to come to your front door," he said softly.

"Ted, I didn't know, I didn't mean..."

"Oh, but you did. Your kind doesn't have to know or mean. What you said is all part of the lifestyle you take for granted. Your kind walks through front doors while mine walks through...servants' entrances.... Maybe I should thank you. You've given me the very thing I needed this morning: that extra ounce of determination to beat your dad, to show him this race is one thing money can't buy."

For an instant she felt hurt. Then she was bristling. As usual he'd taken the upper hand, and what had she done really? Nothing but utter an off-hand remark about the back entrance, the servants' entrance. How could she have known it was he in the truck? She bit her lips.

"I see you still haven't lost your poor-boy chip on the shoulder."

As soon as the words were out of her mouth she knew they were a mistake. He was advancing upon her and seizing her by the wrist, and as always just the touch of him was excitement. She was shivering violently as if it were suddenly cold, and it was still warm. And she'd told herself these past five years she hated him! She tried to twist out of his grasp, but he was too strong. He pulled her to him as if her strength were nothing and gave her a long, searching look.

"When you walked out on me for Rodney, you taught me once and for all the finer distinctions of class. Rich girls don't marry poor boys no matter how attracted they are to them. They might enjoy a fling and a little ardent lovemaking with *them*, but they don't make it a permanent arrangement."

His words stung as he'd intended them to. Half-formed thoughts were whirling in her head. A fling... a little ardent lovemaking with *them*... as if there'd been many men in her life. When there had only been one man and one night... with him. And she'd foolishly thought that he'd cared something for her. She'd been old fashioned and believed such feelings led to marriage. She'd made a commitment to him... before marriage, and he'd tried to take advantage of her. She'd been one in a series of many conquests to him... doubtless!

Left him for Rodney? As if she'd wanted to leave him! He made her sound so cheap!

The hurt went deep, and angry words rushed to her lips to cover it. But before she could speak he lowered his mouth to hers and kissed her ruthlessly. She struggled wildly, but to no purpose. He released her wrist, and his arms circled her waist. He pressed the softness of her body so that it tightly fitted his—his that was lean and hard and powerful.

Suddenly her anger was draining away, and the old, familiar weakening was possessing her. She felt again that old sense of passionate joyful belonging only to him. A strange warmth, an exquisite bliss was filling her. She forgot the old hurt. There was only this moment...now.... Something deep within her—some inner core of happiness that she hadn't even remembered was there—was reawakening for the first time in five years. As always the feel of him was delight and vulnerability and turbulent emotion.

Ted was back in her life, and when he held her it was as if he'd never gone. It was as if there'd never been the gulf of empty years.

Her fingers were in his hair, parting the thick auburn waves. He had always known exactly how to kiss her and where to kiss her that would most arouse her. His lips traveled a leisurely, searing path from her mouth down her cheek to her earlobe. It seemed to her that her blood became hot waves of liquid fire coursing through her arteries. She felt weak—as if she couldn't stand without his support, and she clung to him. He pressed her the more tightly to him with a groan.

She was returning his kisses hungrily. It had been so long. So...so long since she'd felt like this. Five years.... His touch was madness...sweet madness. If only...only he would hold her forever....

She felt him stiffen before he pushed her roughly away.

He took a deep, long breath, "And if I've still got my poor-boy complex, you haven't changed much either. You're still the hot little tease I called Wild Lady."

"How dare you!"

His eyes were traveling lazily from her face downward, and she grew warm all over. "Yes, I dare! What do you expect? You come out here wearing that lacey thing with nothing under it."

"For your information," she said, "I was on my way to the pool when you started ringing the doorbell. I'm wearing a bathing suit under this!"

"Well, you sure can't tell it from here," he said thickly. His eyes were on her face again, on her lips. He turned abruptly from her and strode back to the van and rummaged through it once more.

She knew that she should go, but for some reason she couldn't. Ted Bradley was back in her life—if only for this instant, and in spite of and perhaps because of their long separation, her feelings were more powerful for him than they had ever been.

He emerged from the back of the van once more, a tool kit in his left hand. Her eyes riveted to the gold wedding band that gleamed from the ring finger of that hand.

So...he was still married to Letitia. She remembered he'd had a child.

"You're still here?" Quizzical dark brows slanted upward.

"I thought I'd walk with you on my way to the pool...through the house," she said weakly.

"I can see I'm coming up in the world," was his sarcastic retort.

"Ted.... Please...." She placed her hand on his arm. Her eyes pleaded. "I'm sorry for what I said earlier." Her voice was shaking with emotion.

He saw her distress. "All right," he said curtly, pulling his arm away. "You're forgiven."

She could not stop herself from thinking that he had been back in her life all of ten minutes and their relationship was exactly as it had been. He had done everything that had caused the harsh feelings between them, yet she was apologizing to him.

He was staring deeply into her eyes as if to read her mind and her heart. He looked puzzled suddenly, perplexed. She looked away.

The tool box was clatter on concrete as he set it down and folded her once more into his arms.

"Kit, Kit... what is happening to us? It's almost as if you never left..." His lips were in her hair.

Even as she felt her body responding to his touch, she was remembering he had a wife and a child. She had to stop him.

"Aren't you forgetting... your wife?"

Slowly he pushed her from him. "My wife is dead," he said flatly. "Two years ago she was killed in a car accident. And now I'll find my own way to the pool... through the servants' entrance... if you don't mind." There was no sarcasm in his voice, only pain.

It was obvious he was not over his wife's death. In the face of his grief, she could think of nothing to say.

He swung around on his heels and left her staring open-mouthed after him as he disappeared around the curve in the drive.

Chapter Two

From the height of her balcony Kit watched Ted as he carefully checked each pole and each tie-down of the tent. The languid, easy grace of his great body fascinated her. He strained against a rope and she watched the pull of brown muscles in his arms. She could see he took his work seriously. His checking of the tent was not a casual observation from some faraway, stand-off position.

Kit had returned to her room because she'd sensed Ted's need to get away from her. Suddenly, watching him, she determined to go down to the pool. This was her home after all! She had a perfect right.... She raced from her room, down the stairs, and stopped only when she reached the expanse of sliding glass doors that opened from the den onto the patio and pool area. She caught her breath and slid one of the doors open. Slowly, as though in a dream, she moved to the edge of the pool and laid her wine-colored bathsheet down lengthwise.

She unhooked the lacey cover-up where it fastened at the neck, and let it fall from her body into a puddle of cream froth circling her feet. The swim suit she wore was like an outer skin of olive silk that did nothing to hide her luscious curves. Out of the corner of her eye, she saw Ted stop what he was doing and look at her, his eyes traveling slowly down from the soft swell of full breasts, to her narrow waist, her well-turned hips, and graceful thighs.... He turned away quickly, too quickly, but not before her own pulse was hammering wildly.

She saw the darkening flush of his cheeks; she saw his frown, his attempted nonchalance as he turned his attention once more to his tent. And she smiled. He was pulling fiercely on a rope as she stepped over the cover-up and picked it up. Suddenly the pole he was working on fell, and a section of tent sagged.

"Need some help?" she called gaily.

Gruffly: "No!"

She lay down upon the soft velour and watched his struggles with the tent pole. She could feel the warmth of the tile through her towel, and already the sun was baking on her back.

Once more he had the pole in place and the tie-down taut. Deliberately ignoring her, he moved to the next pole and checked it.

She lay there by the pool trying to fit the pieces together. She should've guessed that Ted Bradley was the owner of the rental outfit and the skipper of *Wild Lady*. She'd known he'd returned to Corpus shortly after he'd married. But it had all happened such a long time ago, and she'd deliberately avoided trying to find out what happened to him—for just the thought of him had meant pain.

Still, she'd heard her father mention his boat, *Wild Lady*. At the time the name had rung a bell. But she hadn't thought...

Wild Lady.... Once long ago Ted had called her that...many times...usually after he'd held her in his arms, sensing her leaping response. She'd thought it had been his special name for her. Now she wondered. Had he named his boat after her? Or, was it merely his turn of phrase? Something he called all his girlfriends?

The past came back in a sweeping rush. The night of that storm...the night she'd almost made love to him in that tiny efficiency apartment he'd been renting off 24th Street in Austin. The night she'd found out what kind of man he really was.

Afterward Kit had supposed such nights of love meant little to him. She had attempted to console herself with Rodney's offer of friendship.

Kit looked up and saw that Ted was staring at her once more. He moved toward her.

"Well, it shouldn't blow away...today anyway," he said in his most businesslike voice.

"I wish it would...blow away...out of my sight. It reminds me of...."

"Always the careless, rich girl out of tune with the harsher realities of Life. That tent cost me a lot of money, and it isn't insured."

Had it always been this easy to get angry at him? "I didn't mean..." she faltered.

"You never mean...do you? But you've reminded me. What happened last night?"

"Read the paper!" she snapped. "Page sixteen!"

"I already have, and if you ask me, that was the luckiest night of your life!"

"I didn't ask you!"

"No, you didn't! But just to show you my heart's in the right place, I'll wish you luck in snagging old Rodney."

"I don't want your good wishes!"

"Well, you have them just the same. After all, I have a personal interest in your success. Who knows, maybe you'll rent the tent from me again!"

"Not on your life!"

He was punching a button on his quartz watch and reading the time. "I can always hope, can't I? But I've gotta get going. The start's at ten, and if I leave right now I'll just make the skippers' meeting. I've gotta show your dad a thing or two about sailing. Remember?"

When he'd gone, Kit flew to her room and pulled a T-shirt and a pair of shorts over her bathing suit. She grabbed her boat shoes and dashed down the stairs to the garage.

She was sinking into the baby-blue leather of her bucket seat and fumbling with the keys in the ignition.

Radials were hugging asphalt and squealing as the Porsche sped out onto the boulevard that followed the curve of the bay from her home to the yacht club.

She eyed the sparkling waters to her right with misgiving. It was still early in the morning, and already the wind was whipping the waves so that white froth laced their crests. A horn sounded impatiently behind her and she turned her attention once more to the road.

So...she'd changed her mind. She would crew for her father this morning. And why not? The race was exactly what she needed to get her mind off...off...things....

Who cared what people thought?

The parking lot near the yacht club was full so Kit had to park near the shrimp boats. As she swung the long, brown curves of her legs out of the car, three shrimpers ceased their work at their nets and leered. When she stepped from her car, they whistled madly. Flushing, she avoided their gaze, finished locking her car, and walked slowly toward the club.

Open masculine admiration from strangers embarrassed her. She'd only exulted in admiration like that from one man—Ted. For some reason she'd always found the intent way his gaze followed her pleasurable and exciting. Rodney had never looked at her like that. The shrimpers called after her in Spanish, but she ignored them and quickened her steps.

Noiselessly she entered the bar of the club, which was a bustle of confusion. The skippers' meeting had just been concluded, and the skippers and their crew members were grabbing paper cups filled with coffee to take with them to their boats where they would finish last-minute rigging.

At first no one noticed Kit, and she viewed the sea of familiar faces uneasily. Many of them had been guests last night, witnesses to the fiasco of her supposed "wedding."

"Hey, Bradley," Marc Clay called. "Did you hear Jackson bought a new heavy-air spinnaker just to help him on the downwind leg of the race?"

At the mention of her father's name, Kit noted his conspicuous absence. Then she looked beyond, through the floor-to-ceiling sheets of glass that formed two walls of the bar, and saw the black hull of *Kitten*, her father's boat, still tied at her dock and her father and her brother, Steve, packing the spinnaker bag. Yards of blowing, ballooning black and yellow silk-like cloth—the new spinnaker—were spilling from the bag. The two men were scrambling to control it.

Then she heard Ted's voice, brash and arrogant. "Hell, Jackson can buy all the sails he wants, but I intend to show him sails and money don't win races. Skippers do!"

Her eyes shifted from *Kitten* to him. He was standing in one corner of the room, one of his great arms gripping the polished brass railing of the staircase that spiraled upward to the dining room. The other arm rested negligently upon the shoulder of a darkly beautiful woman who was wearing a T-shirt like his. *His* wife! But...she was dead! Still, the resemblance was uncanny! Kit had seen Letitia once, five years ago, and she'd never forgotten her dark, almost exotic beauty.

Suddenly Kit was furious. How dare he say such a thing about her father?

Kit's heart was pounding rabbit-fast when she heard her voice, a curious choking sound, cry out as if it had a mind of its own. "Mr. Bradley, I think that remark was rude and uncalled for. My father was merely buying a sail he needed for his boat. I don't think he feels his money can buy races!" She broke off. For one terrible moment she thought she'd strangle on her anger.

Then Ted's eyes were on her; and they were alight with sardonic interest. His great arm fell from the dark girl's shoulder. He smiled broadly.

The crowd hushed and shifted its attention to her. There was a faint buzz in one corner near her, and Kit as did everyone else in the room heard the unmistakable, the terribly cruel words, "You wouldn't think she'd have enough nerve to come here...after last night...." Then the woman, aware the room had suddenly gone silent, hushed.

Kit went red with embarrassment. Why? Why had she called attention to herself? Last night—when she'd stood before these very people—came back in a sickening flash. She'd caused them all such trouble, and she'd made a fool of herself as well.

Then she saw Ted moving toward her. She was dizzy suddenly, and just as she thought she'd faint, his hand was supporting her elbow.

His eyes held hers for a long moment, and the dizzy feeling intensified.

His fingers moved beneath her elbow—warm and electric. Would it always be like this? He had only to touch her, to look at her, and the world would spin. She pushed the disturbing possibility from her mind.

Was his an appeal that all women found as irresistible as she did?

He was strikingly handsome, tall and powerfully built. The blue eyes that studied her face were brilliant, magnetic; and she could not look away. His steady, intense gaze was stripping away all the bandages she'd so carefully wrapped around her heart. Suddenly she was aching as if he'd exposed a deep hurt—that uncovered—was as rawly painful as an unhealed wound.

She grew warm all over. He saw too much. He had no right to come back into her life....

She was angry again and frightened because he could so effortlessly arouse all the old feelings. Did she...was it possible...that she still cared something for him...even knowing the kind of man he was?

"No, it isn't possible!" she told herself desperately. What she felt for Ted had to be physical, nothing more. The wisest course for her to follow would be to avoid him in the future.

She pulled her elbow away from him, noting with satisfaction the quick hardening of his expression. Maybe if he grew angry he would leave. But he didn't. Instead he leaned his great body against the wall behind her and continued to stare down at her.

Her heart was hammering wildly. And only because he was near. Why? Did he attract her because he was different from all that she was used to, different from Rodney and from this roomful of wealthy young men, who skippered the other boats? She viewed their smooth faces, faces unlined by struggle, with distaste. Everything they had had come too easily to them while Ted had fought for everything he possessed.

She admired that in him. His features that were bronzed from work out of doors were rugged. She noted the faint grooves etched between the thick slash of his dark brows. She fought against the desire to reach up and trace the faint lines until they went smooth beneath her fingertips. She noted the long hawklike nose, the square, determined set of his jaw, his bold eyes. She was flushing again as he continued to stare at her in that carelessly reckless yet intense, way of his, smiling insolently, his even straight teeth a flash of white against his swarthy skin. She thought he looked ruthless, almost piratical.

A delicious shiver shook her, and, as if he knew it to be her response to him, his smile widened. She looked quickly away. He laughed as if he had read her mind and seen the battle raging there.

Oh, if she were smart she would run out of the club and away from him at once. Yet she stayed rooted to the spot.

"You couldn't resist the challenge of trying to put me . . . or keep me . . . as the case may be . . . in my proper place, could you?" he said. Again the wide smile, and the Buccaneer gleam in his eyes. "The real Jackson Wild Lady against . . . her name sake, my *Wild Lady*? Should be an interesting race."

Did he mean he *had* named his boat after her? She looked up at him furious again, but her anger dissolved when she saw his blue eyes were twinkling. If he were a pirate, he was in a mischievous mood. He was still smiling as if the sight of her delighted him, and suddenly, in spite of everything, she was smiling too. He was deliberately baiting her, trying to distract her from the woman's malicious remark that had reminded her of last night. He was being kind—in his own peculiar way. For some reason she was inexplicably happy this was so. For the briefest space of time as he looked at her and she looked at him, it seemed to her they were in a world of their own.

As if in a dream she saw his lips move; she heard the deep resonant tones of his voice, breaking the spell, challenging her once more. "So you're gonna help your dad try to beat me? He told me he'd asked you to crew and you'd refused..." He smiled knowingly. "Something...that happened this morning after he left...must've changed your mind." When she still refused to rise to his bait, he hesitated. "Someday, Kit, I hope we'll be on the same side...for a change...." His voice wrapped her with its warmth.

He turned and saw that the dark, exotic beauty across the room was beckoning to him. Smiling, he waved to her.

Then he was leading Kit across the room, and she was acutely aware of his hand lightly touching the back of her waist. Kit knew that heads were turning in their direction, that there was a speculative buzz behind them.

When they reached the younger woman Ted said, "Kit, I want you to meet Phyllis Lanier, my sister-in-law." The dark girl with the fiery gray eyes was glaring at her. "She takes care of my little girl, Missy, for me in the afternoons."

The dark girl jerked her head toward Kit and her thick crop of short curls caught the sunlight and gleamed like black fire.

"Well, I'm happy to meet you, Kit." Her gray eyes, stony with dislike, belied her words. "But, Ted, don't you think we'd better go out to the boat . . . now?"

It was obvious to Kit that Phyllis resented her presence.

"Phyllis, why don't you go out and try to rustle up Rick first. We can't leave without him anyway," Ted said.

"But . . . aren't you coming with me?"

"I'll be along in a minute. I want to show Kit *Wild Lady*."

Phyllis did as he suggested even though she seemed reluctant to leave Kit alone with Ted. For a sister-in-law, she was certainly possessive.

When she was gone Ted turned back to Kit. "Kit, would you like to see *Wild Lady*?" He was taking her hand, and pulling her through the crowd.

Oh, she was a fool to go with him! She should snatch her hand from his and go help her father rig *Kitten*. But when had she ever been sensible about him? She did not snatch her hand away. He led her from the yacht club piers to one of the more undesirable slips—undesirable because it was shallow and the wind and currents brought a veritable floating island of garbage—paper cups, bits of plastic, beer bottles, slicks of grease—to float trapped in the spot where two walls of concrete bulkhead joined together.

"I've been trying to get a better slip for over a year, but they're all taken," he said. "And *Wild Lady* is the only boat with a shallow enough draft to be tied here."

Kit admired the trim lines of *Wild Lady*'s ice-blue, wooden hull. She was a sloop, twenty-six feet long. At the stern the boat's name was a swirl of bold golden script that looked like Ted's handwriting.

He helped her onto the boat, and proudly showed her below. "I made her myself," he was saying. He ran his palm fondly across a piece of decking. "I know every board, every fitting..."

"She is very beautiful, Ted," Kit began.

At her words, he smiled. She noticed that the lines around his eyes were no longer there.

He was about to say something. He seemed eager to, and then he caught himself. He seemed angry suddenly at himself for his own enthusiasm. "She's really nothing, I guess, compared to a fancy rig like your dad's boat, *Kitten*. She's homemade, cheap in comparison, and I'm sure she couldn't impress someone like you."

Before she could reply, he was looking beyond her, and leaping from the boat to help Phyllis who was struggling to carry a heavily laden ice chest to the boat.

Phyllis's eyes were on Kit—accusing. "Ted, it's nine-fifteen. Don't you think we'd better get going?"

"Soon as Rick gets here."

"He's right behind me."

A tall pole of a boy with a thatch of red hair appeared. Rick. Slung over his bony shoulder was a sail bag.

Feeling out of place, as if she no longer belonged, Kit tugged on the dock line. Just as she stepped onto the dock, an angry motorist honked his horn at two pedestrians in his way. Startled by the unexpected noise, she slipped, and if Ted hadn't pulled her swiftly into his arms she would have fallen into the water.

He was crushing her head against his chest. She heard the wild beating of his heart; she felt the hard warmth of his body. She regained her balance, and still—for one long wonderful moment—he held her as if he enjoyed the feel of her against him. Then he released her. She felt his eyes on her face, but she did not dare look up for fear that he would see how shaken she was from being in his arms—if only for an instant.

"Getting clumsy in your old age," he mocked softly. "Hope you're not becoming accident prone like your bridegroom Rodney..."

Angrily she pushed him from her and ran past him. Behind her she heard his quick burst of laughter, but she never looked back.

She was breathless when she reached *Kitten*, and her father, surprised to see her, looked up from his task of uncoiling the main sheet.

"Steve, help her on board," was her father's command. And to her: "You look as if the Devil himself were at your heels." Then his voice became a bark of orders. "Cast off that port line. And now, cast off the starboard line...but hold on to it. Tightly! No...let it go!" When she didn't obey instantly: *"Let it go!"* She dropped it into the water. "Fend off! Fend off!" She leaned her weight against a piling so that *Kitten* wouldn't scrape it.

Twenty-seven feet of black fiberglass backed slowly out of her slip. Steve shifted into forward and moved the tiller. Kit sat back on top of the cabin and tried to stop thinking of Ted.

The sea breeze was ruffling her long black hair as she slipped a bright-red triangular scarf over it. She heard the steady clang of the metal rigging against the aluminum mast, the wash of water curling back from the bow as the boat slipped through the waves, the steady chugging of the diesel, and the cry of a gull behind her. All was like music—soothing.

"Bring her up into the wind, Steve. Not through it! There! I'm going to hoist the main sail."

Kit smiled fondly as she watched her brother follow her father's orders. He moved the tiller with a quiet sureness that was characteristic of him. She always marveled at the way Steve and her father got along. Her father turned into Captain Bly on races, but that never ruffled Steve. Together, the two men made an almost unbeatable combination.

She watched Howard Jackson kneeling beneath the mast and pulling with all his strength on the main halyard. The big sail crawled slowly up the mast; the bottom of it unfurled from the boom that was swinging well over Steve's head as he stood up in the cockpit. Within seconds her father had raised the Genoa, an oversized foresail, also.

"With that Genoa up, I can't see a thing," Steve was muttering. He ran his hand through his dark hair in agitation. "Kit, get up to the bow at once—to the pulpit—and keep an eye out for other boats."

From the pulpit: "*Sashay* is under you, but you're all right. Hold your course. Do you see *Butterfly*?"

"Yea..."

"*Wild Lady*"... Her voice caught and faded into an inaudible murmur at the sight of Ted sitting terribly close to Phyllis. His expression was intense; he was so engrossed in conversation with his sister-in-law that he failed to wave to Kit as the two boats passed one another. Unaccountably this omission on his part hurt much more than it should have.

Kit failed to call out another boat's position and her brother, seeing the other yacht in the nick of time, tacked abruptly.

"Kit, what the devil are you thinking about up there?" her brother called in exasperation.

"Sorry..."

Brother and sister continued shouting back and forth to one another as Kit sighted other sailboats and called their positions to Steve. Her father was setting out lines, checking fittings, and keeping a sharp watch for the white starting flag which would indicate there were ten minutes remaining before the start.

The flag went up, and Howard Jackson instantly punched the button of his nautical-looking stopwatch. Her father took one look across the starting line and frowned.

"Steve, I think we better make a run across that line."

"Tacking..." Steve called.

Uneasily Kit watched the foredeck become white flapping chaos as the Genoa swept across it. Then once more the big sail was trimmed again, and the boat was heeling and moving forward on the opposite tack. She wished they could change the Genoa for the smaller working jib sail. But she knew better than to question her father's judgment. Instead she hung onto the chrome bars of the pulpit for dear life.

Howard Jackson was closely studying the starting line, that invisible line that stretched across the water between a buoy and the committee boat. "Looks like the buoy near the jetty is the favored end of the line, and the port tack will be the favored tack. Which means... that if we cross high up on that end of the line on port tack we won't have right-of-way. There won't be any forgiveness for error."

Fifty boats! It wasn't going to be easy to be in the right spot when that gun went off. *Kitten* would be on a port tack with no right-of-way. If anyone made a mistake or refused to give right-of-way...there could be a collision...

Chapter Three

A burst of fluttering blue—the exact color of Ted's eyes—was hoisted from the committee boat to replace the white, ten-minute flag. Only five minutes remained until the start. Unsmilingly, Kit watched the many boats that were now sailing—all in different directions, seemingly all on different courses. She knew, however, that each skipper was carefully timing himself, trying to figure the wind, and his boat's speed so that he could cross the starting line the precise moment the red flag went up and the gun sounded.

Too many boats—to be at the same place at the same time!

Her father was at the tiller.

"Two and a half minutes 'til the start. We've gotta tack in fifteen seconds."

"*Force 12* is coming up fast," Kit called from the pulpit.

"I see her. We've got room."

Steve was removing the thick coil of Genoa sheet from the chrome-plated winch in preparation for the tack.

"Tacking—now!"

The bow of the boat turned, the air went out of the foresail, and Steve released the sheet. Everything seemed to happen at once.

The foresail crackled like stiff paper and Steve began trimming it on the starboard winch. The main sail caught the wind, and the boom jerked across the cockpit. *Kitten* was heeling again and moving fast.

Kitten heeled at an even more precarious angle as Steve continued to winch the big sail in, and Kit tightened her grip on the metal bars of the pulpit. For some reason she felt unusually nervous. Then she saw the ice blue hull of *Wild Lady* coming up fast. *Wild Lady* was still on a starboard tack. Apparently Ted intended to tack at the last minute. When he did tack he would be almost in the exact position as her father. It was incredible the way the skippers ended up at the same place at the crucial moments.

She observed Ted at the helm, his auburn hair ruffling in the wind, his face ruthless and determined, determined to win at any cost—just as her father was. This time he saw her. For a brief moment his dark face lit with joy. He waved to her jauntily, and she—delighted, too delighted—returned his wave.

Suddenly she heard it. A whir at first, followed by a metallic snap. Her father's voice was a roar in the cockpit. "The Genoa track's pulling out!" Kit watched with horror as the ribbon of stainless track pulled loose from the deck.

Her father was shouting. "Steve! Keep that Genoa sheet on the winch! Kit, get back in the cockpit!"

As Kit crawled across the high side of the deck to the cockpit, a heavy gust knocked *Kitten* over and her low side went under. The winch Steve was working on was completely under water. Slowly the boat righted herself.

Her brother cursed low beneath his breath. "Blast! The winch is fouled! I can't get the sail in!" Louder: "Dad, she's fouled!"

The winch with the layers of overlapping rope looked like a giant silver spool of tangled thread.

Kit saw the big sail luffing, spilling air. The sail was flapping and making so much noise she could scarcely hear anything else.

"Kit, take the helm!" her father ordered.

"But, Daddy, I...I haven't sailed in years. I..." There was no crossing her father when he was determined.

Her father was yelling. "Hold her up...high! Higher!" He grabbed the tiller and pushed it where he wanted it. "There! Keep her heading for that water tower. I've gotta get below! Gotta get the tool kit so I can cut that snarl of sheet off the winch."

Kit fought to point the boat toward the water tower squatting like a giant orange spider on the horizon. Her father disappeared into the cabin and reemerged almost at once with his tool kit.

Without the foresail trimmed in tightly, the boat could not point where her father wanted it to. Kit couldn't see around the big foresail either, and she knew sailboats were everywhere—sailboats on different courses, sailboats she couldn't see.

Steve was intent upon trying to unfoul the winch. Suddenly Kit heard—above the noise of the sail and too-near—the ominous, "Starboard tack! Right-of-way!" Louder: "*Kitten*, give us right-of-way!"

Her father would have reacted with reflex, split-second timing, and tacked, and thereby, avoided the collision. But Kit was sailing, and she was exhausted from her sleepless night. She moved more slowly, too slowly.

As if in a dream, she heard the other skipper's voice—Ted's much louder now, shouting to his crew, "Tack! Tack! Now! *Kitten*'s not..."

His orders became a blur of sound as a sudden gust of air howled, and *Kitten* slammed to a stand-still. Water was again rushing into the cockpit.

Kit heard the terrible sound of wood splintering—*Wild Lady*'s hull breaking as *Kitten*'s bow sliced through it. Another gust screamed, and Kit dropped the tiller. Her father was scrambling to free the main sheet so the main sail would no longer fill with wind and propel the boat forward. Steve was grabbing for the knife in the tool kit so he could cut the Genoa loose and collapse that sail.

Kit froze. This couldn't be happening! It couldn't!

Another gust swept across the cockpit and knocked *Kitten* over, and Kit lost her footing and plunged toward the low side into the water.

When she surfaced, she heard someone screaming her name. Then she saw bearing down on her four tons of white fiberglass! *Butterfly*! And Kris, the skipper of *Butterfly*, did not see her. He was looking instead at *Wild Lady*.

Then suddenly, Ted was in the water with her, grabbing her into his great arms, pushing her out of the way. She heard his words: "Take a deep breath..."

And then she heard no more. Dark waters were curling over her face as he pushed her beneath the waves and held her there. She struggled but to no purpose. He held her with the weight of his body on hers.

When she thought she'd surely drown, when she thought she must open her mouth and breathe water, his body jolted hard against hers and pressed her even deeper into the water. He slackened his grip on her arms. Again she struggled and this time he released her. She fought her way to the surface.

She opened her eyes—burning with salt water—and saw the stern of *Butterfly* near, but moving away. Kris had seen them and tacked. Thank heavens!

Kit gasped for breath, sputtering. Once, and then again. Ted was in the water beside her, and she was relieved to see that he was also all right.

"You okay?" Ted asked. Once more she was sputtering. "Don't try to talk," he said. "Here...hold onto this cushion." He pushed the strap handles of a floating white square into her fingers. She saw the black print that read "*Butterfly*" stenciled onto the top of the cushion. She saw several other cushions, similarly marked in the water nearby. Kris must have tossed them from his boat as he'd passed. Then Kit noticed that Ted's face, usually so dark, was nearly as white as the cushions. She saw the wine-red stains in the water circling him, the dark smears on his blue T-shirt. She remembered how his body jolted hard against hers when he'd held her under. Suddenly she understood. He'd been hit by *Butterfly*! And *Butterfly* was sailing away as if nothing had happened.

Ted had been hit, and he'd shielded her from the impact of that blow with his body. He'd risked his life to save her. If he'd been hit on the head, he could've been...

"Ted, are you..."

He cut her off. "Your dad's got his sails down at last. He's going to pick us up. Hang onto that cushion. I'm not up to any more heroics today on your account."

She heard the purr of *Kitten*'s diesel and saw Steve lowering the aluminum ladder over the stern.

She placed her foot on the bottom rung, and Steve was reaching over the side to help her. At last she stood—bedraggled, dripping and shivering—in the cockpit. Ted was still in the water, and she leaned down to tell him to board.

"Ted..."

For a moment she thought he did not hear her. Then she saw that he was looking past *Kitten* to *Wild Lady*. There was a deathly stillness to his features. At last he tore his eyes from *Wild Lady*, from her badly damaged hull, from the squirts of water Phyllis was pumping out of the cabin, from Rick struggling to fit the small outboard motor into place.

Kit realized in that instant the magnitude of what she had done to him. *Wild Lady* was more to Ted than just a boat. He hadn't ordered her from a boat dealer. He hadn't simply written a check. He'd built her himself afternoons after work. It must've taken him months. He'd put part of himself into her—she was a work of love. And she, Kit, had destroyed *Wild Lady*.

Ted grabbed the ladder with his left hand and—slowly, carefully—pulled himself out of the water and into the cockpit.

"Well, so this is what it's like in the enemy camp," he said, attempting lightness. "High style." His expression darkened as his eyes went again to *Wild Lady*. "I should be over there—with them—helping. Rick still hasn't gotten that motor started."

Kit saw that Ted's right arm dangled crookedly, that his right shoulder was dark with blood stains. He was now ashen from the strain of pulling himself into the boat.

"They'll have to manage," she said gently. "You're in no condition to do anything but sit down."

His hard gaze drifted over her. She was suddenly aware that her soaking T-shirt clung to her curves. "And who should I thank for that, Miss?" he asked brutally.

Her eyes were burning again, this time from tears not salt water. She was remembering his eagerness, his pride when he'd showed her *Wild Lady*. And she'd wrecked *Wild Lady*! And his arm.... It looked broken. That was her fault too. It was obvious although he was trying to conceal it that he was in pain. Why did she always—always—do everything wrong where he was concerned?

His eyes—bold blue and intense with emotion—continued to gaze down at her. His expression was hard, and she wouldn't blame him if he hated her for what she had done. Abruptly he turned away. Shaking with cold, she sat down.

"Sorry about all this, Bradley!" her father said. "Our Genoa track pulled out and the winch fouled. I had to give the helm to Kit. She was in no condition after...last... Well, anyway, I was shorthanded this morning."

Kit sensed her father's deep embarrassment that his boat, his daughter, and therefore, *he* was responsible for the accident. Her father was a perfectionist in everything.

"Daddy, I..." A violent shiver—almost a seizure—shook her as a blast of wind whipped across the cockpit. "I'm sorry...I'm sorry..." Her teeth were chattering so much she couldn't speak.

"You're freezing, Kitten," her father said. "Steve, get some blankets from below. I'm sure Bradley could use one too. Kitten, you don't need to apologize. I needed you to crew, and we might've been in worse shape without you. Bradley, the boy's got your motor started, but I think we ought to follow *Wild Lady* in."

"Thank you, sir."

Steve reemerged from the cabin. "I couldn't find but one blanket."

"Give it to Kit," Ted said.

Steve wrapped Kit in king-sized yellow wool. Ted sat down beside her, and she saw the goosebumps dimpling his tanned arms. He was cold, but she realized he would never admit it.

"Ted, why don't you put part of this blanket around you too? You're as cold as I am."

"I'm okay," he replied in clipped tones.

It was painfully clear he didn't want any contact with her.

"Kitten's right," her father insisted, "It's the only practical solution. Even though it's summer it's always colder on the water, especially when you're wet."

Ted stood up so that Steve could spread the blanket out all the way, and then he sat down once more—this time closer to Kit—much closer. Steve—careful of Ted's injured shoulder—draped the rest of the blanket over his back.

Kit was still shivering violently. Ted sat stiffly beside her, making no move to touch her.

In spite of the circumstances she felt a strange sense of elation that he was near her. She fancied the blanket wrapped them like a cocoon in a private, secret world of their own. His nearness brought back the past. Steve, her father, the scent of salt in the air, the green sparkle of sunlight on waves mingled and blurred.

Five years ago it had felt like this. Ted had only to come into a room, to hold her hand, and he became her world. Once, nothing...no one had mattered to her except him. And then . . . the aching emptiness when she'd broken up with him.

She fought against the old, powerful feeling. He cared nothing for her, Kit, now . . . nor did she care . . . really . . . about him. She didn't! She couldn't! Not now—knowing what kind of man he was. What she was feeling was physical. It was like chemistry—two chemicals exploding when they touched. Was that love?

With difficulty she reminded herself that Ted was no longer part of her life. Somehow she would have to conquer her treacherous feelings for Ted . . . however powerful they were.

Salt spray showered them and brought her attention back to the present . . . to the disaster she'd caused. Howard Jackson was steering *Kitten* so that she followed *Wild Lady* as she limped to her slip. They were moving at a snail's pace, and it would be quite some time before they reached the dock.

"Looks like there's quite a bit of damage, expensive damage, to her hull, Bradley. And your arm will require medical attention as well." Howard Jackson hesitated as if he didn't quite know how to phrase his next words. "I'd like to pay for your medical bills and for the repairs," he began slowly.

She felt Ted's body stiffen. His fingers gripped her arm.

"That won't be necessary," he said curtly.

"Still, I feel responsible. If it weren't . . ."

Again Ted's fingers tightened.

"Jackson, I like to think *Wild Lady* is one thing even your money can't buy. She's mine. All mine. . . . I can and I will get her repaired without your help."

There was no mistaking the determination in Ted's voice. It was as if he'd interpreted Howard's offer to help as a threat to his independence rather than as an offer made out of friendship to help.

Kit held her breath. Her father couldn't possibly understand Ted's refusal to accept his help for he knew nothing of her past relationship with him. He would think Ted rude, and he would be furious.

Oh, why did Ted have to have such a complex about her father's money?

Kitten pitched on a power boat and the tension went out of Ted's grip. He caught his breath and doubled slightly as if he were in pain. But he said nothing.

A long uneasy silence had fallen. Her father, his right hand mechanically guiding the tiller, stared grimly ahead. Kit knew he must be seething with anger and she was dreading the moment when he would explode with some angry retort. She tensed for the probable violent reaction from her father. But the eruption did not come.

Instead she heard her father begin blandly as if he'd carefully considered his answer, "I understand how you feel . . . perfectly. I would have felt the same way myself once."

Kitten pitched again, and this time Ted winced. Kit saw him whiten and press his lips tightly together.

"But here," her father continued, "I can see that arm is painful. At least let me offer you a shot of brandy. I'll get it myself. Steve, take the tiller."

Howard Jackson descended into the cabin and returned almost at once with a column of cellophane-bagged, paper cups and a bottle of brandy—the finest import money could buy. When he'd poured the brandy into a cup, he offered it to Ted.

Ted released Kit and moved his arm beneath the blanket. He took the cup and lifted it to his lips. "It is excellent . . . naturally," he said. "The best. I feel better already. . . ." He drained the cup.

Howard was pouring him another cupful.

Ted sipped the second cup more slowly. The brandy seemed to have an instant mellowing effect on his mood.

"Jackson, perhaps there is a way you could help me get *Wild Lady* back in shape. Kris told me you're an ace when it comes to tuning a mast. When I get the hull repaired, do you think you could give me a hand with the mast?"

"I'd be glad to, of course," her father answered emphatically. He was clearly pleased Ted had requested his help.

The two men began to discuss the technical aspects of sailing. Her father was asking Ted's advice about his broken Genoa track, and Ted was telling him exactly how he would repair it if it were his. Kit listened to them in amazement. They were enjoying one another's company. It seemed almost as though they were old friends.

After a while they fell silent. Steve had gone to the bow with the boat hook to prepare to dock the boat. Howard Jackson maneuvered *Kitten* so that she was as close as possible to the dock so that Ted could easily get off the boat.

Ted was slowly pulling himself to his feet. "Kit . . ." She looked up. His voice was deep, husky. He reached down and brushed a stray tendril of her hair back from her cheek and then drew his hand quickly away as though he touched fire. Slowly he said, "It was almost worth wrecking *Wild Lady* to . . ." She was listening breathlessly, but he did not finish.

Phyllis's voice—shrill with alarm—interrupted him, and he looked up.

"Ted! You've been hurt! Your shirt's all bloody! Your arm! We've got to get you to a hospital!" She glared at Kit accusingly. "This is *your* fault!"

"Phyllis!" Ted's voice was sharp with reproach and the girl became silent at once. More gently: "I know you're concerned, Phyllis, but what happened was an accident. Blaming Kit won't help." He stepped from the boat. Phylis's arms went around him possessively. "Thanks, Phyllis, for getting *Wild Lady* back to her dock."

"Bradley..." Her father called briskly, looking up from securing a dock line, "I'd like to invite you over to dinner if you're up to it. Say Wednesday night. And bring Phyllis too. We can discuss that mast of yours."

"We couldn't possibly come," Phyllis began in a rush. "Ted's been seriously injured. *Wild Lady*..."

"Nonsense, Phyllis," Ted said in a voice of steel. "I'll give you a call, Jackson, about dinner... later tonight. Should know something about this arm by then."

Kit stepped lithely onto the dock. "Ted, if there's anything I can do for you..."

His gaze swept over her and in spite of her soaking clothes she felt oddly warm. But he said nothing; it was Phyllis who blurted,

"I think you've done more than enough for one day, don't you?"

"I didn't mean to. I..." Kit broke off.

For just an instant Ted's manner softened toward her. "I know you didn't." He made his voice low—just her for. More loudly: "I'm gonna check on *Wild Lady* now. Finally figured out something good about her slip—even at high tide, it's too shallow for her to sink in it. She'll just sit in the mud."

Then he turned, as if talking about *Wild Lady* made him impatient to check on her. He strode abruptly away.

Kit watched him slow his pace because of his injured arm. The sight of him, in pain, heading for his wrecked boat, caught at her heart. She started after him. "I've got to find some way to help him. I've got to!"

Phyllis was racing behind her, catching up to her. "Why don't you help by leaving him alone?" she asked vehemently. "You nearly ruined his life once! When will you realize, all you can ever be to him is trouble?"

Kit stopped. Phyllis was right, of course. She no longer had a place in his life. Circumstances—unpleasant ones—had thrown them briefly together again—that was all. Kit watched—dazed—as the two of them disappeared together behind the out-buildings of the yacht club.

Chapter Four

Kit sped into the curving driveway and braked the Porsche to a standstill before three stories of pretentious white walls and turrets capped with red tile gleaming in the sunlight. She left her car parked in the drive and ran toward the front door.

Had it only been half an hour ago that she'd stood on the dock by *Kitten* and watched Ted walk slowly away from her with Phyllis?

She stepped into the house. All was just as she'd left it. The ballroom still stood in readiness for the reception that had never been. The silver punch bowls and champagne fountains gleamed on the elegantly-skirted banquet tables. The three-tiered wedding cake had not been moved. Columns of crystal plates, napkins, and silverware remained.

She gazed around her—the familiar surroundings seemed... different. She had the odd sensation that she was a stranger in her own home. With no regard at all for the upholstery, she sank—still wet from her dunking—into a nearby chair.

She felt lost . . . in a state of shock. Ted had come back into her life and by doing so he'd shaken the structure of her life to the roots of its foundation. Once she'd thought she was over him, and now . . .

How did she feel about him? She honestly didn't know. Everytime he touched her it was like an electric shock to her system. When he'd walked away from her with Phyllis, she, Kit, had felt desolate. She'd thought he must hate her for wrecking *Wild Lady* and breaking his arm.

It didn't make sense to her that his feelings about her should matter. He was a part of her past . . . that was all . . . a painful memory.

The house was funeral-parlor quiet—much too still. What she needed was action—someone to talk to...anything...to distract her from thinking of Ted. But her father and brother had not returned from the yacht club and her mother was in bed with her headache. She didn't feel up to calling Rodney yet. Rodney—there was another problem. What was she going to do about him?

She sprang from her chair and rushed desperately to her room. She changed from her wet clothes into a hot pink T-shirt and jeans.

Ted...Ted.... The name seemed to throb in her head. Almost frantically she brushed her black hair into a ponytail and tied a pink scarf around it. Dressed, she returned once more to the ballroom.

She attacked a stack of crystal plates. She would carry them . . . everything to the kitchen. She had to have something to do or she would go mad thinking of...Ted.

It didn't matter that tomorrow when her mother had recovered from her migraine she would organize the maids to clean away everything. It was imperative she occupy herself now.

Ted.... He had sat so stiffly beside her when they'd shared the blanket. He'd scarcely spoken to her. She paused at what she was doing and her breath caught painfully. It had felt like this five years ago when she'd lost him. Was she going to suffer it all over again? No! She wasn't. She wasn't!

She determined to spend the day putting away all the serving utensils that had been brought out for the reception. When she finished, she made lists of still more things to do.

She viewed the piles of wedding gifts in the den with dismay. Every single one of them must be returned. After all there had been no wedding; there wouldn't be one. She saw so clearly how impossible marriage to Rodney would have been when she still had feelings for Ted.

The kitchen door banged loudly and her brother called out, "Anybody home?"

"In here."

Steve walked into the den and collapsed into a padded armchair. "You'll be happy to know *Kitten* didn't suffer too much damage in our little mishap. There's a small chunk of fiberglass knocked out of her bow—but it isn't serious. Hey—you doing okay?"

"I'm fine."

"You shouldn't feel so bad. What happened really wasn't your fault. I jammed the winch—remember?" There was a lengthy silence. "You called Rod to see how he's doing yet?"

"No, I haven't."

"You ought to, you know. You eaten?"

"No."

"Well, I'm going to grill a couple of cheese sandwiches. You want me to make one for you?"

"I don't think so, Steve. I'm really not very hungry."

"You ought to eat something. Might make you feel better."

"I'm fine—really."

"You sure as heck don't act like it," he said in exasperated tones.

He pulled himself out of the chair as if it were an effort and headed for the kitchen. She knew she wasn't good company, but she couldn't help it.

Steve was right. She should call Rodney. She'd already put it off too long. She dialed the number of the hospital and asked for the extension.

"He... Hello," Rodney answered in his tiniest voice.

Kit always marveled that Rodney, a big blond fellow who looked more like a baby-faced Norseman than a Texas rancher, could produce such a small sound.

"Hello, Rodney. This is Kit. How're you feeling?"

"I'm doing better," he said almost bravely. "The doctor's going to release me later this afternoon. I could come by your house on my way home. It would give us a chance to talk."

Seeing Rodney today was the last thing she needed.

"Rodney, I really don't know if we have that much to talk about today," she blurted.

"You're angry because I didn't show up at the wedding."

"'Angry' isn't the right word, Rodney," she said gently. "I'm having serious doubts about us, and I think you are too. I'm not at all sure but that your accident wasn't a 'blessing in disguise.'" She was using the same turn of phrase her father had. "We may have both been saved from making a terrible mistake."

There, she'd said it. A strained silence followed.

"I've been wondering about that myself, Kit," Rodney said at last. Did she hear relief in his voice? "Freud says there's no such thing as an accident. Lately I'd done quite a bit of thinking about us, but I didn't know how to talk to you about it. You seemed so enthusiastic about the wedding, so caught up in the preparations for it. You and your mother were working so hard, I just didn't have the heart..."

"Oh, Rodney, you should have."

"I'm a coward, Kit. You know that."

"No more than I..."

Although they talked a few minutes longer, there was nothing more to say. When she hung up her engagement was broken.

She turned her attention once more to the wedding gifts. She began separating the gifts from friends who lived nearby from the ones that would have to be wrapped for mailing.

Ted—if only she dared call him and find out about his arm. But he had been so cold, she lacked the courage.

She forced her mind away from Ted and back to the task of separating the gifts. She piled the gifts that would have to be mailed into a mountain. Oh! Surely there wasn't enough brown paper in all the world! This would take days!

She remembered her father's dinner invitation to Ted. Of course he wouldn't consider coming, but if he did.... The thought was disturbing.

The light in the sky had softened when she finally gave up her attempts to wrap the gifts. Six neatly addressed brown packages sat beside the mountain still to be wrapped.

"Nevertheless, six is a start," she thought wearily as she headed to her room.

Though she still wasn't hungry, she was exhausted. She changed clothes, folding her jeans, blouse, and scarf neatly and placing them on her bureau before slipping into a caftan that was flowing scarlet. She belted in her tiny waist with a golden sash. She smiled at her reflection, and the effect was dazzling. The brilliant color brought out her dark beauty. She brushed her hair until it was a wave of black satin falling to her shoulders. She looked exotic—like a Spanish princess.

She twirled in front of the mirror exactly as Ted always used to have her twirl when she'd dressed up for him. If only he could see her now! She smiled again, thinking of the way his eyes had always lit with admiration when he thought her especially attractive.

Then her smile faded, for he would never see her wear the caftan. His eyes would never light with pleasure. She remembered his coldness. Her heart began to beat jerkily as a feeling of hopelessness descended on her. The smartest thing she could do would be to put him out of her mind . . . permanently.

She sank—exhausted—into the softness of her bed. Her mind went blank. She was too tired to think of anything or of anyone, and she fell asleep almost at once.

She dreamed of a man who was tall and dark with strips of gold in his auburn hair. He was twirling her in his arms. She was a blaze of scarlet and gilt. He was laughing and so was she. Then their laughter faded, and they were breathless. His gaze became intense, yet tender. He was holding her tightly and she lifted her face to his kisses. He was so hard and so warm. Yet his lips felt infinitely soft as he nuzzled them against hers.

In her sleep, she smiled. She tossed and murmured his name. Only vaguely did she grow aware of a jarring clamor in the background.

Slowly, reluctantly she awoke. The blue princess telephone was jangling on her nightstand. She fumbled for the receiver and lifted it to her face.

"Hello," she murmured, her voice still thick with sleep.

"Is Howard Jackson there?" The deep, rich tones were unmistakably Ted's.

Clearly he had no wish to speak to her.

"I . . . I don't know," she said. "I'll have to check."

"No. Wait. Kit, is that you?"

"Yes."

"You didn't sound like yourself. I can give you the message just as easily. I'm calling to accept your father's invitation to dinner for Wednesday evening. I'll be bringing Phyllis."

"Oh," she said in a small voice.

"What time should we come?"

"We usually have dinner around seven."

"We'll be there."

He was about to hang up when she stopped him.

"Ted, did you see a doctor?"

"I just got in from the hospital. I have a spiral fracture of the humors in medical jargon. I'll be in a cast for a month or so."

"Oh, no! I . . . I'm very sorry about everything."

"Don't be. A broken arm is a small price to pay for having rescued a damsel in distress—surely."

"I don't know what to say."

"Don't say anything. Just be thankful that I have such a forgiving nature. A lot of men would have been glad to see a woman who'd been as troublesome to them as you have been to me sink beneath the waves and drown."

"I'm sorry I wrecked *Wild Lady*. I know how proud you were..."

"Were you always so obtuse or are you deliberately misunderstanding me?"

"What do you mean?"

"I'm not talking about *Wild Lady*. I'm talking about your jilting me five years ago without so much as a word of explanation or a good-bye."

"You know it wasn't like that."

"No, Kit, I don't."

She bristled at the hard note of accusal in his voice.

"Well, if I ran out on you it was exactly what you deserved! Thank goodness I realized what kind of man you were in time!"

"I think you realized you were falling for a poor man. In the nick of time you set your cap for Rodney, a bona-fide Texas land baron who's filthy in oil and cattle."

This accusation infuriated her.

"I can't believe you have the nerve to accuse me of that when you know..."

"Know what, Kit? That you were used to the soft life. That you didn't want to risk marrying me and being poor?"

"Just because you have a complex about money, don't accuse me of it," she lashed out. "In the first place, you never mentioned marriage to me. In the second, I never had any intention of marrying Rodney for his money!"

"Then what are you marrying him for?" He hissed. "Love? Rodney does not seem like the type of man you would find...exciting."

She bit back the angry words that rushed to her lips. His question went too deep. She'd almost told him that she'd only turned to Rodney out of loneliness in an attempt to forget *him*, the only man she'd ever loved. But that was something he must never never know. She would keep her pride intact at least, even if he'd broken her heart.

When she hesitated, he said, "You see . . . you want to continue living in your grand style, only grander. You know, Kit, when I first met you, I thought you were different. I thought you were the kind of girl...but now isn't the time to go into my foolish misconceptions about your character. I'll just say this morning was typical of our relationship—your ordering me to the servants' entrance...as if that's where I belong. I see very clearly that you're the type who gets a big thrill out of flaunting that large diamond you wear. With the Starr money behind you, you can have lots of diamonds. You can go anywhere, do anything, have anything. Do you know what that makes you, Kit? Don't you know what women who sell themselves are called?"

"Don't say it!" she cried. "Don't you dare say it! You don't understand me at all! If either of us had faulty character, it's you."

With that she slammed the phone down onto the receiver and lay back against her pillows as hot and angry as a curl of flame.

How different from her dream was the reality of her relationship with him!

Kit half expected Ted to call back and cancel on the dinner party, but he didn't. By Wednesday afternoon she was a nervous wreck. He would be coming in just a few hours. How could she face him now that she knew how he felt about her? She tried to comfort herself by rationalizing that she had an equally terrible opinion of him.

That evening she dressed carefully. She selected a low-cut, emerald-green sundress with a tightly fitting bodice that clung to her breasts and narrow waist. It had a full skirt that swirled in graceful folds below her knees. She slipped into green high-heeled sandals that accentuated the shapely curves of her legs as well as the daintiness of her ankles. She brushed her hair until it sparked like blue-black fire. Her skin glowed like rich cream, and her black eyes were sparkling as if she were actually looking forward to the dinner party instead of dreading it.

At the precise hour of seven when the library clock was chiming, the doorbell buzzed. Once and then again. She realized with dismay she would have to answer it because Steve and her father were out by the pool getting the charcoal fire started and her mother was in the kitchen with the cook. She dashed nervously toward the door, her green skirts flying, the rapid tapping of her high heels clicking on the saltillo tile.

She flung the door open wide. Lounging with menacing ease against a pillar like a great, dark tiger with a bandaged paw, was Ted. His tall, muscular build seemed to fill the doorway, his large presence dwarfing her. Navy slacks snugly fitted his narrow hips; the crisp cloth of his pale blue shirt stretched across the width of his firmly muscled chest.

His bold, sardonic gaze swept downward over her from the softly oblique line her black hair drew against the smoothness of her forehead, slowly over her body to the tips of her toes neatly buckled into their green sandals. His eyes lit with appreciation, and he whistled softly.

She gasped. She went warm all over and hated herself and him as well because he could so easily fluster her.

"You look very nice tonight," he said silkily. "But you certainly took your time answering the door." When she still said nothing: "Aren't you going to ask us in?"

She felt curiously weak all over. Why did her senses respond in such a way to this infuriating man?

"Yes . . . of course. Where's Phyllis?"

"She had to go back to the car to get her purse. Oh, here she is."

"Hello, Phyllis," Kit said as graciously as she could under the circumstances. "Won't you come in?"

Phyllis gave an abrupt little shake of her head which Kit took to be a nod of agreement. The girl kept her smouldering gray eyes downcast as if she disliked Kit so intensely she had no wish to even look at her.

"Mother's in the kitchen. Steve and Daddy are outside lighting the fire," Kit said, attempting to cover the awkwardness with small talk. "Could I fix you a drink?"

"I'd like a beer," Ted said smoothly as if he felt perfectly at ease. "Phyllis, how about you?"

"Nothing, thank you," she managed.

Kit led the guests out onto the patio where Howard and Steve welcomed them. Then she escaped into the kitchen. Her mother was pouring ice tea into glasses.

"Mother, I can do that." Kit pulled a beer out of the refrigerator. "Why don't you take this out to Ted."

"*Querida*, don't you want to?"

Sharply: "No."

Her mother looked at her quizzically. "*Querida*, sometimes I don't understand you at all. When I was your age I would have wanted to take a drink out to a man like Ted Bradley."

Kit's hand that gripped the pitcher of iced tea shook. "Please! Mother!"

Kit tried to find things to busy herself with in the kitchen to avoid going out onto the patio. She'd never learned to cook and usually avoided it. She was placing rolls on cookie tins when she was startled by Ted's voice—vibrant and deep—directly behind her.

"If only you were wearing a ruffled apron you'd be the picture of domesticity, Kit. Somehow this new you is a surprise."

"Is it?" she replied without amusement. Why did he have to make the situation more difficult than it already was? She knew he disliked her. Why couldn't he just leave her alone?

"I think you're deliberately avoiding me," he said with alarming accuracy.

"And would that surprise you after our telephone conversation? I would think you would at least apologize for insulting me so..."

"I never apologize for the truth."

"That wasn't the truth."

"Wasn't it?" There was a watchful, puzzling glint in his blue eyes as if he found something about her difficult to understand.

"What did you come in here for anyway?"

"Phyllis changed her mind about that drink after all. She wants a beer."

"You'll find one in the refrigerator."

He opened the refrigerator door and pulled out a beer. Then—beer in hand—he came toward her. Although he was smiling, he looked ruthless...menacing. She was stiffening.

"You needn't bother to avoid me, Kit. If I want your company I'll seek it."

He was pivoting to leave her, when several ice cubes slipped through her shaking fingers and splattered onto the floor. He stooped and retrieved them for her, tossing them carelessly into the sink on his way out.

His meaning was obvious. She wouldn't have to avoid him, because he had no intention of seeking her out. His words hurt—much more than they should have.

He was so coolly arrogant, so supremely self-confident—so indifferent to her now...

Throughout dinner the talk centered around racing although any mention of the accident was scrupulously avoided. Steve, Howard, and Ted were enjoying one another's company immensely. Anitra laughed merrily when one of the men made a joke. Only Phyllis—who stared moodily down at her untouched dinner plate when she wasn't glowering at Kit—and Kit failed to enjoy themselves.

After dinner the group moved into the den. Kit helped her mother serve after-dinner drinks. The men continued to discuss sailing. During a heated debate over the proper headsail to use in heavy air her father began to search through his stacks of sailing magazines for one issue in particular that had an article in it that would illustrate the point he was trying to make. Suddenly he remembered where it was. He was on the way to get it, when the telephone rang. It was a business call for him. He placed his hand over the receiver and summoned Kit.

"Kitten, would you mind going into the library and seeing if that September issue isn't on the table?"

"Not at all." She was only too glad to escape.

Her father excused himself to take the call in another room.

Ted was staring at her when she left the room, her hips swaying provocatively beneath the soft fabric of her green skirts. She walked self-consciously down the hall toward the library; self-conscious because she knew that he was still watching her in that boldly intent way of his and that he would continue to watch her until she vanished from his sight.

Why did he take such pleasure in annoying her?

She was rummaging through the magazines on one of the library tables, when Ted entered the room. She whirled to face him. He closed the double doors behind him so that they were completely alone together in the library.

His virile, blue gaze held hers until she looked quickly away. Every inch of him was handsome, she thought weakly. Why did he have to be so impossible? She steeled herself against his appeal as she remembered his accusations.

"Did you think you'd found another chance to escape?" he asked softly. He was smiling and she somehow found this apparent attempt at friendliness even more disturbing than when he'd been insulting.

"You heard my father," she replied coolly.

"Looks like he's going to be tied up on the phone for quite a while. That will give us a chance to talk."

"We have absolutely nothing to talk about."

"That's where you're wrong. I noticed you aren't wearing Rodney's ring tonight. Could it be that you found our conversation enlightening, and you've decided to mend your ways?"

"I found our conversation thoroughly disagreeable and not at all enlightening. I had already broken the engagement to Rodney *before* you called."

"Really? Why?"

"Because..." She broke off disconcerted. What could she say? She had no intention of telling him that her feelings for him had been the chief reason for her decision.

"I suppose you felt humiliated by the way he stood you up at the altar."

"That wasn't the reason."

"Then... what was the reason?"

"It's none of your business."

"Well, nevertheless, the important thing is that you're free again. I'd like to ask you out. Say tomorrow night. Why don't you come over to my place, and I'll cook dinner for you. If you weren't after Rodney's money, I'd like to know exactly why you ran out on me five years ago—not that it's important any longer. I'd just like to clear the slate."

"I can't believe you're asking me to dinner after the way you insulted me. I don't want to have anything more to do with you."

There was only the faintest tightening at the corners of his mouth. Then his lips curled as blue eyes that were too-knowing swept her. "You kissed me too passionately Sunday morning for me to believe that."

"Oh... Oh..." She was sputtering.

His voice drawled languidly. "I think you owe me one night. After all I broke my arm saving your neck, and you did wreck *Wild Lady*."

"Oh, all right.... When you put it like that."

"We'll make it eight o'clock. That'll give me time to pack Missy off to Phyllis's so we can be alone."

"Where do you live?"

"You won't have any trouble finding it. I just moved into a townhouse south of here a bit... on Ocean Drive..." He told her the number.

Then he leaned forward, the contours of his muscles rippling beneath his crisp shirt as he picked up the September issue of the sailing magazine. "I imagine your father is off the phone and will be wondering where the two of us are. He's going to have to work to prove his point. He's dead wrong about that headsail!"

"You don't think you make mistakes, do you?"

He looked up at her quickly and something—some emotion she couldn't read—came and went in the depths of his eyes. The moment was fleeting. His expression hardened almost at once, "Oh, I wouldn't say that." His tone was derisive, and a flicker of uneasiness raced down her spine. "I made one about you, didn't I?"

His words were shattering—like a bullet searing the soft tissue of her heart.

He left her then badly shaken from their conversation. Her date with him would serve as his brand of punishment for past grievances. How would she endure it—knowing that he disliked her?

She tried to cheer herself with the thought that it would only be one night—a few hours.

What could possibly happen in a few hours?

Chapter Five

Kit—the tires of her Porsche squealing—swerved onto the ribbon of asphalt winding down to the bay toward Ted's townhouse. She was late because she'd taken such pains with her appearance. This morning when she'd gone through her wardrobe she'd realized she didn't have anything special enough for tonight. Remembering how Ted had always admired her in bright colors she'd gone shopping and bought a new red dress. She'd justified the expense with the thought that if she was going to do battle with one of the most impossibly arrogant men she knew, she needed all her feminine armor intact.

And it was intact. Her freshly shampooed hair caught by a red silk headband fell in soft, raven clouds to her shoulders. Gauzy red cloth drifted over her curves, clinging, revealing, enhancing. She knew Ted would think the rich color brought out her dark beauty. The top of the dress was strapless and elasticized so that it molded her breasts and slender waist; the soft fabric of the skirt was swirling accordion plates. She'd applied perfume, Ted's favorite scent.

But in spite of the dress she felt apprehensive. After all it was only armor. She still had to battle her dragon.

Uneasily she remembered last night and how he'd bested her. She remembered his parting words—words that had cut her deeply—when he'd said he'd made a mistake about her. She hadn't been able to forget either his words or the contemptuous tone of his voice when he'd spoken them. If only she didn't care what he thought of her!

Well, tonight...tonight wasn't going to be a repeat performance of last night, she vowed silently to herself. She was going to be careful to be polite but impersonal. How, exactly, she could accomplish this, was unclear.

Again tires squealed. She was driving too fast and all because she was late and nervous about her dinner date with Ted. She knew that in spite of all her careful plans to keep their conversation on safe topics and thereby preserve her composure, Ted would be in charge of the evening, and the evening would go as he directed it.

The drive curved unexpectedly, and a blur of red bounced directly in front of her. Kit—mindlessly terrified—stepped down on her brakes hard. The car slid to a standstill just as a pretty, dark-haired child bounded out from behind a parked car after the ball.

Kit put on the emergency brake and stepped from her car. The child was trying to retrieve her ball from a clump of Natal Plum.

"Ouch! Sticky!" The child turned toward Kit for help, the thorns and her ball her only concern. Her great cobalt-blue eyes implored—misting.

Kit was still not over her fright that she could have hit the child. She felt cold to the pit of her stomach. Her knees were so weak she almost wobbled as she walked toward the little girl. She pulled the ball from the brambles. The child's hands were eagerly outstretched.

Kit said, "Darling, you mustn't.... You mustn't ever...." She was shaking so much, even her words seemed to shake. "You mustn't chase this ball just anywhere. If the ball goes into the street, please don't run after it. Not ever! Go get your mother..."

Before she could finish the child seized the ball and said defiantly in a voice quivering with pain, "My mother is dead." Then with the quickness of a little savage she darted away from Kit and disappeared toward the pool area.

Poor little thing! She was just a slip of a child. And no mother. She probably wasn't five years old. Such a spirited little darling with those saucy black curls framing that pixy face, those great big blue eyes.

Kit was still wondering vaguely who the child could belong to and why that person wasn't seeing after her properly as she climbed back into her car.

Slowly she drove toward Ted's townhouse. The color had gone out of the water and clouds; two flamingos, their great wings flapping languidly, were splashes of brilliant pink as they flew low over the darkening waves.

Kit pulled into a parking place not far from where she thought Ted's townhouse must be. She was still badly shaken from nearly having hit the child. She couldn't possibly face the ordeal of her date with Ted without giving herself a few minutes to calm down. She sat for a long time and watched the sun sink below the horizon. It was dark when she slung her purse over her shoulder and headed toward the townhouses. The breeze fanned her skirts, swirling them around her slender form.

The night was black velvet sprinkled with diamonds; the moonlight was silver ribbons spreading across the bay. And Kit, racing toward Ted's townhouse with the graceful lightness of a sea sprite, was as young and lovely as the night.

She paused, breathless. She was staring at the cluster of townhouses trying to determine which was Ted's. They were all so alike, great sloping shadows in the darkness, differing only in that some were unlighted and others lighted. Ted had called her earlier that afternoon and given her specific instructions how to locate his. She began to count the buildings and headed in the direction of one which was cheerily lit. Its large plate glass windows facing the bay were as brilliant as bars of glowing gold. She noticed the fuzzy shadow against the drapes of what looked like an etagère. Yes, it was his! She could make out the numbers above his lighted front door.

She knocked on his door several times and no one answered. She looked at her watch. She was a few minutes late. She'd been so upset over nearly running into the little girl that she'd sat in her car far too long.

She decided he might have stepped out for something. Perhaps he'd lacked some ingredient for the meal and when she'd been late, he'd decided to do a bit of last-minute grocery shopping. It never occurred to her he would stand her up. He'd been determined last night to make her accept his invitation, and then this afternoon when he'd called, he'd been equally forceful.

Perhaps something had happened. Well.... She waited another couple of minutes and then scribbled him a note and pinned it to his door. She decided to return to her car and drive down to a little convenience store where she'd spotted a pay phone and call him. Perhaps he'd been running late and was showering.

She headed back toward her car. She was almost to the pool when she saw out of the corner of her eye, a blur of something bounce toward the pool. In the distance—as if it came from the pool, she thought she heard a faint splash.

She turned from the pool in the direction of the parking lot. Suddenly she heard—again from the pool area—a squeal, desperate and high-pitched followed by a splash, larger than the one before.

And then—nothing. No sound other than the murmur of banana leaves rustling gently as the wind swept up from the bay.

She was about to hurry on toward her car, but something, some warning of danger, stopped her. She turned and saw floating quietly on the aqua waters of the pool like a cherry decorating a fancy drink, a bright red ball. She was remembering bright blue eyes thickly fringed with sable lashes set in the face of a pixy. Where was the little girl?

A quiver sliced through her. Truly afraid, Kit was running toward the pool. Beneath the ball, almost at the bottom of the lighted pool she saw something dark. Forgetting her watch and her purse, she plunged into the water with them and dragged the object to the surface.

She swam toward the shallow end of the pool, pulling the child with her. She lifted the little girl into her arms and carried her up the steps out of the pool. The child opened her mouth and gasped. She took a second breath. No water sputtered up. She was perfectly all right.

Hugging the little girl to her closely, Kit sank into one of the poolside chairs.

"I was holding my breath," the child explained brightly. "You didn't have to jump in 'cause I know how to swim. My daddy taught me."

The wind gusted around them and the two of them shivered with cold.

Kit remembered her purse—still at the bottom of the pool. She saw that her wrist was bare. Her watch must have fallen off in the scramble.

"I got you all wet," the child said. "And big people don't like to get wet. Your red dress is all ruined. Are you mad?"

"No, I'm just thankful you're all right."

She was remembering how carefully she'd dressed, how carefully she'd arranged her hair. She wouldn't be female if she didn't feel a twinge of dismay. She remembered her watch and purse. Still, those things were unimportant.... "You and that ball!" She hugged the child fiercely.

Then they were laughing—Kit a little hysterically and the child with sheer delight.

"I must get you home," Kit said at last. She would take the child home and go home and call Ted and explain why she couldn't make it tonight. She couldn't possibly face him now—looking as she did.

Reluctantly the child agreed. "We'll go to Daddy's house first." She skipped off toward a nearby townhouse.

Kit was too distracted by everything that had happened to read the lighted numbers above the door.

She was ringing the doorbell when the child said, "Ever since my mother died I've lived with my Aunt Phyllis. Daddy lives next door...."

Then the door opened and Kit was staring up into the boldest of blue eyes. Ted's handsome face went dark with alarm.

"Princess! Kit.... What happened?"

For one long moment Kit was too stunned for speech. Her red silk headband fell at a crazy angle across one eye. Her dress was dripping like a soaked dishcloth. Doubtless her eye make-up was smudged beneath her eyes. She remembered ruefully how she'd planned to be the picture of sophisticated composure this evening.

"My ball went into the pool," Missy cried. "Then I fell in trying to get it out, and the pretty lady jumped after me." The child hushed, breathless, and shivering in the air-conditioning.

"Your Aunt Phyllis has been looking everywhere for you, Missy." Ted said sternly. "You shouldn't have run off."

"I know," the child said, her big blue eyes—so like his—solemn.

"Kit, come inside. I'll call Phyllis and tell her Missy's safe. I'll find something dry for you to put on."

"That really isn't necessary. I'll just run on home."

"Oh, no you don't!" His good hand was on her elbow, and he propelled her into the room which was as boldly modern in decor as the architecture outside. "I got your note. The reason I wasn't here was because I was down on the beach searching for Missy. I don't know why I didn't leave the door unlocked."

She was vaguely aware of white walls on which hung large, abstract paintings, of sleek furniture done in earth tones, of brown carpet—plush—stretching across the room, of sheets of glass looking out onto the moonlit bay. And on the wall directly opposite the windows and over the sofa was an enormous slash of silver with beveled edges. The mirror was bold—like the house, like the man who lived in it. The mirror reflected the loveliness of the scene outside.

"I wouldn't dream of letting you go home like this, shivering. You'd catch pneumonia," Ted was saying.

He led her to a chair and overruled her protests that she was too wet to sit on it by saying that it was upholstered in leather and couldn't be hurt by a little water. He brought a blanket and wrapped her in it; he brought her a long-stemmed crystal goblet filled with amber liquid. He insisted that she drink it. Only too late—as it flowed scalding down her throat—did she realize it was brandy.

He was kneeling before her, his knees sinking deeply into the rich brown carpet. She saw that he was refilling her goblet.

His eyes were on her face and they were electric blue. She went warm all over. She was remembering again that other time—was it only Sunday?—when she'd been shivering with cold and they'd sat together beneath the blanket. She was dizzy suddenly. She was afraid to take the goblet from his hands because she was trembling. It was just the cold and the brandy combining... surely...

He was reaching beneath the blanket. He caught her wrist in his large brown hand. She knew he must feel the leap of her pulse as her heart quickened. Again she felt a treacherous warm tide of feeling wash over her.

He placed the goblet a second time in her hand, saying, "Just sit here and relax while I call Phyllis."

She sank back feeling cozy and cared for as he went to the phone. Slowly she sipped her brandy, watching him.

Tonight he wore black slacks and a shirt of the deepest blue—the color of his eyes. She saw the column of his dark throat above the unbuttoned top of his shirt. Once—when she'd felt like this—she would have been free to press her lips against the warm flesh of his throat, and he would have drawn her into his arms and responded passionately.

Feeling strangely heavy, she placed the goblet on the glass table beside her and lay back against the chair.

He went to the telephone; and when he dialed Phyllis, there was no answer.

Missy, her black hair shining wet, was a bundle of exuberant energy bouncing into her lap and snuggling into her arms to share the warmth of her blanket.

"I've brought Joseph," the child said. She thrust a large, white, stuffed rabbit—a little worn from love—up to Kit to admire. "I want him to meet you."

"Hello, Joseph, I'm Kit."

"That's almost like cat. Rabbits like cats. Or anyway Joseph does, and he's a rabbit."

The child continued to chatter gaily, describing the peculiarities of Joseph's personality. Joseph wasn't an ordinary rabbit. He was special. And he didn't like carrots either. He preferred chocolate as apparently his little mistress did.

Kit, in turn, told the child a story. The child listened—rapt. Once while she was telling her the tale, Kit looked up and saw Ted watching them intently, but when he saw her look up, he turned quickly away.

Time passed pleasantly until Ted, who had finally reached Phyllis, decided it was time he took Missy to her aunt's.

Missy wanted to remain on Kit's lap and listen to another story. It was only with the greatest effort that Ted persuaded her to leave Kit to go to her Aunt Phyllis's. Missy was at the door holding her father's hand when she suddenly broke out of his embrace and raced back to Kit. Impulsively she flung her arms around Kit's neck and kissed her on the nose. Then she was skipping nimbly back to her father.

Ted was gone for at least a quarter of an hour. His heavy footsteps sounding on the concrete walkway outside signaled his return. The door opened abruptly, and he entered the room. Kit heard the lock click firmly as he shot the bolt. Then he moved toward her with the silent, menacing grace of a large cat stalking his prey. She shrank against leather upholstery. She was alone with him, and she felt strangely alarmed. Her heart hammered wildly as if she were his prey.

Ted sank into the thick carpet at her feet.

"Sorry I was gone so long," he said in husky tones.

"That...th-that's all right..." she managed a little breathlessly because of his dangerous nearness. As always she felt powerless against his virile appeal. Just the proximity of his body to hers affected her senses.

His dark face was grave. "How can I ever repay you, Kit, for saving Missy?"

"It was nothing."

"It was everything...to me," he contradicted. His voice held an intimate quality that was even more unsettling to her than his nearness.

"Missy was in no danger. She said she was holding her breath."

"Missy is a poor swimmer at best. She can hold her breath like a champ, but if you hadn't come along when you did, I very much doubt if she could've gotten out of that pool alive."

"Oh, no!" She let out a little horrified gasp.

"So you see...how much I owe you." The tones of his voice were rich and deep—and unnervingly intimate. He was reaching beneath the blanket for her hands. He took them in his, and as always at his touch she shivered. "You're cold. We've got to get you out of those clothes."

He drew her up from the chair and the blanket fell from her. He pulled her—unresisting—into the warmth of his arms and led her toward his bedroom.

Everything seemed to happen as if in a dream. She saw his bed—its headboard, gleaming chrome, its spread a vivid splash of blue, the very color of his eyes. It stood in the center of the vast room beneath a large painting of a pale blue sailboat flying before the wind. *Wild Lady*...before...the accident. Her eyes riveted to the bed.

Again she sensed the danger, and she stiffened in his arms. He led her toward his dressing room and bath area.

"I want you to relax. Take a warm bath. I'll go next door and get some dry clothes from Phyllis."

"Really...you mustn't... None of this is necessary. I'll just go on home. I'll be fine. Really I will." She finished through chattering teeth.

"You're in no condition to know what is necessary," he said firmly. "You're shaking like a leaf. I want you to do just as I say. You can leave your wet clothes..."

"Leave my wet clothes? As if it's perfectly all right for me to undress in your bedroom while we're here alone! What if someone were to come by and find me like that? One of your neighbors..."

"None of my neighbors would dream of coming over at this hour unless I invited them," he said smoothly. "And I have no intention of letting you catch your death of pneumonia because of your Victorian morals. It's clear to me that you think I might be planning to take advantage of this situation. But let me assure you, I'm not. I'm deeply grateful to you, Kit, for what you did tonight. And I want to repay you by doing what anyone would do. I'm simply offering you the comfort and convenience of my home so you can bathe and change into something warm and dry. Is that so awful?"

He sounded almost hurt. His dark face was gravely handsome, his voice sincere. He was merely being courteous. She felt a pang of guilt to have doubted him.

"No, it isn't awful at all," she said weakly, feeling foolish for her unwarranted suspicions. "And it would be nice...very nice...to bathe and slip into dry things."

"I'm glad that's settled."

"Wait! My gold watch! And my purse!"

"What about them?"

"They're at the bottom of the pool..."

"I'll get them with the boat hook while you're bathing." He was at the door, pressing the button of the doorknob.

"There," he said. "When I pull the door closed, it will lock, and you'll be safe... from me." His lips parted in a broad, rakish grin that made her feel guiltily uncomfortable. It had always been easy for him to read her. She thought he was secretly amused because of her suspicions about him. Without saying another word, he left her, pulling the door shut behind him.

She went to the door and pressed her fingertips to the doorknob. He'd been as good as his word. It was locked. Feeling reasssured and a trifle ashamed that she'd doubted him, she went to the dressing room area and began to undress.

She really was being frightfully cold to him. And he was being so good to her, so considerate. Ever since she'd arrived, he'd done nothing other than be solicitous of her every comfort. She remembered the blanket, the brandy. He was going to bring dry clothes. And more than anything, his gratitude to her for saving his child, had touched her. She removed her clothes and lay them on the marble counter in the dressing room.

Bare feet touched the cold baby-blue tile of his bathroom floor. Beige Turkish bathsheets hung on chrome bars. She turned on the water and fingered its warm flow until it was just the right temperature. She saw a child's jar of perfumed bubble bath on one corner of the tub. Missy's no doubt. Impulsively she sprinkled the bubble bath into the water, and then as the sweet-smelling bubbles began to build like a foam mountain, she slipped into the tub and lay back languidly.

For a long time—it seemed half an hour—she lay there soaking. She hadn't meant to, but the water was so warmly pleasant. And she had been blue with cold.

At last she forced herself to bathe and shampoo her hair. Then she stepped from the tub and wrapped herself in a thick Turkish bathsheet. She wound a small towel around her hair so that it looked like a turban. She unlocked the bathroom door, and as she stepped through the doorway, shining in the dressing room mirror was the vision of her own loveliness. She scarcely glimpsed the reflection of her breathtakingly beautiful face, the rosy flush of her cheeks, the crescent of gleaming black hair just visible beneath the folds of her turban.

Where were her clothes? Ted's clothing littered the bright blue bedspread.

She saw black slacks. She saw his blue shirt in a careless heap. His shoes . . . all thrown down as if he'd hastily undressed. Her own clothes were nowhere to be seen.

Then she heard the sound of music playing softly and drifting in from the living room. Her heart beat with short little spasms. It was the very music he'd played the night he'd almost made love to her so long ago. A saxophone was playing low and sexy.

She should have known she couldn't trust him! But he'd been so courteous, solicitous, so grateful to her for saving his child that she'd been taken in.

The music enveloped her and for one long moment she remembered the beauty of their last night together. Nothing he could have done other than play that music could have brought their time of love back more poignantly. Tears were in her eyes, and she lifted her fingers to push them away.

Oh, he was horrible! Horrible! Too horrible for words! Just the sound of that music brought back the hurt. How could he have played it?

She was filled with murderous fury. She was shaking with it. If he thought for one minute that he could seduce her just because he'd given her two glasses of brandy, tricked her into removing her clothes, and put on that record, he had another thought coming! She wasn't that weakly sentimental! And to think he'd used his child, to accomplish this! He was low and it was obvious he had a poor opinion of her as well.

Holding the bathsheet tightly so that it couldn't fall, she rushed to the door. She saw that strangely the small button in the doorknob was still pressed down. How had he gotten it? Never mind.... His type knew all the tricks. There was no time like the present to give him a piece of her mind. She'd set him straight once and for all about the kind of girl she was.

She heard sounds from the living room, but she ignored them. She opened the door and called loudly, "Ted, you bring me my clothes this minute. I'd like to get dressed and go home before someone comes and finds me..."

"I'll just bet you would!"

"Phyllis!" she was gasping. "What...what are you doing here?"

"I could ask you the same question if the answer wasn't all too apparent!" Phyllis was pale with rage; every inch of her quivered with that same emotion. "In answer to *your* question: The door was wide open so I came in to get Missy's ball. When she remembered she'd left it here, she refused to go to sleep until I promised to come over and get it."

Kit scanned what she could see of the living room for any sign of Ted, but she couldn't find him. Where in Heaven's name was he? Surely if he could be found, he would explain.

"Phyllis, this isn't what you think. It's all perfectly innocent."

"Innocent!" She was pushing past Kit and striding into the bedroom. Her eyes were on Ted's clothes. Then she returned to the living room. "You must have a strange definition for that word. It's plain as day what's going on." She turned to face Kit once more. "I should have known you'd try something like this! Your ego just can't take the fact that a man jilted you—"

Kit drew a sharp, quick breath and flinched. She couldn't blame Phyllis for drawing the conclusion she had. She herself was convinced that Ted had not planned an *innocent* evening. But she couldn't understand why Phyllis was so hostile... unless... she were interested in Ted for herself. Aloud she said, "For your information, trapping Ted is the last thing I have on my mind at the moment. Where is he anyway? He'll set you straight."

"You tell me. It's obvious you *know* him... far better than I do."

"Oh..." Kit was angry too, and she was finding it increasingly difficult to hold her temper in check.

Just then the door leading into the kitchen from the utility room and garage opened and closed. Both women heard the refrigerator door open. Then Ted, holding a news magazine in his good hand and an unopened beer in the other, stepped into the living room. At first he did not notice the girls because he was avidly reading an article in the magazine. Then setting the magazine on the counter, but continuing to read, he opened his beer. Kit sighed loudly and impatiently as he flipped a page. He looked up.

His lazy gaze took in Phyllis—still white and quivering with rage—as well as Kit clad only in his towel, and he smiled. His smile, which Kit was sure was motivated by amusement rather than friendliness, only infuriated her the more.

She saw that he was dressed only in a thick velour blue robe, its wide sleeves concealing his cast. His chest—tanned and muscled—was a V of darkness against the blue of his robe where it opened down the front.

Her mouth went slack. She couldn't believe what she was seeing. What was he doing in that robe? His hair was wet and rumpled—as if he too had bathed or showered...perhaps with her...or as if she'd run her hands through it while they'd made love. In spite of her anger she was aware of an odd breathlessness at the sight of him—so virile and overpoweringly masculine dressed only in his robe.

With a look of dry amusement curving his lips, he lifted the magazine from the table and would have resumed reading it had not Kit snatched it from his hand and tossed it onto the carpet.

"Ted...what are you...but never mind.... Tell Phyllis...tell her the truth about us...and what happened here tonight."

"Don't be ridiculous! Phyllis doesn't expect an explanation." He moved across the room to the stereo and turned it down.

"Tell her the truth," Kit hissed.

"All right," he said lazily.

Phyllis interrupted him with a burst of impatience. "Ted, you're absolutely right. I have no interest in hearing an explanation. What you do is your own affair."

Ted lifted his beer can to his lips Then he settled himself into his large overstuffed chair as if that finished the matter.

"Put that down and tell her!" Kit cried.

"All right . . . if you insist. Do you mind if I make myself comfortable first?" He plumped a cushion under his cast with maddening slowness. "The blasted thing is awfully heavy." He turned toward Phyllis. "The facts are quite straightforward. Kit was the one who jumped into the pool to save Missy. Her clothes got wet in the process, and she decided to take a bath and change . . ."

Phyllis couldn't resist a question. "Isn't that Kit's red dress on your sofa?"

Kit saw the rumple of bright red—her dress! Her undergarments—dry now—were also piled on the sofa.

"Those clothes certainly look dry to me," Phyllis commented.

"They are *now*," Ted said quietly.

Phyllis caught the edge in his voice and relented. "Well, as I said earlier—what the two of you do or don't do . . . is none of my business. What I *would* like to know is where's Missy's ball. I promised I'd find it for her."

"It's in the kitchen sink," Ted said. He waved one hand toward the cubicle brightly covered in foil wallpaper that was his kitchen.

Phyllis went to the kitchen and returned with the ball. Ted got up and joined her at the door. "Phyllis, bear with me . . ." Ted said. "I can see by Kit's scowl that she isn't at all happy with the way I've explained things. I can't let you leave without putting this mess in the proper perspective. As a woman you should understand how much importance women attach to morals and their reputations. No matter how things look . . . I have the most honorable of intentions toward Kit."

“Really, Ted, I told you none of this is necessary...” Phyllis said faintly.

“Nevertheless...” Ted insisted, opening the door for her. “I will tell you. I had wanted Kit’s parents to be the first to know...but under the circumstances and because you are family...I’m going to marry Kit.”

Chapter Six

I'm going to marry Kit." Ted's words rang in Kit's mind. Had he gone mad?

Phyllis had practically collapsed against him when he'd said that. The poor girl had looked shattered as he'd led her from his townhouse to her own.

"I thought she'd never leave," Ted said, interrupting Kit's thoughts. He was shooting the bolt in the front door after Phyllis had gone. "We're alone at last!"

His eyes went over her, forcing an awareness in her of her body and his virile response to it. Worse still, he forced her to be aware of her own answering response to him. His voice went deep and husky. "Do you have any idea what the sight of you in that . . . only that . . . does to me, Kit?"

She felt curiously light-headed, treacherously aroused by his words.

His large brown hand was on the dimmer of the light switch. As if by magic the lights dimmed to a romantic glow. He came toward her. The dim light caused a shadow to flicker across his dark features.

She watched him—mesmerized. Her pulses quickened in anticipation. She was unable to prevent the flush which swept her cheeks, but she managed to meet his gaze which was as direct as ever.

"Don't come near me!" she cried breathlessly. His eyes were on her fingers nervously clutching the towel about her. "*You* stay away from me!" She was terribly aware of the feel of terry against her breasts, of the feel of it—soft—against the smooth flesh of her body. Oh, if only she were properly dressed, she wouldn't feel at such a disadvantage.

"You're shrinking against that chair with all the terror of a prim virgin who thinks she is about to be..." The omitted word hung in the vast silence of the room. She saw his teeth flash white in the darkness. "Odd; but I have the distinct impression you're scared of me, Kit."

"Ted Bradley!" She stiffened with outrage. She longed to be able to honestly refute that remark. He was so smug; he felt himself so superior to her. "I'm not afraid of you! I'm... I'm angry.... Furious...."

"Then I want to know why you're so angry at me?" he asked innocently.

She watched with wild relief as he sank down into his overstuffed chair instead of coming nearer to her. Thank heavens he'd decided *for once* to follow her bidding! She felt on much safer ground.

"As if you don't know."

"I don't. That's why I'm asking."

"You tricked me out of my clothes pretending to be grateful about Missy."

"I was grateful. And I didn't trick you out of your clothes."

"Then while I was taking a bath you removed my clothes..."

"Only to put them in the dryer," he replied with an easiness that only angered her the more.

"And you took off your own and threw them on the bed."

"I couldn't reach your purse and watch from the edge of the pool with the boat hook. I had to change into my swimming trunks—which strangely enough I keep in my bedroom." He opened his robe so that she could see he was wearing his bathing suit under it.

"Well, you put on that record...that same record you played the last night..." She was becoming flustered.

"It happens to be a favorite of mine."

"And where are the clothes you promised to get from Phyllis?" she countered, determined to catch him.

"I didn't think it would be necessary to involve Phyllis since you took such a long bath and yours were dry before you finished."

"You didn't bring them to me..."

"Would you have wanted me to? You were bathing, remember. I thought you might object if I showed up in the bedroom when you were getting out of the tub. And I can see by the way you're overreacting to all this, that you would have."

Kit thought she detected a barely perceptible smile on his face, mocking her. She blushed furiously. He always bested her!

"You have an answer for everything," she said, admitting her defeat.

"Are you quite finished with your interrogation?" he asked after a brief silence. He was no longer smiling; his blue gaze raked her thoroughly and she remembered with a start all she wore was his towel. When she said nothing: "What I want to know is why you would think I would do all the things you've accused me of? What have I ever done..."

"As if you don't know..."

"I don't. And I'm getting sick of all your insinuations—that I mistreated you in the past. When it was you who walked out on me."

"I don't want to talk about the past."

"Why not? Have you developed a conscience after all these years?"

His steady gaze probed her face for the answers she refused to give him. His calm, deliberate manner was unnerving.

"I want to go home."

She was edging slowly toward the puddle of bright red cloth on the sofa, but, before she could reach it, he read her mind. He sprang from his chair and seized her clothes. The flimsy material of her undergarments flowed through his fingers and fell upon the carpet. His blue eyes, lazy with amusement, gazed down at them and then up at her. She was increasingly aware—and by his expression it was evident he was too—that she was naked but for his towel. She felt her cheeks grow warm. Oh, if only he wouldn't look at her like that!

"Give me my clothes so I can go."

"You're very beautiful when that Latin temper of yours catches fire."

"Give them to me!"

He sat back down in his chair, still holding her dress. A brief grin curving the corners of his mouth teased her.

"Sit down and relax. You're not going anywhere yet!"

"You would keep me here against my will?"

"Until you hear me out."

"I've heard all I want to hear for one night."

"Not quite. Unless you intend to run out of here naked without your car keys. I'm certainly in no mood to loan you that towel."

"You took my keys?"

"I didn't take them. I retrieved them from the pool along with your purse and watch." She heard a faint jingle as he held them up for her to see. He smiled pleasantly. "I suppose you could go knock on one of my neighbors' doors. I'm sure you'd find someone willing to help you."

"You're...insolent and crude." He only laughed. "You think all of this is hilarious. Phyllis will probably tell everyone she knows. What if she calls my family—as if there hasn't been enough gossip about me. I'll never be able to hold my head up in this town."

"Phyllis would never do anything like that, and I think you're attaching too much importance to what unimportant people think."

"You couldn't possibly understand. You don't have a decent bone in your body. You're twisted...and horrible...and...and..." She failed to think of an adequate insult.

"I get the picture. But if you're quite through with your insults, I have a plan to help you, a plan that will be the salvation of your reputation."

"I think you've done more than enough for one evening."

"Nevertheless, hear me out. *You can marry me.*"

"What?"

"You heard me. *You can marry me.*"

For that she had no answer. She lapsed into a moment of stunned silence.

He'd said something to Phyllis about marrying her. But she'd thought it a crazy taunt; she hadn't believed he'd been serious. She saw now that he had meant it. His dark face was grave as if he'd never been more serious in all of his life. He was watching her face intently as if he were hanging on her next words, as if he were hoping she would say... What? What could such a perverse human hope for under the circumstances? His proposal was outrageous!

Never had she felt further from understanding him than she did at this moment. He looked expectant, almost eager as if her answer were very important to him, as if this were a bonafide proposal...

And how...how could she answer him under the circumstances? She felt a strange eagerness as she wouldn't have dreamed she could at his words. They seemed to ring in her ears like music. *"You can marry me. You can marry me."* And for some idiotic reason marriage to him seemed like the most natural thing in all the world.

Nothing that had happened in the past few days seemed to matter beside that. She no longer cared that Rodney had jilted her. All that was important was that Ted, Ted had asked her to marry him.

She fought against the emotions that were sweeping her, the old familiar weakening, the hunger for his touch. She loved him as she had never loved Rodney. Why hadn't she realized it before? Rodney was just a man she'd spent time with because she couldn't have the man she really loved. Without Ted her life had been empty. Even though he'd been infuriating these past few days, she'd felt alive as she hadn't since he'd left her. She'd felt! And for five years she'd felt nothing.

Now she knew by her powerful emotional response to his proposal that her feelings for Ted stemmed from love.

But there was so much she didn't understand. Letitia. His marriage. His abrupt reappearance in her life. What were his motives behind this proposal? She would be foolish to assume he was romantically attracted to her just because she was in love with him. He couldn't love her. Nor had he mentioned love to her.

He must have some other reason—other than love—for wanting to marry her.

She was remembering the past: that golden, scarlet, crisp October when she'd fallen in love with him. He'd courted her ardently, pretending to love her so cleverly. She'd never detected he had the slightest interest in any other woman. She'd been so young and naive—easy prey for a man like him.

Then she'd found out about Letitia, and she'd run from him. Later she'd learned from friends that Ted's adopted father had died. Ted dropped out of law school then because he didn't have enough money to continue his education and help his mother. Mrs. Bradley had given her son all the insurance money from her husband's death, and Ted had started his own business. He'd married and begun a life that no longer included Kit.

Just thinking of it and she was hurting again as if it were only yesterday. Clearly she'd just been one of many women in Ted's life. No! He wasn't asking her to marry him for love. She knew him too well to believe that. He had some other less noble motive. What was it?

"At least you didn't say 'no' right off the bat," Ted said, breaking into her thoughts. "That's something."

"Well, I should have." It would never do to let him suspect how vulnerable she felt where he was concerned. She actually—fool that she was—wanted to marry him. She loved him. *She loved him.* The realization was still new to her. What would he do if he knew the extent of his power over her? The thought hardened her voice. "I wouldn't marry you if you were the last man on earth. If I didn't know before how terrible you are I do now."

"And what have I done that's so terrible? Would you prefer me to kneel before you and take your hand in mine and beg you to marry me? Yes, that's it. I can see it shining in your eyes. You're an incurable romantic, Kit."

Before she could do anything other than gasp in horror he sprang from his chair and was kneeling at her feet. She shrank back into her chair as he seized her hand, her free hand that wasn't fearfully clutching terry cloth around her.

"Why, Kit you're trembling."

"If I'm trembling, it's with rage." She pulled frantically at her hand, but he held it tightly.

"I don't think so. You're trembling because I'm touching you. Remember, I know you." He hesitated. "You were thinking earlier that I was planning to seduce you, weren't you?"

Her eyes widened at this truth.

"And I'm wondering if that isn't what you secretly longed for. I haven't forgotten our kiss in the drive," he continued softly.

"No.... No..." She was backing away from him. She tried to draw the edges of the towel closer about her body. If only he wasn't so near. If only she could escape from him. But where? Where could she go without her clothes? To his bedroom? She could lock him out. She knew from experience that wouldn't work.

He increased the pressure of his grip. He was pulling her from the chair, down onto the carpet beside him.

"There...that's better. I'm tired of playing games, Kit. I want you as I've never wanted any woman. And you want me too."

"I don't want you! I don't!" Her pulse raced, mocking her swift denial.

"We're going to settle this argument tonight once and for all."

"Oh, no!"

He was pushing her body down onto the thick pile of the carpet and positioning her beneath himself. Oh! He knew exactly what he was doing! She struggled wildly, but he was far stronger. And he held her beneath him almost effortlessly. She was panting with fury and with something that went deeper than fury, something he was deliberately trying to awaken.

His good fingers closed around her fingers that were holding the edges of the towel together and he ripped the towel from her body so that she lay naked beneath him. Carelessly, triumphantly he flung it aside. His gaze swept insolently from her blazing eyes, over her breasts, across the flat of her stomach, down the curve of her thighs. He missed nothing. "You're beautiful, Kit. Even more beautiful than I remembered." As she cried out he muffled her cry with his lips. She pushed against his chest but it was like iron. She tried to toss her head, so that he could not kiss her, but he brought his good hand up and held her face still. His kiss was long and searching and she writhed—but in vain—to escape him. His lips left hers, and he was murmuring endearments in his softest, huskiest voice.

"Kit, I've been such a fool.... We've wasted so many years."

She was about to answer him, but his mouth closed over hers once more. He was parting her lips with his tongue. His kisses became urgent and possessive, ruthless. Her hands were reaching up and circling his neck. She was pulling him to her tightly. She felt the hard warmth of his lean body, and thick hairs of his chest—bristly—against the rounded softness of her breasts.

She was shivering as if she were cold, but she was warm. He had been out of her life for five years, but her body remembered the delight of his and betrayed her. She was opening her mouth and kissing him as passionately as he was kissing her. All of her resistance against him was flowing out of her. She wanted him; she couldn't help herself. She loved him as much as the night she'd loved him so long ago when she—thinking their love would last forever—had almost given herself to him.

She forgot his treachery and was only aware of the feel of his hand moving gently over her, tracing the supple curves of her body. She felt his lips on hers. Then he was kissing her on her cheek, her neck, her earlobe. She felt his breath—warm—in her hair.

Oh, she wanted him; and he knew it. Her heart was beating fiercely, joyously as she waited for him to possess her.

Then, just as she thought he would take her, he seemed to catch himself and stop. He shuddered violently. Then he held her to him, breathing deeply as if to check his passion, before he pushed her roughly away. Blindly she saw him grab the bathsheet from the sofa and pull it over her.

"I think I've proved my point," he said brutally.

"What?" She felt stunned; cheated. She'd been on the verge of surrendering herself to him because she loved him, and he'd been trying to prove a point.

"I wanted to prove to you once and for all that you want me as much as I want you. And I think—stubborn though you can be—even you will admit I'm right now."

How could he . . . how could he . . .

"I won't admit..." she broke off, strangling. In another minute she would be crying. She had never felt so hurt, or so lost in her whole life.

"Admit it, or you might drive me to further lengths to prove it to you."

"I admit it," she said slowly, reluctantly. He smiled; his eyes were brilliant. "You needn't look so smug," she said in what she hoped was her coldest voice, "I only kissed you like that because I couldn't help myself. I..."

"Exactly. And I can't help myself where you're concerned either."

"That's no reason to ask me to marry you."

"I didn't say that was why I was asking you to marry me. A man my age looks for more in marriage than that."

"I...I..." His face was blurring in tears. She tried unsuccessfully to blink them back. He hadn't meant any of his kisses. Even his passion for her was phony. He'd only used her to prove some idiotic point. He'd been playing a cruel game to boost his much-too-conceited ego. To prove his power over her. Now he was conversing as if nothing that had happened between them mattered to him. She began to weep bitterly and hated herself for doing so.

"Kit, darling. You're crying. I've hurt you."

He'd called her "darling."

Between sobs: "And no doubt that proves even further how susceptible I am where you're concerned."

He pulled her—unresisting because she was too upset to fight him—into his arms. His hand stroked her hair.

"No matter what you think, Kit, I don't want to hurt you. You're very special to me. That's why I'm not going to make love to you tonight even though I want you more than I've ever wanted anything." His whole body shook violently. "I want you. You don't know what just holding you like this is doing to me. But this time I want things to be right between us. We're going to marry first."

She pushed against him and he let her go. She wanted to believe him, but because she wanted to so much, she couldn't let herself. Once long ago he'd betrayed her trust, and she couldn't allow herself to trust him again. She reminded herself he'd been kissing her as if he wanted her desperately, and he'd only been trying to prove a point. Wasn't trickery dishonesty? Didn't that prove he couldn't be trusted?

"Why do you want to marry me?" she blurted.

"Don't you know me well enough to know the answer to that?"

"No! I don't think I know you at all. I don't suppose I ever did, even though once, I thought I did. You pretended to love me, when all the time..."

As always when the past was mentioned, his face darkened. His lips twisted into a grim, cynical smile. "I think you and I would do best to forget the past," he said evenly. "Our discussions about it always dead-end. Let's sum it up by saying we both made mistakes, but if we've learned from them, we don't have to repeat them. As for why I want to marry you, I have my own reasons. But I'd rather not discuss them now. We'll discuss them over dinner."

He'd talked about mistakes. Did he mean he was a changed man? Did he mean he wouldn't turn to another woman if she were to resume her relationship with him?

"I won't be staying for dinner," she said coolly. The last thing she wanted was for him to realize how much she hoped that what he'd said would prove true. "I'm going to leave . . . as soon as . . ." Her voice lacked real determination.

"Oh, I don't think you'll be leaving just yet. Remember I've still got your car keys. And that towel you're hugging so fiercely belongs to me."

"You . . ."

"It's nearly nine-fifteen. I know you're hungry."

What was the use? He always had his way with her. "I'll stay."

"That was easy." Blue eyes flashed with triumph. "Sometimes you can be very difficult to persuade." He laughed jauntily then, and threw her her clothes. "There's an ironing board in the utility room you can use."

Kit blew her hair dry with the hair dryer Phyllis kept at Ted's for Missy. She'd pressed her red dress so that it looked almost as fresh as when she'd put it on earlier in the evening.

She switched off the hair dryer. Piano music—low and melodic—was drifting into Ted's bedroom. She heard Ted—brisk and purposeful—moving about in the kitchen. The scent of a charcoal fire was in the air.

She began to brush her hair. Unconsciously she began singing the lyrics of the lovesong the pianist played on the record. Then she caught herself and stilled the brush in mid-air. She was singing—and she only did that when she was very happy.

Slowly, carefully she placed the brush on the cambrian marble counter. She hadn't been this happy for a long time. And it was all because it seemed Fate had turned back a page of time. Rodney was out of her life. She was with Ted, and it seemed to her they were young and in love and planning to be married.

Oh, if only...if only...things were as wonderful as they seemed. She heard the crisp sounds of Ted's knock on the door. "Kit, are you ready for me to put the steaks on?"

She heard her own voice, a stranger's, call gaily, "Yes, I'll be right out."

They ate out on the terrace beneath a canopy of stars. Two candles in hurricane lamps glimmered from the center of the table. The moon was high and the bay was soft silver ripples. But Kit was so aware of the tall, dark man who sat opposite her, she scarcely noticed the beauty around her. Being with him—as if she belonged with him—was almost too wonderful to believe.

Dinner was superb. Ted cooked—as he did all things—well. The meal was simple: romaine lettuce sprinkled with toasted sesame seeds, finely grated Swiss cheese, and Italian dressing; sauteed mushrooms; fresh green beans garnished with sliced water chestnuts; Texas toast, and steak. And of course he'd remembered her favorite wine.

Throughout the meal Ted was attentive. He acted to perfection the part of ardent suitor. Kit had to work very hard to keep her guard up. At last she asked the question foremost on her mind.

"You said if I stayed for dinner we would discuss your reason for wanting to marry me."

"Suppose I said I had only one reason—that life without you these past five years has been empty."

She caught a strangely husky note in his deep voice, and she almost believed him—because she wanted to so much. She steeled herself against the sincerity of his manner.

"I wouldn't believe you," she said harshly. "Remember I'm not the naive little girl you knew five years ago.

I've learned a few things about life. You married Letitia. You have Missy..."

"Still, my life is incomplete without...you... without a wife."

"I don't believe you," she repeated. She was afraid to show how desperately she hoped he cared something for her. "Remember you have already proved your point tonight—about how susceptible I am where you are concerned. You think you can persuade me to believe anything because I...I..." She'd been dangerously close to say that she loved him.

"Because you what?" He seized her wrist, and when she didn't answer him his fingers tightened until she cried out. "Because you what?"

His eyes were fastened on her face with an intensity that alarmed her. She was afraid he would see her love for him.

"Because...I...I'm such a...because you think I'm such a little fool."

He released her abruptly as if in disgust.

"Is that really what you think?"

"Yes."

"Then you're right! You are a little fool! That's not what I think at all! You used to understand me so well. What's happened to us, Kit?"

"Five years," she said bitterly. "Five long, empty years."

"Empty? Were they empty for you too?" He no longer sounded so angry.

"No! I don't know why I said that. It's just that you confuse me."

"I don't mean to."

"You still haven't told me your reason for wanting to marry me," she persisted stubbornly.

She felt, without seeing, because his face was in the shadows, his gaze linger upon her features. She knew that her expression was tight and guarded. He must never, never know what she felt for him. At last he answered her.

"Well, suppose I said I need a wife to look after me. I'm tired of living alone . . . and then my bookkeeper just quit at the store." He spoke evenly, as if he were interviewing her for a prospective job instead of telling her why he wished to marry her.

"Surely you could hire someone to replace her."

"Not someone with your mind for numbers. I have accounting problems with my ranch and construction company as well."

"Your ranch and your construction company?"

"Yes, your poor boy's made good. But we won't go into that because I wouldn't want to think you were marrying me for my money."

"I would never marry anyone for money!" she flared.

"Wouldn't you?"

She remembered he'd accused her of marrying Rodney for that reason.

"We were discussing your reasons for wanting to marry me," she replied coldly.

"So we were. There's Missy. She needs a mother."

"You have Phyllis to care for her, her own aunt. She'd be much better for her than I would."

"I don't think so."

"Phyllis only lives next door. Looks like the perfect arrangement."

"Then looks are deceiving. Like you, I thought it would be perfect for all of us at first. Phyllis and I have a good relationship with one another. I bought the two townhouses side by side. The second townhouse was to be an investment as well as a convenient place for Phyllis to live and see after Missy. She pays a nominal rent. I thought I could help her get on her feet financially. She's had some problems the past few years. Well, things went along all right for a while, but then it became apparent that Phyllis spoils Missy. You saw what happened tonight."

"So you want to marry me for your own convenience. You need a wife and someone to look after your child. You've said you want me physically, but you haven't mentioned love. I don't suppose that in a 'marriage of convenience' love matters. I do want to make it clear, though, that I'm no more in love with you than you are with me." Her pride drove her to say that last.

He pushed his chair back from the table and stood up, his muscular body rigid with tension. When he spoke his voice was hard.

"I want to marry you, Kit, if you'll have me. Apparently we've lost the ability to trust and understand one another. I'll let you draw your own conclusions as to what my motives are."

He turned and left her then. She heard the sliding glass door slam shut behind him.

For a long time she stared miserably out onto the glistening bay. The scent of salt spray and jasmine filled the air.

She wanted him. She loved him. She would marry him. She knew she would be behaving foolishly to do so, but she couldn't stop herself. Without him she would always be unhappy. If she married him there was a chance—however remote—he might come to love her.

She heard his movements in the townhouse and turned to observe him. He'd poured himself another glass of wine. She saw him bend and turn up the stereo. Again he was playing the saxophone music he'd played the night they'd made love.

She went to the glass door and pushed it open. The music was vibrant and soothing like warm liquid passion filling the room.

"Have you made your decision yet?" he asked quietly.

"Yes. I'll marry you . . . on one condition."

He swept her into his arms and before she could even attempt to resist, he kissed her. Slipping his arm around her waist, he drew her across the room. He opened the drawer of a cabinet and pulled out a tiny velvet box.

"I think it's time we made it official," he said.

He handed her the velvet box. Slowly she opened it. She gasped. An enormous American-cut diamond—at least two carats—set in a simple setting of yellow gold flickered in the dim light. Slowly, carefully she removed it, and he slipped it onto her finger.

"Ted . . . Ted . . . it's lovely," she murmured.

He was staring deeply into her eyes, his expression unfathomable. She fingered the ring in shy delight.

Impulsively she sprang onto her tiptoes and threw her arms around his neck and hugged him. Her fingers were clasped together at the back of his neck, and he brought his face down to hers. She kissed him lightly on the cheek. She had meant only to embrace him affectionately. She had not anticipated his response.

His great hand moved behind her head, forcing her face to slant against his. His mouth covered her lips in a long, searing, demanding kiss. She could feel the fiercely rapid thudding of his heart against her breast. She felt the heaviness of his cast around her back as he crushed the slender curves of her soft body against the threatening hardness of his. She gasped weakly, and she felt his breathing quicken. She heard him groan.

She was aware of his fingers moving downward from her neck to the zipper at the back of her sundress. Deftly he parted the zipper and the dress was slipping from her shoulders. She felt the warmth of his hand moving across her flesh. And as always his nearness, his desire for her, and his touch produced a wild answering thrill in her. Her whole consciousness was stimulated by the taste, the feel, the smell of him.

She was kissing him with a passion that matched his own. She felt a mad impatience to belong to him completely. He was pulling her across the room and drawing her down onto the sofa. His kisses became deeper, longer; the caressing touch of his fingers—intimate fire. She was breathless with longing for him, shivering gently with ecstasy.

His mouth traced downward from her lips to her earlobes. She was moaning softly as she lay limply beneath him. She felt the blistering heat of his lips as he gently kissed the tips of her breasts. Her fingers were intertwined in his auburn hair and she held him to her fiercely so that he would go on kissing her there forever and ever.

His voice was a low murmur. "My darling, Kit. You're all I can think about, all I want. Let me make love to you now."

His hand moved slowly downward.

The deep husky sound of the saxophone enveloped them. *The same sound as before. Before—when he'd almost made love to her and—before she'd lost him!*

The grip of her fingers in his hair slowly weakened. The memory of his treachery was dampening—like throwing cold water onto fire. While some of the heat of that fire may remain, the flames go out.

Oh no! No! No! She must find a way to stop him before it was too late, and she was lost. She forced herself to break away and because that was the last thing he expected, it was easy to do.

"I said I'd marry you on one condition," she said thickly. Her fingers shook as she brushed her hair back from her face.

"What? What in hell are you talking about?"

"I'll marry you if you promise me you won't touch me. Do you understand? I don't want you to make love to me—ever."

"Kit..."

"I mean it. Don't come near me. Not tonight...or ever."

"Kit, I don't want to promise that. I want you. I lo..."

"Don't say it! You'll say anything to a girl to make her give in to you. Surely I should know that by now." He was staring at her as if he couldn't believe what she was saying. "Is that understood? If we marry, you must promise not to touch me. Not even to kiss me. The only reason I'm considering marrying you is to save my reputation—which will be in shreds because of you!" When he said nothing: "I won't marry you if you don't."

His eyes hardened; his mouth twisted. Slowly he sat up on the sofa. He pulled the edges of his shirt together and began to laboriously button them with his left hand. When he spoke his voice was deep and cold.

"I see Kit, you're set on being a fool. You seem determined to ruin things between us again."

Her voice was equally cold. "Will you promise?"

"Yes."

He arose from the sofa and slipped his belt through the loops of his dungarees. She was terribly aware of him as a man—of his height as he stood over her, the breadth of his shoulders, his muscles tapering to his narrow waist, the purposeful movements of his fingers at his belt buckle—those same fingers that could touch her gently and make her flesh burn like fire.

He was at the door. She heard something jingle faintly and watched as he tossed her keys onto the carpet at her feet.

Then he pulled the door open, and stepped out into the night. He slammed it behind him, and she was left alone.

She had won! He'd given her his word. But why did her victory feel so hollow?

Chapter Seven

The day of the wedding dawned clear and bright. Kit was in her room waiting to make her appearance. She wore a gown of ivory lace that hugged the curves of her body more provocatively than a wedding gown should. Never had her waist looked tinier. The neckline was low and scalloped.

More than a month had elapsed since the night Ted had proposed. She had not seen much of him since that evening. He had been out of town for two weeks on business at his ranch. She had been busy with preparations for the wedding. When she had seen him he had been coolly polite. He had kept to their bargain—he had not touched her.

Why was he marrying her? He had agreed to forego the physical side of marriage and his recent lack of attentiveness was beginning to make her wonder if he was really all that attracted to her anyway. Could such a marriage work? Was she a fool to rush into it? Her rational mind told her that she was, but love wasn't rational. And she loved him.

Kit had wanted a small wedding after the disaster of the first one, but the small garden wedding had mushroomed into an enormous affair.

Kit shakily fingered the rope of pearls at her throat—Ted's wedding gift to her—as she studied the milling crowd beneath her balcony. She would have to go down soon. An enormous yellow and white striped party tent—bigger even than the one they'd rented a month ago—stood in readiness for the wedding and reception to follow. Her mother had hired a band at the last minute.

A small wedding! Kit laughed nervously at the thought. Although they'd sent invitations only to family, in the past month her sociable mother had invited everyone she'd talked to on the telephone, everyone she'd run into, however casually.

"I just couldn't leave *them* out, *querida*," she'd explained over and over to her daughter as the guest list grew longer. And when Kit had stormed about the band: "*Querida*, it just wouldn't be a wedding without music. You know how we all love to dance."

Kit had seen to only one detail of the wedding herself. She'd had a small replica of the giant wedding cake made. The smaller cake was chocolate on the inside, and she'd had it made for a certain little girl who loved chocolate.

Anitra came to her room and told her it was time for her to come down.

"Mother, is he..." She lowered her voice and whispered in Spanish, the language they used sometimes when they were alone. "Is he here?"

Her mother reassured her in Spanish. "*Sí, querida.* He has been here from the first. He is so anxious to marry you. And, oh, he is so handsome today. Dressed in dark blue. His suit is the color of those darker rings around his eyes. He has such beautiful eyes. So blue. So expressive. I have watched them fill with love when he looks at you."

Kit thought her mother was too effusive about Ted's love for her, but she relaxed a bit. At least—this time—she wasn't going to be jilted.

They were married.

The band was playing a Spanish polka, and Ted was claiming her for his partner. In spite of his cast, he held her tightly and moved with that flowing grace that was characteristic of him.

"And so now, Kit, you are mine."

"In name only."

"You have a strange idea of marriage."

"You promised to go along with it."

"And for a month, I've kept my promise. But I'm growing weary of that promise, aren't you? Remember we are married now."

The music was ending, and before she could answer, Steve was asking her for the next dance.

"Kit, I'm happy for you today," her brother said as he whirled Kit across the dance floor beneath the tent.

Kit looked past Steve and noticed that Ted was dancing with Phyllis. Phyllis looked unhappy although she was beautiful in a gown of blue threaded with wisps of gold. Ted's expression was tender with concern as he bent his head low and talked to her. Suddenly Phyllis broke from his arms and ran across the lawn as if she were desperate to get away from the wedding activities. Ted was right behind her. Kit watched miserably as he caught up with her, and seized her by the hand. He led Phyllis—still holding her by the hand—away from the crowd toward the water.

The music stopped and Kit was hardly aware that it did so. All she could think of was Ted—with Phyllis. Why didn't he return? Where had they gone? What was their relationship? Was he in love with her? Was she in love with him?

Steve led his sister from the dance floor, and her father, smiling proudly, joined them and began discussing the next yacht series. But Kit wasn't listening to them; she was aware only of Ted's lengthening absence from the wedding festivities.

Another Spanish song was played and then a western song. Kit found herself only half listening to those who spoke to her. Her gaze kept straying toward the lawn stretching toward the seawall that was hidden from her view by a clump of oleander and olive trees. Phyllis and Ted still had not returned.

At last her mother came and told her that the photographer wished to take a few more pictures of her and Ted together.

Kit wandered across the lawn in search of Ted and Phyllis. At first she could not find them because the foliage at that end of the estate was dense. Her father had had it planted for privacy.

She heard them before she saw them. Their voices were clear and distinct like sounds carried across water.

Phyllis was talking in a tear-choked voice. "You'll never make me understand why you're marrying her. You don't love her! You couldn't!"

Not wanting to hear another word, Kit called to them loudly. She gave Phyllis a moment to compose herself before she joined them.

"The photographer wants to take more pictures," she said simply, feeling miserable and embarrassed that she had interrupted them.

Ted slipped his good arm through hers. He seemed genuinely glad to see her—almost relieved. "Phyllis is worried about how Missy will react to our marriage," he said in explanation of Phyllis's tear-streaked face. "But she hopes we'll be very happy together." He eyed Phyllis sternly, daring her to object to his explanation. "She wants to keep Missy at her house for a little while—to give her a chance to adjust to our marriage."

Steve was coming across the lawn. "The photographer..."

"We're coming," Kit answered.

Steve pulled Ted to one side to ask him something.

Kit turned to Phyllis. "Phyllis," she said gently, "I won't try to take your place with Missy. I hope you know that. But I do intend to give her all the love I can possibly..."

Phyllis didn't wait for her to finish. "You don't fool me for a minute, Kit Jackson! You couldn't care less about Missy! And you are the last person Letitia would have wanted raising her child. I know you've wanted Ted for a long time. Letitia told me how you tried to take him away from her!"

"Phyllis, that's not true."

"You're just a spoiled rich girl who thinks she can have anything or anyone she wants. You'll ruin Ted's life and Missy's too... He deserves a different kind of woman. A woman more like..."

Phyllis never finished what she would have said, for Ted was saying smoothly, "Girls, are you ready?" He took Kit by the arm and led her back to the house.

What would Phyllis have said, had she completed her sentence? Was she in love with Ted herself? Was that it? Did she think Ted loved her in return? Was that why she thought Kit couldn't make him happy?

Kit was beginning to have real doubts about the wisdom of her hasty marriage.

The photographer had a last-minute inspiration.

"Let me get one more picture of you two," he said to the newlyweds. "One of you kissing."

Before she could resist, Ted was pulling her into his arms, crushing her to him. She saw the determination on his face, the glint in his eyes. He smiled down at her triumphantly. She knew he was remembering his promise not to touch her or kiss her. Just as she knew he was going to seize this opportunity to kiss her in spite of that promise. She twisted her face to evade his lips, but he was too quick for her. She felt the warmth and wetness of his open lips cover hers and linger there nibbling slowly, softly, and then insistently until her lips parted as well.

The camera had ceased its mad clicking, and still he kissed her. Still he pressed her slim body against his own. In spite of herself and the circumstances she enjoyed the hard, masculine feel of his body against hers, the intimacy of his lips on hers. Her brain was spinning; she felt dizzy and breathless from his kisses. But he did not release her.

She could almost feel her resistance weakening. As always her need for him betrayed her, and she lifted her arms and circled his neck.

His triumphant chuckle tickling her throat warmly brought her back to reality.

"You see, that promise is as hard for you to keep as it is for me."

She pushed against him, but he held her to him.

The photographer was thanking them. "That's great. Just great!" His camera clicked one final time.

"It certainly is," Ted agreed. He was smiling broadly down at her.

He was laughing then as he held her to him, and so was she. Phyllis and her angry words were forgotten, and Kit was hoping fervently that somehow, someway the two of them could find a way to be happy together.

The festivities were far from over when Ted insisted that they leave. Kit had changed from her wedding gown into a demure three-piece suit that was done in three shades of lavender. Ted tucked her into his low-slung sports car. Anitra, tears of happiness streaming down her face, bent down to kiss Kit. Then Ted was in the car beside her and stepping on the gas pedal. Rice showered them, and cans tied to the rear bumper of their car were clatter on concrete as they sped away into the twilight.

Kit watched the incessant crashing of the waves against the concrete bulkhead beneath her as she waited at Ted's front door for him to return from the car with the rest of her things. She heard his heavy tread as he approached. She watched as he set her suitcases down.

"Isn't it tradition that a groom should take his bride in his arms and carry her over the threshold?" he asked.

"I'm surprised you care for traditions."

"I don't, unless they suit my purpose."

He was staring down at her, his gaze direct and piercing. Then before she could stop him he pulled her to him and held her tightly.

"Kit, this is the beginning of our life together."

"Aren't you forgetting your promise?"

The mere mention of it seemed to enrage him.

"My promise . . . !"

His mouth came down hard upon hers, forcing her lips apart. He kissed her hungrily, passionately, no longer with restraint. Just as she was dizzy from his kisses his lips left hers.

With one movement he was stooping. His left hand traveled over her body, and he grasped her at the knees, lifting her and swinging her onto his left shoulder. He held her there, slung over his shoulder like a heavy sack, as he struggled with his keys and the lock on his front door.

"Put me down!" She kicked at him wildly. "What do you think you're doing?"

"Be quiet! I'm carrying you across the threshold." He was slamming the door and bolting it, forgetting their suitcases and leaving them outside.

"You certainly have a strange way of doing it," she said as he carried her across his living room and into his bedroom.

"And you, my darling, have only yourself to thank for that. Remember if it weren't for you, I wouldn't have a broken arm, and I could carry you properly."

He flung her onto the bed and before she could do anything other than gasp he was on top of her. Her black hair spread in gleaming ripples across his bed. Her black eyes were luminous.

"You are very beautiful, Kit," he said softly. "Very beautiful. And I want you. I want you more than I've ever wanted you. We're married now..."

"You promised," she said weakly. She tried to keep her body stiff beneath his.

"I know I did, and I've kept that promise for a month. Do you really want me to keep it now?"

Oh, he was close, too close! She couldn't think! A lock of his thick hair had fallen across his tanned forehead. He was terribly handsome. Just the feel of his hard body covering hers... She was so, so vulnerable to his appeal, and he knew it.

With his fingertips he traced and retraced the curve of her ear. She was gasping. He knew, too well, what his touch there did to her.

"Do you?" he repeated his question.

He brought his lips to her throat and kissed the mad pulsebeat there.

She moved underneath him. Slowly she lifted her hands and caressed his rough cheeks. She pulled his face to hers and kissed him tentatively on the lips, and then because she could not stop herself, more passionately.

She should despise herself for her weakness, for giving in so easily, but she couldn't. She was too caught up in the joy of the moment, the joy of his wanting her. And she wanted him; she wanted to belong to him completely—even if he could never be hers in the same way. She knew that being with him would be beautiful, and she would treasure the memory of it always—even if she lost him again.

Suddenly she was thinking of beautiful things: Missy smiling fleetingly, pink flamingos flying low over darkening waves, and wild olive blossoms blooming and blowing in the wind. Were these things less beautiful because of the transient quality of their beauty, or were they all the more precious because they couldn't last?

Life was like that too, wasn't it? Filled with beautiful moments that couldn't endure. She knew she had to surrender herself to the beauty of this moment. Living life to the fullest meant taking risks. She knew she was risking her heart to love him a second time. But if she didn't take the chance, she would have to go on as she had. Anything, even that terrible hurt was preferable to feeling that strange, hollow emptiness that was not being alive at all.

She was aware of his hand moving gently, beneath her chin and down the curve of her neck to rest upon the swell of her breast. He was staring at her in wonder, as if he thought her very beautiful. He was unfastening the tiny buttons of her blouse. He bent his head and with his lips nudged the silken edges of her blouse aside. He was unhooking the bit of lace that was her bra. She felt his lips warm and nuzzling on her flesh once more, finding the ripe softness of her breasts, and kissing them until she was shivering with pleasure.

He helped her to sit up. He was pushing her jacket over her shoulders, helping her slip out of her blouse. His eyes went over her, and the sight of her—her full rounded breasts, the smoothness of her olive skin—inflamed him. He smiled at her tenderly before crushing her to him. Her hair was tumbling about her shoulders and he buried his face in its rich darkness and kissed her on her neck beneath her earlobe. She heard his voice, vibrant with passion, murmuring love words to her.

With shaking fingers she unbuttoned his shirt. Deftly, in spite of his cast, he pulled it off. Then he held her to him for a long moment as if she were very dear to him. She felt the thick hairs of his chest against her breasts, the incredible heat of him.

If only he really loved her, as she loved him, she would have been completely happy. But he only wanted her physically!

Though eyes blurred with desire she watched as he hastily undressed and then undressed her. He was pulling her to him and covering her body with the long length of his. She was trembling and so was he.

"You smell sweet—like flowers," he murmured. His hands gently caressed her body as he kissed her.

Her mind seemed to go blank for a while. She forgot her doubts about him. She was aware only of her driving need for him. His kisses became more urgent; his body moved purposefully, pliant to hers, responsive to her slightest movement. His touch was like fire and ice. One moment her flesh seemed to burn and the next she was shivering. He was embracing her tightly, and for one long moment, it seemed to her that they were one—not only physically but emotionally and spiritually.

The tension drained from them, and still he did not move from her. He held her, cradling her in his arms.

Time passed. Except for a sprinkle of lights across the bay all was blackness and silence outside. He was holding her still, as if he couldn't bear to let her go. And strangely she felt even closer to him afterward than she had when he'd made love to her.

The terrible thought came to her. What would happen if she lost him now...after this wonderful moment of shared closeness. How could she bear it?

His lips sought hers again and he kissed her gently as if he truly loved her. And suddenly, for no reason at all, she was weeping. He kissed her eyelids that were wet with tears and her cheeks that were also tear-wet.

He spoke softly. "Why are you crying?"

"Because...because..." In that moment she could do nothing but be honest. "Because—before—I lost you."

She felt his muscles tense. "You didn't lose me, you left me. Remember?" he said in a voice that was now tinged with bitterness.

He pulled away from her. The closeness that had existed between them was gone. In the darkness she was aware of him fumbling for his clothes and hastily dressing. He left the bedroom and went into the living room.

Why did the mention of the past always anger him? She lay back, tears smarting in the back of her eyes. After a while she drifted into an uneasy sleep.

An hour later the phone rang. Although Ted answered the extension in the living room before it rang twice, Kit woke up. Who could have called them on their wedding night? She felt increasingly uneasy when she heard the front door click softly shut. Ted had gone out without bothering to come in and explain to her where he was going.

While he was gone she bathed and dressed in a pair of tan slacks and a green silk blouse. An hour passed and he didn't return. At last she decided to go out and see if he'd taken the car.

She found his car where they'd parked it earlier. He was on foot unless someone had come by for him.

She decided to search the beach. She stepped from the pebbled walk onto the lawn that sloped downward toward the seawall.

Suddenly she saw him. He was standing on the concrete bulkhead, holding a woman in his arms. Phyllis!

Involuntarily Kit stepped deeper into the shadows.

Ted's head was bent over Phyllis's, and he seemed to be talking earnestly to her. But, because of the rhythmic lapping and splashing of the waves against the bulkhead, Kit could not hear what he was saying.

As she watched them she felt frozen—in a state of stunned shock. Phyllis...and Ted.... Ted had made love to her and then gone to Phyllis. It seemed to her that tonight was a bitter repetition of the past.

Somehow she managed to get back to the townhouse. She sat down on the couch. She felt cold like ice—cold to the marrow of her bones. Her stomach was queasy. All of the warmth she'd felt for him when he'd made love to her was gone and in its place was a terrible, hollow coldness.

Why had she married him? Why hadn't she seen something like this would happen? He hadn't changed.

Ted came in a few minutes later. His face looked tense and strained. Doubtless he was dreading returning to his wife. Was he regretting their hasty marriage as she was?

"Where did you go?" she asked quietly.

He hesitated only a second. "For a walk. It's a beautiful night."

"Did you run into anyone out there?"

Again he hesitated. Evasively: "I pretty much had the place to myself."

His half-truth was incriminating. Clearly he had no desire to tell her he'd met Phyllis. If their meeting had been innocent, wouldn't he have told her?

He came to the couch, and when he sat down beside her, she shuddered. He pulled her to him, and at first, he didn't notice that she was wooden in his arms.

His lips seemed to burn her flesh. She tried to pull away, but he caught her to him fiercely. His mouth came down hard on hers. What was the use of fighting him? She let her lips remain cool and passive beneath his.

He drew back. "What's wrong, Kit?"

"Everything," she wanted to say, but she said nothing. If she mentioned Phyllis, he would probably put together some half-baked explanation that wouldn't satisfy her anyway. Then they would argue, and what would that accomplish? There was no way she could make him be faithful to her, if he didn't choose to be. She wasn't his jailer.

"Nothing," she said in a small, tight voice.

"I can see by the look on your face that something's wrong."

If she didn't know better she would think he was genuinely concerned. She marveled at his duplicity.

"I'm just tired, that's all. And if you don't mind, I think I'll go on to bed."

"I was hoping we could have dinner together."

"You'll have to count me out."

"Kit, this is our wedding night."

"Believe me, unlike you, I haven't forgotten it for a minute." With that she arose from the couch, and would have marched to the bedroom had he not jumped up and grabbed her.

"Now what in the world is that supposed to mean?"

"I don't think I need to spell it out. Figure it out for yourself."

She left him then, and went into the bedroom. He made no attempt to follow her. A few minutes later she heard the front door shut and she knew he had gone out.

She cried herself to sleep wondering if he'd gone to Phyllis.

The next morning she wakened to the sound of Ted in the kitchen, to the smell of eggs and bacon and biscuits cooking. She was about to get up when he entered the room, a cup of coffee in his hand. "Feeling better?" he asked.

Her heart flip flopped crazily at the warmth in his voice. He was smiling down at her, a smoldering light burning in his blue eyes at the vision of her in his bed.

"Yes," she murmured, averting his gaze. Just the sight of him this morning—handsomely masculine—and she felt shyly nervous. She realized how vulnerable she was to his appeal. He had only to smile to disarm her.

"Good." He leaned down and brushed her forehead quickly with his lips. She knew she had only to respond and she would feel the wondrous rapture of his lips on hers, of his arms circling her in a passionate embrace. But the inner demon of doubt still possessed her. She endured his kiss stiffly, and he withdrew his lips. He handed her the cup of coffee. He smiled at her again; this time his smile showed the strain of control. "Don't get up. This morning I'm going to serve you breakfast in bed to make up to you for not taking you on a honeymoon."

"I never expected a honeymoon."

"You're very understanding. I will take you on a trip as soon as I can get away from the business. That's one of the penalties of being in business for yourself—you can't always leave when you want to. Right now I'm developing a tract of land on the Intercoastal Canal near Aransas Pass for an oil company. We're dredging a canal and building docks. I just can't leave in the middle of it. This is our big season. We have several cattle sales coming up and those mean tent rentals and table and chair rentals."

"From what you say, I gather your businesses are doing well?" Gingerly she sipped the steaming coffee. She felt much more relaxed with him than when he'd first come into the room. He'd expertly maneuvered their conversation onto safe ground.

"They are. When other areas of my life did not work out, I put all my energy into them." His face had darkened. "But now . . . that I have you, I'll want to spend more time at home." Again the intimate tone of his voice sent her pulse beats tripping.

He did not pursue the subject further. Instead he returned to the kitchen and left her to finish her coffee.

They spent the rest of the day alone together, and she almost succeeded in pushing Phyllis from her mind.

That afternoon he took her to the shipyard where *Wild Lady* was in dry dock for repairs. Ted told her he'd hired professionals to do most of the work because he wanted her to be ready for the next yacht series.

"This time, with you crewing for me instead of for your father, I won't have any trouble beating him. I won't have to worry about someone running into me," he teased.

That afternoon he told her things about himself she'd never known before. He told her of the first ten years of his life, the years he'd spent in a foster home before he was adopted. He told her how he'd longed to have a family like hers, how he'd longed for security.

"At Christmas rich people used to send us baskets of food and cheap little presents so our Christmas wouldn't be quite so bleak at the foster home," he said. "Sometimes we would even get to ride down Ocean Drive to see the Christmas lights as a special treat. We would pass by some of the homes that belonged to the people who so carelessly made those donations. Kit, I don't know if you can understand what it is to have nothing . . . and to want so much." His voice caught with remembered bitterness.

"I've made a lot of money, Kit. It took a lot of money before I learned it wasn't just money I wanted. It was love and security as well. Happiness. I was starved for it." He set the tool he'd been working with down. He was reaching for her and pulling her into his arms. He held her close. "There was a time when I wanted all those things so much I almost hated anyone who had them. Having Missy helped. I didn't want her to grow up with all the twisted feelings I had. And now that I have you to help me raise her, I know she'll grow up taking for granted all the things I missed. She's going to love you—and soon. And in time we'll have children of our own . . ."

If only Kit hadn't known about Phyllis, the afternoon would have been idyllic. The knowledge touched everything with a strange bittersweetness.

Ted took her to dinner at an elegant restaurant overlooking the bay. The dining room was softly aglow with candle light; beneath them the bay like a sheet of smooth glass reflected the night beauty of the city and its lights. Throughout dinner he gripped her hand as if he could not bear to sit through the meal without touching her.

When they returned home he immediately drew her to the bedroom and into his arms. She tried to push away from him, saying she was tired. He paid no attention to her protests.

"I can't let a wife of mine fall into bad habits," he teased, his gaze possessively roaming over her face. She was acutely aware of his fingers in her hair, of his nearness, of the warmness flowing like a treacherous flood through her. "Tomorrow night it will be a headache or some other bit of nonsense. When all the time you want me as much as I want you."

"Oh, you're impossibly conceited," she whispered in a shaky voice that betrayed all too clearly she was not immune to his appeal. "You think you can have any woman." She was thinking achingly again of Phyllis, of him holding her close to him in his arms.

"We're not talking about any woman. We're talking about you. It's you I want—you I intend to have. Have you forgotten that you belong to me? That you're my wife?"

She struggled in earnest, but he was stronger, and more determined. His mouth closed over hers in a long kiss. And as always, her will to fight him drained from her.

He bent her backwards and she felt the bed beneath her, and his body on top of hers. Then she was aware of nothing but the swirling mad bliss of his touch, the ecstasy of his embrace as the fire of their passionate desire leaped into roaring flame.

She was lost, as he'd known she would be.

His mouth followed the curve of her chin to the hollow of her throat. Slowly he undressed her. She felt the body warmth of his hands at her bare waist, pulling her body against his, molding her to his length.

Her own fingers combined the thick auburn mane that was his hair. Her lips found his once more in an ardent, drugging kiss....

When it was over, he fell asleep almost at once, but she lay awake remembering the thrill of his touch, the heat of his kisses. He'd clasped her to him, his fingers pressing against her spine as if she'd belonged to him utterly. She'd felt hot like an overbright star—sparkling with light, flaming with glory.

When it was like that between them she found it difficult to believe he could love another woman as he did her. She could not doubt his passion.

Still, the vision of him holding Phyllis in his arms was indelibly stamped on her brain.

Weren't men different from women? They didn't always love the women they desired. But she loved him! Fiercely!

Yet the thought that he might love Phyllis was tearing her to pieces. She couldn't endure marriage to a man—even Ted—if he wasn't faithful.

What was she going to do?

Chapter Eight

Kit stirred drowsily, awakening. The bright glare of morning sunlight was slanting through the partially opened floor-to-ceiling draperies. Outside she saw an expanse of summer sky—brilliant blue. The bay was undulating green glitter. Then the man beside her stretched sleepily. She felt the hard warmth of his fingers move across the bare flesh of her stomach as he moved nearer and snuggled against her.

She stared down at his face, partially concealed by the tumbled sheets. Red highlights glinted in his tousled hair. Sleep had smoothed the lines from his face, and his gentle expression was strangely at variance with his virile, rugged features. He pressed his lips lightly to her shoulder, and where his lips touched her, her skin tingled.

She almost hated him because she loved him so much. He was capable of hurting her as no other man could. Effortlessly he aroused her deepest emotions; carelessly he disregarded her for another woman. He had done it in the past, and she was almost positive he was doing it in the present.

He had talked of learning from past mistakes, of changing. She was beginning to realize, he hadn't meant a word he'd said.

The telephone rang, and Ted answered it. Kit could tell by the low, intimate tone he used as well as by the fact he was discussing Missy that the caller was Phyllis.

To Kit's horror she heard him invite the other girl and Missy to dinner that evening.

When he hung up the phone, he rolled over and kissed Kit leisurely on the throat.

She tried to spring away, but he was holding her down.

"I think we overslept," she said coldly.

"Did we?" His voice was lazy. "Surely the world expects that of newlyweds."

His lips were hot and searching, and her own senses were quickening, ready to drag her into the powerful undercurrent of his desire. In another minute he would be making love to her. Longing quivered through her like fire tongues flicking as she forced herself to twist away from him.

"It's almost seven thirty," she said tautly. "Aren't you supposed to be at work by eight?" She pulled the covers over her rigid body.

This time he heard the impatience in her voice; he sensed the tension in her.

"Don't tell me you're going to start nagging me this early in our marriage," he replied lightly. "The store opens at eight, but I own it, remember? I don't have to be there until I get there."

He was bending over her to kiss her again, and a sigh shuddered from her lips. She shrank from him. She mustn't, she simply mustn't let him! He didn't love her, he only wanted to use her. She pushed him away.

He sat up, the sheets falling from him and exposing his furred, muscular chest. He was staring down at her quizzically as if he were trying to understand her mood. Then his expression hardened. He reached for his quartz watch and clipped it around his wrist. She knew he'd decided to curb his desire because that was what he thought she wanted. Fleetingly a pang of disappointment, keen and sharp like a knife's edge, winged through her. She'd denied them both the rapture of physical love, and it hurt. He turned back to her, and when he spoke his tone was harsh.

"Well, if I have to get up, so do you, madame. It's time you learned there's more to being a wife than being a bedmate." He raked his eyes over her until she blushed. "You're so anxious to see me off to work—well, I'm just as anxious for you to get into the kitchen and fix my breakfast. I have a long day ahead of me, and I don't intend to face it on an empty stomach." When she made no move to follow his instructions: "Or do you intend to remain the spoiled little rich girl who can't even boil an egg?" he finished.

"I...I..." She was about to say that she couldn't possibly cook his breakfast because she didn't know how. His blue eyes were on her face, boldly challenging her as he waited for her to answer. "Of course I can cook!" she cried out. "What do you want to eat?"

"Well, I'll be thoughtful and keep it simple. How about three boiled eggs, toast, bacon, and coffee—black. You should be able to manage that." The faintly taunting tone of his voice implied that he very much doubted she could.

Of course she could manage that! Housewives all over the country did it for large families. Why couldn't she?

When she heard the sound of water streaming in the shower, and of him whistling safely inside it, she slipped from the bed and into a robe. She went into the kitchen and began the task of preparing his breakfast.

Nothing is ever as easy to do as it seems. The eggs broke as they boiled and became knotty, rubbery stretches of white in the turbulent water. How long did one boil eggs anyway?

She forgot the toast. She was removing it smoking from the toaster when Ted, stuffing his shirt into his trousers, entered the kitchen.

"I thought I smelled breakfast."

"Don't tease me," she said miserably. "I burned your toast. Those eggs look like rubber."

"What happened to the bacon?"

"Oh! I forgot about it completely." She was pulling the frying pan out of the cupboard. "It will only take a minute."

"Never mind."

Tears of frustration were filling her eyes.

"Brides are supposed to burn toast and cook rubbery eggs," he said gently in low-pitched tones.

Then before she had time to resist, he was pulling her into his arms and kissing her. Her heart leapt with alarm at his touch. When she pushed him away, he frowned but said nothing.

"And new husbands are supposed to eat what their brides cook," she answered with flashing temper.

He ran tap water into his coffee and carried his cup to the table. He ate his breakfast in silence. When he finished he said, "I'll do the dishes while you get ready for work."

"Work?"

"You don't think I'm going to have a wife lying around the house when she could be useful to me. I'm sure your father let you lounge around to your heart's content between trips to Europe, but you're married to me now and I'm not nearly so rich as he. I need your help in the business. I told you my bookkeeper quit, and I'm falling behind on my books. I think it's high time you put that college education of yours to work."

At his words her black eyes sparked with fury, but again he was challenging her. And she could not refuse him.

"All right. I'll be ready in a few minutes," she replied tightly, and went to the bedroom to dress.

When she returned, dressed stylishly in apricot Qiana, fifteen minutes later she found Ted reading the paper.

"Well, I'm ready," she said coldly.

His voice went equally cold. "Good." He arose and opened the door for her. They stepped out into the sunshine.

As they drove to the store, he said, "I think you heard me invite Phyllis to dinner tonight. We haven't seen Missy since our wedding, and I want her to feel that she's a part of our lives."

"You invited them without asking me."

"I'm asking you now. If you want to do something different tonight I can call Phyllis and cancel. She's very understanding."

"I'm sure you think she is," Kit said sarcastically.

"What is that supposed to mean?"

"Nothing."

"I didn't like the tone of your voice."

"Sorry. Maybe I don't like the situation."

"What in heaven's name are you talking about now?"

He drove the car into the parking lot of his store and stepped on the brakes. She was about to get out, when his large brown hand wrapped around hers.

"Not so fast," he said, his voice ominously soft. "You're not going anywhere until we get this cleared up. You've been acting strangely all morning and I want to know why."

A quick sideways glance on her part, and she saw the hardened set of his jawline and the angry fire of his eyes. She was going to have to tell him something, but, she certainly didn't feel up to discussing Phyllis with him this morning. The hurt went too deep. She was convinced he would invent a lie to explain his involvement with his sister-in-law. Her mind searched desperately for something to divert him.

"Maybe I don't appreciate you asking them to eat dinner...when...you know what a terrible cook I am. Have you forgotten what I did to breakfast? I couldn't possibly cook a meal if I can't boil an egg. We would all die of embarrassment...if my cooking didn't kill us first...."

He was looking at her oddly. "Are you sure that's what's bothering you?" His look held a silent warning that she be truthful. "You look awfully worried..."

"Of course that's what's bothering me..." She avoided his gaze.

The tension in his grip relaxed.

"Then you have nothing to worry about. Tonight I'll do the cooking."

Ted's store was a centrally located modern brick building on a busy thoroughfare. It had large plate glass windows to show off his equipment and party rental items. He led her through the store to a newly remodeled office. It was done in blues—her favorite shades. The desk was gleaming white. The wallpaper was delightful. Blue twists, shells, were arranged on silver foil.

"Ted, it's beautiful." Her eyes shone with delight.

"I hoped you'd like it," he said. There was an answering light in his eyes as they shared a quick moment of mutual joy. Involuntarily she felt herself responding to him. "I had it remodeled just for you. Phyllis helped me."

"Phyllis?"

"You knew she works out of an interior design studio nearby, didn't you? She did my townhouse too. I told her your favorite colors."

"I didn't realize..." she was murmuring.

The mention of Phyllis spoiled her happiness in the lovely office. Why did he bother pretending he'd done all this for her? No doubt he'd relished the excuse to be with Phyllis.

"I bought you a new calculator," he was saying, "and a small computer. I thought when you organize my books we'd put them on the computer. I'll teach you how to operate it. That will give us something to do in the evenings when we're not doing something else. ...I know how you love to play with numbers." Through the thick sweep of her black lashes, she glanced quickly up at his lean, towering profile. His eyes were gleaming as he looked down at her. It was all too easy to read his mind, and she stepped back nervously. "Your passion for numbers is only exceeded by your passion for..."

"Stop it!" she said irritably. "I thought you were going to show me your books."

"So I was."

Ted showed her around the store, and she marveled at how well-run it was. If only the books were as orderly as the rest of his business. He was using an intricate hand system for his books that was not only time consuming but gave little information. No wonder the bookkeeper had quit.

He showed her his office and his files. When she knew where all the information she might need was located, he left her sitting at her desk poring over a stack of ledgers, his check book, bank statements, and day sheets that were piled high on top of it. She became so absorbed in her work that she scarcely noticed when he kissed her cheek and said good-bye as he left shortly before noon, saying he had an appointment with his doctor to have his cast removed.

Two hours passed and when he did not return she began to wonder where he was.

Suddenly her inner doubts about him attacked with renewed force. He could be with Phyllis. Discreetly lunching in some out-of-the-way, romantic restaurant. With trembling fingers she laid her pencil on top of one of her ledgers.

He'd said he had a doctor's appointment. Why couldn't she simply trust him as a wife should trust her husband?

The vision—graphic and hurtful—of him holding Phyllis in his arms returned. Then she remembered the old hurt when she'd called him all those years ago and Letitia smugly, triumphantly had answered the phone. He hadn't changed. Why had she ever thought he could.

All at once—perhaps because it was nearly two o'clock and she hadn't eaten since breakfast—she felt weakly tearful. Or perhaps it was the strain of having controlled her feelings ever since she'd seen him on the beach with Phyllis.

She sought for control of her emotions and failed. Bursting into tears, she buried her face in her hands and sobbed.

She should have known where marriage to him would lead. She should have been wiser and prevented this new pain.

A knock sounded faintly at her door, and she looked up. The last thing she needed was a visitor now. Her pain was private, not something she wanted to share with anyone.

The knock sounded again, and she wiped at her eyes.

"J-just a minute."

Before she had a chance to compose herself, Rodney pushed the door open. "Kit? I see Bradley's got you up at his salt mine."

She looked up, unpleasantly startled that it was he, and managed a terse, "Hi, Rodney."

His back was to her as he pushed the door closed. He still hadn't noticed anything was wrong. With tear-wet palms she brushed at her eyes once more.

"Bradley here? I needed to discuss the terms regarding the tents and other items I want to rent for my cattle sale."

"I'm sorry, but he's out," she said in quick dismissal.

"Well, I sure need to talk to him. Haven't got all day." Rodney paced impatiently; she saw he was as uncomfortable in her presence as she was in his. Suddenly he blurted, "Hey, are you okay? Your eyes are all red.... Have you..."

She interrupted him quickly. Rodney was the last person she would confide her troubles to. "I-I must have gotten some dust in my eyes. These ledgers have been up there for months." She pointed upward to the top of the filing cabinet. She was a poor liar and was sure he wouldn't be fooled for a minute. To her surprise, he believed her.

Swiftly he leaned over her desk, and just as swiftly she cringed away from his inspecting gaze. "Maybe I should have a look," he said. "They're really red." Before she could stop him he tilted her face upward and touched one of her eyelids with a roughened fingertip. His face hovered just inches from hers. "There! Got it!" he exclaimed triumphantly. "It wasn't dust. An eyelash. That's all."

It was then that Ted, tense because he was running late, burst into the office without bothering to knock. At the sight of Rodney leaning over Kit he stopped abruptly in mid-step.

"What are you doing here, Starr? And why is the door closed?"

"I was waiting for you—to discuss terms for the cattle sale rental." Rodney moved away from Kit and faced Bradley.

"Then come into my office and we can discuss them," Ted said in a cold, low voice.

The two men departed. Half an hour later Ted buzzed Kit on the intercom.

"I want to see you in my office at once," he ordered.

When she entered his office, he arose and pulled out a chair for her.

"Rodney's gone?" she asked, avoiding his searing gaze because it made her feel oddly uncomfortable.

"Obviously."

"Did you get the rental?" she asked nervously.

"Of course."

His abrupt manner made her feel even more nervous. "Well, I'm glad of that," she said, faltering. "What was it you wanted to see me about?" When he didn't answer, she looked up and into eyes that were so dark with fury she scarcely knew him. His expression was cold and hard.

"I want you to explain that touching little scene I broke up in your office."

His accusing scrutiny of her features made her feel defiant. "Nothing happened that requires an explanation," she said stiffly.

"You were in his arms."

"I was not! I..." She was about to say, "I was crying... and Rodney interrupted me." But she couldn't say that because then he would demand to know why she'd been crying. She was too emotionally drained to even attempt to explain to him how she'd felt when she'd seen him holding Phyllis. Just the memory of it hurt. How could she possibly talk about it—to him. She didn't want to hear some glib lie that would supposedly explain everything, a lie she would desperately want to believe.

"Tell me!"

"He was removing an eyelash because my eye was watering," she hedged.

His eyes were on her face, and he was staring at her intently. She felt increasingly uncomfortable. His gaze was penetrating; he saw too much. She hadn't told him the whole truth, and she was sure that fact was guiltily written on her face. When she tried to look away he sprang from his desk and cupped her face in his large brown hands. He stared at her for a long moment. At last he released her.

His eyes were the deepest, darkest shade of blue. "You've never been any good at lying, Kit," he said. "You've been acting very strange all day. I'm wondering if you're regretting our marriage. Did you call him when I left at noon? Are you planning to see him again? Kit, are you sorry you broke your engagement to him—and married me?"

He was still staring at her closely through narrowed eyes, as though he thought the answers to his questions would be inscribed on her face. She flushed guiltily and squirmed.

He had no right to question her like that. She should be questioning him. After all he was the one who was actually involved with someone else.

She remembered him holding Phyllis tightly in his arms with the waves swirling around them. They were in love; it was obvious. There could be no other explanation. If he was in love with his sister-in-law, why did he care what she, Kit, did in any case?

He didn't; he couldn't really care, she decided bitterly. He was just proud. He didn't want it known his wife might be the unfaithful type. It wouldn't reflect well on his masculine image.

"Kit, what does Rodney mean to you?"

"He means nothing to me! And I don't like being accused of things when I'm not guilty! Why won't you believe me?"

"Perhaps it has something to do with your walking out on me five years ago without telling me why. It's a little hard for me to trust you when I remember that." He grasped her wrist. "Tell me, Kit, what is going on?"

He seemed determined to believe her guilty. He did not trust her! If only she had the proper sense of humor she could have laughed, the situation was so absurd. But she was too deeply hurt.

He was implying that she wanted to have an affair with Rodney when all the time he was probably actually having one with Phyllis. The irony of it tasted bitter in her mouth, and she swallowed convulsively.

He had no right to accuse her unjustly! And she had no desire to accuse him although he was guilty! The situation was hopeless.

"Would you please let go of me," she said at last. "You're hurting me." When he released her, her wrist was red from his touch.

"Tell me, Kit, what's going on!"

She looked up from rubbing her injured wrist, straight into his eyes. "I've told you the truth, and I have nothing more to say," she replied flatly. "But it's clear what kind of woman you think I am. I don't suppose that should surprise me—considering the kind of man you are. Living the way you do, it's no wonder you think I'm capable of being married to one man and sneaking around to see another. But, you can relax, I'm not cheating on you. And I won't—ever. I am not that kind of person. Your masculine pride is intact—I'm sure that's all that matters to you—really—in any case."

"Damn it, Kit. I couldn't care less about my 'masculine pride' as you put it. All I've ever cared about is . . ." He seemed to think better of what he'd intended to say and paused. Kit wondered if he'd almost said the name "Phyllis." He continued, "And I want to know what you mean by such remarks as 'considering the kind of man I am.' I'm getting a little sick of your insinuations. Insinuations you refuse to explain. Perhaps now is a good time to bring up the past. I'd like to know why you left me when we were in college."

"You were the one who once said our discussions about the past always dead-end. And I see no reason to explain the obvious. Now if you'll excuse me, I think I'll take the rest of the afternoon off. I don't think I could accomplish anything further; the atmosphere isn't conducive to work. Anyway, I'm sure you haven't forgotten for one minute that you invited Phyllis over. I need to go to the grocery store and straighten the house."

He didn't so much as twitch an eyebrow at the mention of Phyllis's name. Grudgingly Kit had an odd sense of admiration for his superb ability to conceal his true emotions.

She stood up, and for a minute, she didn't think he was going to allow her to leave. He was staring down at her so hard, she thought he could see right through her.

"All right," he managed more calmly. "We don't seem to be getting anywhere with this discussion." He thrust his hand into his pocket and produced his key. "Take my car. If I need to go somewhere, I'll take one of the vans."

Kit spent the afternoon getting ready for their dinner guests. She'd never felt less in the mood for a dinner party. The bitter words lingered in her mind, and she felt acutely unhappy.

She'd been a silly, romantic fool to have married him. She irrationally thought that her love for him would be enough to solve all their problems. But she hadn't anticipated his involvement with another woman. He probably thought it his right to be married to one woman and in love with another....

Ted returned home in time to start the fire for the steaks. Kit had already put potatoes into the oven to bake and tossed a salad. She'd gone to a bookstore and bought herself two cookbooks. She'd also gone to a bakery and selected a chocolate cake for Missy.

When Ted came in from the balcony where he'd been tending the fire, he did not offer to apologize for the unpleasant scene that had passed between them. His blue gaze raked coldly over her, taking in every detail of her appearance. She was wearing her green sundress again—he'd told her several times he thought she looked especially beautiful in it. She'd piled her hair high on top of her head in a new hairstyle she'd seen in a magazine. But if he found her attractive, he did not say so.

Instead he went to the bar and mixed himself a drink. She observed his mouth set in a thin, forbidding line; the angular planes of his face were harsh. She couldn't help noticing he'd mixed himself a double. Was her company so unendurable for him that he needed a stiff drink to stand being near her?

Her eyes smarted with tears. How was she going to make it through this evening—entertaining Phyllis?

Ted was showering when the doorbell rang, so Kit had to answer it. She pasted what she hoped was a warm smile on her face and opened the door. She didn't want to give Phyllis the satisfaction of seeing how unhappy she really was.

Missy bounded into the house.

"Kit, where's Joseph?" Her bright, blue eyes danced.

"You know he's upstairs just waiting for you to come visit him."

The child dashed up the carpeted stairs.

"Come on in, Phyllis," Kit said in the cheeriest voice she could muster.

Phyllis eyed her with a frosty, gray stare and a quick twist of her lips and stepped inside.

Ted came out of the bedroom. His auburn hair glistened with wetness. He was wearing a pale blue shirt that was open at the throat. Kit watched the hard contours of his muscled leanness ripple beneath the cotton fabric of his shirt as he moved toward Phyllis. He was wearing corduroy jeans of a darker shade of blue that were belted around his narrow waist. Kit caught the fragrance of his after-shave, the fresh laundry-smell of his shirt.

"Hello, Phyllis. I'm glad you could come. You look beautiful." His drawl was painfully resonant with warmth and friendliness.

Kit was reminded he'd scarcely spoken to her since their argument at the store. Nor had he complimented her appearance even though she'd worked very hard to look nice for him. Unhappily Kit watched him bend over Phyllis and kiss her lightly on the cheek as he helped her out of her jacket.

"I'm . . . I'm glad I could come too," Phyllis answered in choked tones.

"Princess." Ted's voice was vibrant with emotion. Missy was descending the stairs dragging her battered rabbit friend and carrying several story books. "Let me help you with all that." He lifted her and her things into his arms. "What's my little princess been up to?" He set the child down and bent to her level, and she told him about the pet gerbil Amie Rodgers had brought to kindergarten class that morning.

Throughout dinner conversation was stilted, and Ted did most of the talking in an effort to cover up the awkward silences. He was very friendly to Phyllis and tried hard but without much success to see that she enjoyed her evening.

Phyllis scarcely ate a bite of food. She spoke only when asked a direct question. It wasn't difficult for Kit to understand how she felt, for she herself felt the same way.

To Kit, Ted was civil, but his manner lacked warmth. Kit was sure that Phyllis sensed there was something wrong between them. After dessert Missy decided it was story time.

"I want Aunt Phyllis to sit here and Daddy here," she said, plopping down on the couch and indicating either side of her small self. Kit realized the child wasn't intentionally leaving her out. Missy just wasn't accustomed to her yet and didn't know how she fit into her life.

Kit was clearing the dishes from the table as Phyllis and Ted joined the child on the couch.

"Would you like to read 'Cinderella?'" Phyllis asked innocently.

"Isn't that the one about the wicked stepmother?" the child queried.

"Yes, dear, it is," Phyllis said in carefully measured tones, looking up from the brightly-colored story book and staring with direct coldness across the room at Kit.

Either unaware of or determined to ignore the undercurrents in the room, Ted began, "Once upon a time there lived..."

Watching them read together—their dark heads bent over the book—Kit thought they looked like the ideal family. Each adult took turns answering Missy's eager questions. It was obvious this was a ritual they all enjoyed that had gone on ever since Letitia's death. The resonant cadence of Ted's voice filled the room, and Kit had never felt more left out in her life than she did listening to the three of them reading and discussing "Cinderella."

Later Missy decided she wanted her daddy to take her down to the water and search for crabs. When they left, Phyllis offered to help Kit with the dishes, and Kit could think of no way to refuse her.

After a strained silence, Kit attempted small talk.

"You look awfully nice tonight in that dress, Phyllis. In fact, this may surprise you, but I almost bought one like it the other day myself when I was shopping."

"Really, why didn't you?"

"Well, I just didn't have the time to try it on what with the wedding preparations and all."

Phyllis almost dropped the plate she was drying at the mention of the word "wedding," but she managed to catch it before it hit the porcelain sink. She pressed her lips tightly together and made no comment as she dried the plate furiously.

"I love the office you decorated for me, Phyllis. I thought the wallpaper was lovely."

"You just won't stop, will you? I decorated it for Ted—not you!" Phyllis said cruelly. "I'm sure you must've realized that! And furthermore, you needn't try to entertain me with your mindless chatter. Nothing you have to say could be of the slightest interest to me." She set the plate down on the counter with a clatter. "I know that sounds rude, but I just can't be a hypocrite like you. I know you don't like me any more than I like you."

Kit gasped.

"Not that you should. As I've said I don't like you either. And I don't like what you're doing to Ted and Missy. It's obvious to me that Ted is very unhappy. He hardly said a word to you tonight, and that's not like him. You've only been married a few days, but I guess he's finding out what kind of woman you are."

"Phyllis," Kit interrupted in a quiet voice, "you are in my home as a guest, and you have no right to say these things to me. If you can't be pleasant, you'll have to leave. I'm not up..."

"You always expect to get your way, don't you?" Phyllis challenged. "Well, this is the real world and you're all grown up. Your wealthy father can't give it all to you anymore. It's time you learned just wanting a man and trapping him into marriage aren't enough to keep him."

The front door opened and slammed shut before Kit had a chance to retaliate. Missy bounded into the room chattering about all the sea creatures they'd seen and the fisherman she'd talked to.

Kit sighed with relief, and Phyllis lapsed into a long and stony silence until Ted escorted Missy and her home.

As soon as they were out the door, Kit went into the bedroom. Phyllis must have felt very sure of herself as far as Ted was concerned or she would never have said those things she'd said in the kitchen. Dismally, Kit changed into a filmy nightgown the color of flame. She put on a matching see-through peignoir. Phyllis's words seemed to repeat themselves in her brain as she uncoiled the length of her long black hair and let it fall like a thick veil to her shoulders. She brushed her hair free of all tangles and then went to the bed.

She knew she couldn't sleep—she was too distraught. She selected a mystery novel Ted had read and recommended and slipped into bed with it. Although the novel was written by an author whose tight prose and fast-moving tales usually kept her reading spellbound from the first sentence to the last, she couldn't get past the first paragraph. She read it over four times before she closed the book and set it in her lap.

What was wrong with her? Why couldn't she just accept the fact that Phyllis and Ted were in love and step aside so they could be happy together? But the thought of losing Ted completely was devastating. She'd been through that once before. She had a stubborn streak as well, and she loved him so much she kept clinging to the flimsy hope that things could work out.

She placed the book on the beside table. She might as well turn out the light. She couldn't read anyway.

After what seemed an eternity of lying sleepless in the dark, she heard the sound of Ted's footsteps outside and of the front door opening and closing. She heard his tread—heavy upon the plush carpet as he headed toward their bedroom.

He opened the bedroom door slowly and switched on the light. She kept her eyes squeezed tightly shut and pretended she was asleep.

"I doubt very much you're asleep," he said perceptively. "I want to talk to you." He crossed the room with long rapid strides and sat on the corner of the bed at her feet.

"Well, I don't want to talk to you," she said, sitting up and brushing her mussed hair back from her face. Something about the authoritative tone in his voice upset her. She blinked her eyes against the brightness of the now-lighted room.

"Don't you think it's a mistake to go to bed with this argument between us," he said in softer tones, his blue eyes somber.

"Yes, I do, but as I didn't start the argument, I don't believe it's up to me to clear the air. I seem to remember it was you who falsely accused me of chasing after Rodney. However, if you're ready to apologize, I'll listen."

"I have no intention of apologizing about anything," he said grimly. "You still haven't told me what you were doing in his arms."

His steady blue eyes never left her face. His face was white and drawn—like that of a man bleeding from an internal wound. Still, he was handsome, the handsomest man she'd ever seen. But his arrogant assumption of her guilt enabled her to steel herself against his appeal.

"Ted," she begged abruptly, wishing there could be peace between them once more although she was unwilling to relent from her own position, "you must believe that what I told you earlier was the truth. You must!"

"Without any further explanation?"

"Yes."

"You ask too much," he said at last in a quiet, toneless voice.

Her heart sank with bitter disappointment. He refused to believe in her; he refused to trust her.

Anger flared in her suddenly. He'd been with Phyllis for over an hour, and he had the nerve to resume this ridiculous argument with her!

"You have your nerve!" she began, her black eyes flashing. "You think you can do exactly what you please and it shouldn't make any difference at all to me. You've been with Phyllis for over an hour, and have I said one thing? No!"

His hard gaze flicked over her. When he spoke his voice was tight with control. "My relationship with Phyllis is not at all the same thing. I was over there putting Missy to bed—you know that."

"No, I don't!"

"Phyllis is my sister-in-law! I have to see her from time to time because of Missy. She also happens to be a very good friend of mine. You're just throwing this out as a red herring."

"Am I? It's all right for you but not for me. Is that it?"

"You were in Rodney's arms," he accused. "I saw you myself."

"And you were holding Phyllis in your arms on our wedding night," she wanted to lash out. But she didn't. As always her belief that he would lie glibly and she would foolishly long to believe him stopped her. Aloud she said, "I told you all he did was remove an eyelash from my eye."

Wearily he rose from the bed. He began pulling out blankets and sheets.

"What are you going to do?" she asked shakily.

"I'm going to sleep on the couch, if it's of any real interest to you," he replied steadily.

Then he left her, and she felt numbed with the pain of his rejection and lack of faith in her.

Was this to be their marriage? Coldness and distrust? It was almost morning before Kit fell into a troubled sleep.

Chapter Nine

The sun—hot and angry—like a great ball of flame hovered on the horizon where water touched sky. Pink light was filtering through the bedroom draperies when Kit stumbled out of bed.

Ted was knocking briskly on the door.

"Come in," she called, pulling her filmy peignoir hastily over her shoulders.

"Thought I heard you up," he said.

His dark skin was shadowy beneath his eyes; he hadn't slept any better than she. His long frame probably hadn't fit the couch too comfortably.

He was shirtless, wearing only the bottoms of his blue pajamas. A towel slung carelessly over one shoulder was white against the mat of dark hair covering the breadth of his bronzed chest. Weakly she observed the contours of his muscles, his hard leanness. She wished there was some way she could make him believe her.

But, more than that she wished there was some way she could make him love her.

Without another word to her, he went to his closet and began rummaging through his clothes, taking some out and throwing them on the bed. The pile began to mount.

"What are you doing?" she asked tonelessly.

"I think you can see that for yourself. I'm moving some of my things upstairs."

Her voice almost caught in her throat, but she managed, "Why?"

"I would think you'd be grateful instead of so inquisitive," he answered, his voice hard, his blue eyes cold. "I seem to remember that you wanted me to marry you on one condition: that I not touch you. Well, I promise you, I have no intention of touching you again. Not that you would care. Lately you've made it very clear you want to have as little to do with me as possible." He grabbed a handful of hangers on which hung his suits, slacks, and dress shirts. When one of the shirts slipped from the hanger, she rushed to retrieve it. "I can manage without your help," he said curtly.

Stung, she made no further attempt to assist him.

"You're still furious about Rodney's visit to the store, aren't you?" When he made no reply, she said, "Why won't you believe me when I say nothing happened?"

"I've told you. You're a terrible liar, and you lied about Rodney. Or at least if you didn't actually lie...you're holding something back. And I keep wondering what it is and why."

"There's nothing between Rodney and me."

"There had better not be! I'm not the kind of man who wants to share his wife with any man."

"There isn't another man."

He made no reply.

"Does this mean you want a divorce?" she asked hesitantly.

He threw the hangers onto the bed. He came toward her and seized her by the wrist, pulling her up hard against him. The peignoir fell from her shoulders revealing clearly to him her lovely curves in the filmy nightgown. His gaze drifted slowly over her body, and she blushed hotly. The knowing look in his eyes made her acutely conscious of his blatant virility.

"No! It doesn't!" he rasped in a strangely hoarse voice. "And don't mention that word to me again."

He released her hand, and resumed his task of removing his clothes.

So—he was still furious because she hadn't explained Rodney's visit to his satisfaction.

She almost screamed that she was the one who should be angry—not him. That he was blaming her for what he himself was guilty of. That it was his own guilty conscience tormenting him.

During the succeeding weeks she saw little of him. He threw himself into his work with a vengeance and began to work late into the evenings. She knew that he was doing it deliberately so he could avoid her. When she was at his store, he found excuses to be at some construction site. When she was at home, he said he had to work after hours at the store to catch up on paper work. Evenings when he didn't work, he either went over to Phyllis's and visited with Missy or down to the yacht club to work on *Wild Lady*.

Their marriage consisted of coldly polite salutations passing between them in the mornings and evenings.

Kit was desperately unhappy. She'd lost weight. If she hadn't had her work at the store to occupy herself with, she would have gone mad.

She loved him—still, but their marriage seemed hopeless.

It was the evening of the Starr ball, the night before the Starr cattle auction. Ted had spent two days at the Starr Ranch personally supervising his men setting up the tents, and dancefloors, tables and chairs.

When he came home early that evening, he looked exhausted.

She was already dressed for the ball in a gown that was simple in design and stunning. The dress was wine red; the deep color enhanced her own dark coloring. The soft material rounded beneath her breasts and fell to the floor.

She was brushing her black hair when he came into the bedroom. His skin was tanned mahogany brown from the long days spent in the sun; his wind-blown hair glinted gold. He sagged wearily against the door frame, his gaze traveling slowly over her. Tired as he looked, just for an instant she saw a faint leaping light in his eyes. He wanted her. She knew it. But he didn't want her to know. Abruptly he looked away.

A wave of tenderness rushed through her at the sight of him looking so haggard. "Ted, you really do look awfully tired," she said gently. "Maybe we should stay home and have a quiet evening together."

His eyes went over her again and his expression darkened. "I am tired, but I would prefer to go to the party," he said tonelessly. "I need to go... for business reasons. I'll just take a quick shower and change."

He left her and trudged heavily upstairs. When he was gone she wanted to collapse onto the bed in tears. He hated her. She knew he did. He preferred going to the party when he was exhausted to spending an evening home alone with her. He had said nothing about her new dress and how lovely she looked in it. Although it was a small thing, this omission hurt. She'd tried so hard to be beautiful for him, hoping his attitude toward her might soften.

She'd seen desire in his eyes, but he'd fought against it. He disliked her so much he didn't even want to find her attractive.

They rode in silence to the Starr Ranch. He made no attempt to talk to her. Occasionally she would catch a glimpse of his features as the headlights of a car passed them. His face was full of menace—he looked almost dangerous. It seemed to her that her mere presence provoked him in some way she could not understand.

As they turned from the highway onto the curving asphalt drive that led to the ranch house, the moon—golden and full—was just rising. They were directed by a ranch hand to a canopied walkway that led to the enormous sprawling mansion.

The party had a flavor that was distinctly Texan. If only things had been right with her marriage, Kit would have enjoyed herself. The scent of hickory and barbecue wafted in the crisp, cool night air. Kit heard the whine of western music. She saw that although some of the guests that strolled arm-in-arm across the lawns wore formal gowns and jewels, others wore boots and cowboy hats.

Matt Walsh, Rodney's older cousin and one of the owners of the vast ranching empire, was one of the hosts. He came to greet them. Her own brother Steve with Alicia Walsh, Matt's younger sister, on his arm was right behind Matt. Alicia, golden and lovely in the moonlight, wore a gown of yellow froth.

"You did a great job with the tents, Bradley," Matt was saying.

Movies flickered across one large screen in a nearby tent to acquaint guests with the cattle and horses that would be auctioned on the following day. Hors d'oeuvres were being served beneath another tent.

"And, Kit," Matt continued in a fatherly way, "you look gorgeous. I think marriage suits you." He took her hand in his and led her beneath the canopies across the grounds. He offered her and her husband hors d'oeuvres. Shrimp teriyaki and petite finger ribs were being grilled over open flames.

Matt was trying to be hospitable. In spite of Matt's friendliness, Ted's mood darkened with each hospitable comment the other man made.

Matt was complimenting Kit. "Bradley, I'm sure you're aware that your wife epitomizes the beauty of South Texas. She represents how beautifully two cultures—the Spanish and the American—can blend. Tonight she looks like a Spanish princess."

The lines beside Ted's mouth tightened as Kit blushed, laughing nervously, and thanked Matt for his compliment, but Ted said nothing. He merely drained his drink and reached for another. Kit could see that it was going to be a long evening.

The sound of Spanish music drifted from the porch where *mariachis* were singing and playing their guitars. Kit absently tapped her foot in time with the music.

Matt was telling them of the notable guests. "The governor, of course, always comes, and tonight an Arab prince is here. I'll introduce you to Namir after a while. An African prime minister...cattle buyers from South America..."

Conversation turned to cattle; and Steve, Matt, and Ted began discussing the auction. Kit knew Ted was interested in buying some stock for his ranch in The Valley.

A small dark man in flowing white robes approached. He seized Kit by the hand and introduced himself as Prince Namir. His English was impeccable. He seemed filled with energy. His black eyes flashed and his hands moved nervously as he talked. He paid her outrageous compliments, and she found herself laughing at their absurdity. He told her she had harem eyes, that she was like a desert flower. When he asked her to dance, she accepted.

As Prince Namir danced with her she glanced occasionally in Ted's direction. He was still conversing with her brother.

Prince Namir danced with her once, twice, and then a third time. His energy was boundless. The music stopped and he asked her for a fourth dance. She was about to refuse him, but as she glanced again toward Ted, she saw that he was now talking to a beautiful, elegantly-clad woman.

"Why not?" Kit responded pertly to the dark Arab, and he hugged her to him.

The dance was a fast one, and when it ended she was laughing breathlessly. Prince Namir led her from the dance floor. Ted was still talking to the beautiful woman.

When Prince Namir offered her a glass of champagne, she hesitated. She hadn't eaten, and champagne on an empty stomach... Then she giggled, "Why not?" She felt hollow, as though she were filled with a strange coldness. Perhaps a glass... or two would warm her and make her forget...

She sipped her champagne and noticed the beautiful woman laughing at something Ted had said to her. Then she saw him laugh. Achingly Kit thought that it had been so long, too long... since he'd laughed with her.

Ted was dancing with the woman now, and he was holding her close. Then Kit watched them no longer, for Prince Namir was back and demanding her attention for himself.

When dinner was served, Prince Namir was again at her side. The dinner menu featured chicken curry with condiments: chutney and raisins, over wild rice, chilled tenderloin; baked acorn squash filled with fresh pineapple. The salad consisted of whole marinated artichokes, mushrooms and crisp lettuce leaves.

Kit couldn't eat a bite. She had no appetite. She did however watch Namir gobble every morsel from his plate. When dessert was served he selected tart lemon bars and fruit-glazed Brie. They in turn quickly vanished from his plate.

When he finished his meal, Namir again gave Kit his full attention. Again he paid her absurd compliments, saying he pitied the sultans of old because she had not been one of their harem girls.

"And have you a harem, Prince Namir?" she asked. What was the harm of flirting with him? It had been so long since her own husband had made her feel attractive.

He laughed as if he found that idea delightful. "Er…not exactly. I have one wife…and…er…occasionally…I meet other women who delight me as you do. Our customs are different from yours. We make allowances for the nature of men. You Americans set too much store upon fidelity."

She thought of Ted and found Prince Namir's remarks ironic. "And your wife… she thinks as you do?"

"What she thinks does not matter. She is only a woman. We have our customs."

"Sometimes I think they're not so different from our own."

"I do not like to talk about my wife when I'm with a woman as beautiful as you," Prince Namir said.

"Don't you? How exceedingly thoughtful." She giggled merrily up at him as she sipped her champagne.

After dinner he asked her to dance. The music was slow, and he held her close, pressing her to him. She looked over his shoulder once and was aware of Ted watching her from the shadows. He looked lean and darkly elegant, but his expression was so harsh, she could have wept. But she was at a party and she was determined to have fun. When the dance ended Prince Namir handed her another glass of champagne. She drank it hoping it would blot out the dark vision of Ted's countenance.

Other men asked her to dance: Steve, her father, Matt, and men she'd met only for the first time at the party. Once the governor himself claimed a dance. As she whirled in their arms she was unaware of how devastatingly beautiful she was with her wine-red gown swirling around her lithe figure, her black hair shimmering in the moonlight. She laughed too frequently, but if her laughter sounded strangely brittle as it blended with the music, no one seemed to notice. She appeared the picture of gaiety even though her heart was breaking.

She found herself suddenly alone. She was reaching for a third glass of champagne, when a large brown hand clamped around her wrist.

"I think you've had enough for one evening," Ted said.

The moon washed all color from his face. Only his eyes were alive. They flashed brilliant like the blue fire of a gas jet.

For some reason she was afraid of him. "I was just having fun," she said defiantly.

Matt, Howard and Steve were approaching and to avoid talking to them, Ted said, "I want you to dance with me. I have something to say to you."

"Well, I don't have anything to say to you!"

Just as the three men joined them, she twisted free of Ted's grasp. "If you'll all excuse me..." She tried to make her shaking voice sound light. "I promised Prince Namir this dance." Then she raced off into the night.

She danced again and again and again. She wanted to dance until she was too exhausted to think or feel anything about Ted. Several hours passed before she realized that she had not once caught sight of him since he'd asked her to dance. Where was he? She glanced at her diamond wrist watch. It was nearly three A.M.

When most of the guests had gone, Kit began searching for Ted. She ran across the grounds until she was breathless. Where had he gone? A branch of a twisting live oak snagged her gown and tore it, but she was so distracted she scarcely noticed.

Matt came to her. His pale hair gleamed like a silver halo in the moonlight.

"Something wrong, Kit?"

"I was looking for Ted."

"I think I saw him leaving with your brother and his date around midnight."

"Leaving...without..." Her voice faltered.

Matt eyed her sympathetically. "You two having problems?" Her eyes were over-large and glazed with pain. There was no sign of the gay creature who'd whirled madly in the wine-red gown. She nodded mutely. "Let's go see if your car's still here," he said gently. "If it is I'll drive you home."

The car was parked exactly where they'd left it earlier. The keys were in the ignition, and a terse note was clipped to the visor, which read,

"Kit,
Tried to tell you I was tired and ready to go.
Caught a ride with your brother. Ted."

Matt was opening the door for her. He slipped behind the wheel.

"Matt, you don't have to drive..."

"You're in no condition to drive, Kit," he said in a determined voice.

They drove home in silence, the only sounds that of the big engine's purr and that of Kit crumpling and uncrumpling the stiff paper Ted had scribbled his note on.

When they arrived at her townhouse, it was unlighted.

"I'll come inside just for a minute to make sure everything's all right," Matt said.

Together they went inside. Kit switched on the lights and went from room to room, her voice echoing as she called to Ted. There was no sign that he'd even been there.

"Matt, where could he be? It's nearly four A.M.?" she asked worriedly.

"You said the two of you have been having problems. He could..."

His remark set her thinking along a different track. Phyllis! He could be over there.

How she summoned the courage to dial Phyllis's number she never knew. But she had to know if her worst fears were true. She couldn't go on doubting him. When Phyllis answered in a fuzzy voice, Kit blurted, "Phyllis, this is Kit. I'm terribly worried about Ted. He hasn't come home from the Starr ball and I was wondering if you know where he might be."

"He's here. Asleep." Phyllis replied icily, before hanging up on her.

He was asleep at Phyllis's! Her worst suspicions were true! Something seemed to shatter inside her.

"Kit, is he..." Matt's hand covered hers that was holding the buzzing receiver. He hung up the phone.

"He's with Phyllis," she replied dully.

"I doubt if it's the way it seems. Ted wouldn't..."

"It's exactly the way it seems. He did the same thing before..." she wailed desperately.

She was in his arms without knowing quite how she got there and he was pressing her head against his shoulder.

Keys were rattling in the lock of the front door, and Ted stepped inside. He looked completely exhausted. His eyes were red, the dark flesh beneath them puffy and shadowed. His elegant navy suit was badly wrinkled. His hair was disheveled and tumbling over his brow. Every inch of him seem to sag with weariness, and for a split second Kit's heart went out to him. Then she remembered he'd spent the night with Phyllis.

When Ted saw her in Matt's arms, his face hardened, his eyes glittered with emotion.

"Darn you, Kit!" he muttered at last. Then more to himself than to her: "I don't know why I'm blaming you. I should have known the kind of woman you were when I married you." He was advancing upon her. "You don't know me very well if you think I'll put up with a wife who chases every man she sees and then brings one home for the night." He gripped her by the hand, pulling her away from Matt. "I want you out of here! Now! Take your things and get out!" He picked up her evening bag and wrap she'd set on a chair and pushed them into her fingers. "Come back for the rest of your things during the day—when I'm at work—so I won't have to see you again!"

"Ted, I can explain. It's not what you think."

"I said get out! Both of you!" An odd smile twisted his lips. He released Kit's hand, and moved toward Matt. Never had he looked so ruthless... so menacing.

Matt stiffened. "Bradley, you're jumping to the wrong conclusion."

"Walsh, if you're smart, you'll get out like I asked—before I lose control..."

"Ted..." Kit began weakly, desperately.

"Get out, Kit! I don't want to see you—ever again!"

Chapter Ten

A splash of sunflowers was bright gaiety against the stark flat stretch of cactus and brown grass that was the Starr Ranch. The Jackson Lincoln and its occupants sped beneath the ebony trees that lined either side of the asphalt road that wound past the big ranch house and the adobe brick horse stables to the shaded arena where the cattle auction would be held.

"I really wish you'd let me stay home," Kit said to the group in general.

"You need to be out with people—not at home moping," her father declared.

"The auction will take your mind off your troubles," Anitra amended gently. "Perhaps this will be the very thing to help you put this . . . this lovers' quarrel into the proper perspective."

Matt had caught a ride with them because he'd driven Kit home the night before and left his own car at the ranch. "If you want me to talk to Bradley, Kit, I will," he offered. "There's no reason for the two of you to separate because of a misunderstanding over me."

"No! I've told you there's much more to it than that! And there's no reason for all of you to concern yourselves with my problems. I'll handle them my own way."

"You're not doing such a terrific job of it at the moment, Sis," Steve said. "You may be as mistaken about what he was doing at Phyllis's as he is about Matt. The two of you need to sit down and have a long talk."

Though Kit could appreciate the logic of Steve's statement, she knew that such a "talk" would never be possible. She'd seen the look of implacable hatred on Ted's face when he'd thrown her out last night.

He was probably deeply relieved to have her out of his life for good. Whatever attraction he had for her, whatever whim had prompted him to marry her no longer existed. She was simply in the way. He wanted Phyllis not her. Why couldn't he have realized that long ago? Before they'd married? Before they'd gotten involved with one another all over again? She knew that losing him this time would hurt far worse than losing him the first time.

Now she was a woman. She'd experienced the deepest sexual and spiritual fulfillment in his arms. She knew that no man would claim her heart again in the same deeply complete way he had.

Anitra, her daughter's problems forgotten for the moment, was chattering gaily, but Kit wasn't listening. She felt dead, as though she was only going through the motions of being alive. Would it always be like this—without him? She remembered the five long empty years before he'd come back into her life.

Kit saw the future, the years of her life stretching before her, and without Ted, they seemed a lifetime of desolation. She sat quietly, her hands folded in her lap, her whole body taut, as she struggled for composure. Her lips pressed themselves into a tight line. She made no attempt to brush away the single tear that spilled over her eyelashes and traced a glistening path down her cheek. She was not even aware that it had fallen.

The Jacksons drove past open cattle trucks parked along the side of the road. After they passed a cluster of shorter horse trailers nestled beneath the shade of a few feathery salt cedar, Howard maneuvered the car off the road and onto a field that was being used as a parking lot and parked the car. They got out of the car and headed for the arena.

Spanish music was a slur of sound; the scent of cattle and horses was in the air. Barbecue was being served beneath the shade of several large party tents. Kit saw, perched on high stools at one of the many tables covered with red-checkered table cloths and not too far from the band, Ted, Phyllis and Missy. They were eating barbecue.

Ted looked even more haggard than he had the night before. He was wearing a red and green plaid western shirt, faded jeans and boots. His cowboy hat was pushed back from his face, and she saw that his auburn hair was uncombed, that a lock of it kept falling across his dark brow. His face was darkly shadowed as if he hadn't shaved. He looked up and saw her just as a voice on the loud speaker announced that the auction would begin in ten minutes, and Steve placed a hand beneath her elbow to lead her to the arena. As soon as he saw her, Ted turned quickly away as if the very sight of her caused him pain.

He was free of her. Didn't he realize she was willing for him to live his life as he wished? She would place no further claim on him. She wondered if he felt guilty to be with another woman when he was still legally married to her.

The shade of the covered arena was welcome after the brilliance of the Texas sun. Spanish guitars whined in the background as some of the ranch workers watered down the sawdust in the auction block that resembled a cattle pen. Only the faintest breeze stirred the air.

Kit watched as Ted, his hand cupping Phyllis's elbow, found a seat not too far from her. Not once did he turn to look at her.

The guitar music faded, and the rumbling voice of the auctioneer began. The crowd murmured as a small, fat cowboy led two thousand pounds of excitement, a Santa Gertrudis bull, into the arena. The small cowboy handled the powerful bull with expert ease as if the animal were no more than a small dog he was leading on a leash.

With the careless disregard of children playing with play money, wealthy ranchers began bidding and the bull's price quickly soared to five figures.

Three bulls later Kit watched Ted's hand go up. He was bidding on one of the finer bulls Matt had mentioned the night before. The bidding went hot and fast, and when it was over Ted had purchased a very fine piece of livestock. He bid on two more bulls with impeccable bloodlines and bought them. After he bid on the third bull he got up and ushered Phyllis and Missy out of the arena. Never once did he glance in Kit's direction, and she knew that he was avoiding her deliberately.

Kit's heart was an aching place in her breast. She could barely sit through the auction. Oh, why had she let her parents bring her? She should have stayed home. It was terrible seeing Ted with Phyllis. He, on the other hand, obviously felt perfectly all right or he couldn't have come and bid on three bulls as if nothing of any consequence had happened to him.

It was a relief a few minutes later when Howard came to her and said her family was ready to leave.

The big Lincoln sped back toward town. Anitra chattered gaily. Kit stared silently and unseeingly out the window.

Farmland like black felt pierced with oil derricks stretched on all sides of the speeding car. The terrain was stark and vast and empty, the sky a brilliant sweep of blue, blurring at the horizon because of the heat waves.

Kit brushed at the tears falling lightly down her cheeks. She felt her heart was like the view outside—a vast, aching emptiness.

A week passed—the longest week of Kit's life. She still hadn't felt up to returning to Ted's townhouse for her things.

It was eight o'clock in the morning. Saturday. The start for the first race of the new yacht series would be at ten. Kit's father had insisted she come down to breakfast.

She was buttering her toast when Howard announced, "Kit, I need you to crew today. Jake just called and he can't make it."

"Daddy, surely you haven't forgotten the disaster..."

"No, I haven't. But I need you, and you need to get out of the house. It isn't good for you to spend so much time alone in your room. Besides you don't have a thing to worry about. I won't let you near the tiller."

"Is Ted..."

"Yes, he'll be racing. *Wild Lady*'s back in the water. I helped him tune the mast the other evening."

"Then I definitely won't go."

"Yes, you will. It's time you thought of someone besides yourself for a change. I need you."

When he put it like that, she couldn't refuse him. They were at the pier rigging *Kitten*, when Kit looked up and saw the ice blue hull of *Wild Lady* slicing through the waves. He and Phyllis were sitting very close to one another in the stern of the boat, and the sight of them together was a vicious pain in her heart.

Ted saw her then, and for one long minute his eyes fastened on her as he drank in every detail of her appearance. Then he tacked abruptly, and *Wild Lady* headed off in another direction.

Had he noticed how much weight she'd lost in the past seven days? Had he seen the bluish half-moons beneath her eyes—evidence that her nights were long and sleepless? And if he saw, would he care that she was desperately unhappy? After all, *he had Phyllis*.

Wild Lady was the last boat across the starting line.

"Looks like we won't have any worries where Bradley's concerned," her father commented. "He's definitely chosen the wrong tack."

Kit, who was hanging onto *Kitten* for dear life, observed *Wild Lady* tacking away from the fleet toward the shore.

"He won't improve his position doing that," her father continued. "His judgement's way off."

At the windward mark Ted was even further behind than he'd been at the start. Kit couldn't imagine what was wrong. Her father said that he'd been on *Wild Lady* Wednesday night and the boat had sailed perfectly.

Howard Jackson finished way ahead of all the other boats; Ted finished way behind them.

After the race, Howard told his daughter and son that he wanted to have a drink in the club before returning home.

The white-coated waiter was taking their orders. "What will you have, Mrs. Bradley?" Skip asked her. His pencil hovered over his notepad as he waited for her to make up her mind.

"I guess I'll have a Coke...with a touch of lime in it," she responded indifferently. His pencil was scribbling on paper when Ted and Phyllis walked into the bar. Kit looked up and saw them. "No, Skip, let me change that," she amended hastily, "to a . . . a martini. And make it a stiff one."

She observed Ted's appearance achingly. In spite of his haggard expression he looked terribly handsome. His auburn hair was tousled from the wind. His white shirt—its top three buttons undone—was startling white against the darkness of his massive, darkly-tanned chest. He wore dungarees—neatly belted around his narrow waist. She saw the rippling contours of his muscles, his taut leanness.

She noted that the lines about his eyes were unusually deep—that he looked tired. She saw that his lips were parted in a half-smile over something Phyllis was saying.

Never had having drinks with friends been such an ordeal. How she'd ever gotten through it, she never knew.

Her father was basking in glory. He was the undisputed victor. Everyone surrounded him and congratulated him. They were asking why he'd selected his smaller spinnaker rather than his heavy-air spinnaker.

"Just by feel," he answered proudly. "I felt like the light-air spinnaker would do the job."

"I sure miscalculated on that one," Marc Clay said. "Did you see the knock-down we took?"

"Well, you needn't feel too ashamed, you placed second," Kris said. "Bradley over there seems to have miscalculated on everything." There was no malice in his voice. He was just teasing good-naturedly. "Sorry about that, Bradley," he added in louder tones. "But you've gotta expect a few remarks when you bomb out. You usually do so well. It's not often we get the chance to rib you."

Bradley looked up from his drink and smiled at Kris, but he made no comment. His blue gaze went to Kit. Then abruptly he got up, pouring the rest of his drink into a paper cup, and escorted Phyllis out of the bar.

"What's with him anyway?" Kris asked, perplexed after Ted left. "He's not himself these days. He's really falling down on the construction job at Port A. He's never there. It looks like there's going to be unscheduled delays.... And have you noticed how bad he looks too?"

Howard and Steve exchanged knowing glances. Then Steve gave his sister a penetrating look, which made her feel ill at ease.

She pushed her chair back from the table. "Well, I for one am finished with my drink. I'll wait for you all in the car."

Outside she paused to cover her hair with a triangular scarf, when a familiar voice—deep and vibrant—sent an electric charge coursing through her.

"I guess I owe you congratulations on your victory today," Ted said impersonally.

She turned to face him. "Why...why...thank you," she murmured. "I'm sure you realize how little I had to do with it."

"You're looking very beautiful, Kit," he said in a strangely tight voice.

"Oh...why...thank you." His compliment caught her completely off guard and she didn't know how to react. She felt flustered. She knew she was blushing furiously.

Her fingers were twisting and untwisting the ends of scarf beneath her chin. She was so nervous she couldn't tie a simple knot.

He saw her predicament and set the ice chest he was carrying down onto the pavement beside him. "Let me help you with that," he said smoothly.

Startled, she tried to back away from him, but a parked car was directly behind her blocking her escape. He came toward her and covered her hands with his larger brown ones.

She pulled her hands quickly to her side. She felt limp and weak. He was so near. And as always his touch affected her. His long fingers were deftly securing the scarf beneath her chin.

His blue eyes on her face seemed filled with longing. She noticed that although he'd finished tying the scarf his hands lingered just for an instant at her throat in what was almost a caress.

"Kit, I never did give you..."

She never knew what he intended to say for Phyllis joined them at just that moment. "Ted... Oh...hi...Kit. Congratulations. Y'all did great!" Only the hard steel gray of her eyes belied her friendliness. "Ted, I was wondering where in the world you were. The Jarvises are on the boat, and I can't serve them drinks without that ice."

"I was just coming, Phyllis."

Phyllis slipped an arm through Ted's possessively. "See you around, Kit," the girl said in dismissal.

"Good-bye, Kit." Ted leaned over and picked up the ice chest.

"Good-bye..."

Kit hated herself because she'd felt so hopeful the instant before Phyllis had arrived. Ted had been so friendly, so nice.... She'd almost believed that he was going to ask her for an explanation of Matt's presence that night in the townhouse. She'd almost believed that such an explanation could make a difference between them. Then Phyllis had come, and Kit remembered with renewed forcefulness that he was in love with Phyllis, that he'd spent the night with her. No explanation could change the way things were between them. Her innocence was not the issue; his love for Phyllis was.

Two weeks later Ralph Jackson, Howard's younger brother, arrived to spend part of his six-week vacation with the Jacksons. Uncle Ralph was one of Kit's favorite relatives, just as she was his favorite niece.

"I don't like seeing you so depressed," he said one afternoon as they fished off the Jackson pier.

Silently she slipped a shrimp onto her hook and cast it once more into the blue-gray waters.

"I don't like being this way, but there's not much I can do about it," she replied at last, keeping her eyes glued to the bobbing cork.

"Anitra told me you were separated from your husband, that the two of you haven't been married very long."

"Uncle Ralph," she began gently, "I really don't like Mother discussing my personal problems with everyone. And I don't want to discuss them either. I'd much rather hear about Stavanger, Norway and your exciting job over there as an oil executive who's having a hand developing the North Sea."

"I thought I'd bored you silly with all that last night."

"Why did you choose overseas work...so late in your career?" she asked, relieved he'd let her maneuver him into a different topic of conversation.

"Now we're getting on sticky ground again—my personal problems," he replied easily. "But unlike you, I've gotten to the point where I can talk about mine. After Mary and I divorced I just wanted to get away from everything and everybody that reminded me of our life together. Stavanger is a complete change from Texas, and I was out there only a short time when I felt much better about everything."

Kit wasn't listening to Uncle Ralph any more. A change of scene...the idea held a strange appeal for her. If she were to leave Corpus she wouldn't be constantly running into Ted and Phyllis together. Perhaps a move would enable her to forget her problems as Uncle Ralph had forgotten his.

"I wish there was some place I could go...like Stavanger," she said half-aloud, half to herself.

Uncle Ralph heard her. "Are you serious? I mean *really* serious?" The sunlight was glinting in his silver hair.

"Yes." She looked up and met his direct gaze. "Oh, Uncle Ralph, I'm miserable here. I can't think of anything except..." Her voice broke.

"I know, honey," his voice was filled with compassion as he patted her gently on the back. "I've been there." Then in a lighter voice he said, "I seem to remember you have an accounting degree from UT?" When she nodded he continued, "I'm going to need a bookkeeper for about six months. The girl who's been working for me is going to take a leave of absence because of pregnancy complications. I was planning to hire the wife of one of my other employees for the position, but if you were interested..."

"Oh, Uncle Ralph, thank you. It would be a life saver."

"You're sure there's no chance for you and your husband?"

"I'm sure," she whispered heavily.

Anitra and Howard were dismayed that evening at dinner when Ralph and Kit told them their news.

"Norway? But, *querida*, you haven't even tried to work things out with Ted."

"He doesn't want to work things out, Mother," Kit said firmly. "He doesn't care about me. Our marriage was a mistake from start to finish."

"You'll never make me believe that—not for one minute! Have you seen him lately? He looks brokenhearted."

Sharply: "Mother! I really don't want to talk about Ted! I've told you that before!"

"But, *querida*, if you go to Stavanger with Uncle Ralph for six months, you're sure to lose him."

"Mother!"

Conversation flowed around Kit, but she scarcely listened. After a time she became aware of her mother's voice louder than usual.

"*Querida*, your head must be in the clouds!"

"What were you saying, Mother?"

"I was talking about Marc Clay and that party he's having tomorrow night for the skippers and their crews."

"I told you before I couldn't go."

"But, *querida*, you're going to have to go—as a special favor to your father and me. As you know Mom isn't doing at all well, and Howard has said he can fly me up to San Antonio so I can see her over the weekend. We really can't get away any other time. That means that no one from our family will be at the party to represent *Kitten*."

"What about Steve?"

"He has other plans he can't change."

"I'm not up to a party, and I'm sure Ted was invited too. I certainly don't want to risk running into him."

"From what I understand, Ted is in The Valley at his ranch," her father said. "I think you ought to go to the Clays' party. You need to get out more. And, Kitten, I know Ralph would enjoy going."

If Ted wasn't going Kit saw little harm in going herself. She did need to get out, and she knew Uncle Ralph loved parties. It would be the perfect way to entertain him.

The next evening Kit selected a floor-length gown that was a drift of lime green. The chiffonlike cloth seemed to float around her as she moved about her room getting ready for the party. She wore her black hair down about her shoulders.

After applying a soft shade of lipstick to her lips, she eyed her reflection in the mirror critically. The dress was so simple, she decided, she needed to wear some jewelry. Her long, carefully manicured fingertips fingered several pieces of jewelry in her jewel case.

She lifted Ted's pearls—cool and lustrous—from black velvet and held them tentatively to her throat. The effect was stunning. Suddenly she was remembering when he'd first placed them around her neck. She'd been so much in love with him, so hopeful that their marriage would be a happy one. Just the thought of it and tears were filling her eyes.

She couldn't possibly wear them. Slowly she dropped the pearls back into the jewel case. Instead she chose a simple twist of gold and fastened it at the nape of her neck. If it wasn't as lovely as the pearls, at least the mere sight of it brought back no aching memories.

Heads turned at the party when a tall, distinguished-looking gentleman ushered his raven-haired niece through the entrance of the Clay mansion.

"Kit, darling," gushed Judith Clay, "you look stunning tonight! It's so good to see you out!"

"Judith, I'd like you to meet my Uncle Ralph..."

Marc Clay was hugging Kit to him and kissing her affectionately on the forehead. Then Ralph and Kit entered the living area of the house to mingle with the other guests.

The house was a perfect setting for the beautiful people who filled it. It was boldly modern in design—its living room ceiling slanting upward three stories to a sky light. Lush hanging baskets of trailing green vines hung from the high ceiling like living chandeliers. It was a house of many windows. Here one would always feel the presence of the sea.

She wandered through the house introducing Ralph to the other guests and exchanging bits of nonsense with friends. Still clinging to Ralph, she led him onto the terrace overlooking the bay. The wind blew her hair back from her face. The house stood high upon a bluff. Some distance beneath her she watched the waves run across the soft sand and crash against the bulkhead.

Kit and Ralph stared across the bay. She pointed out the harbor bridge—a crescent of sparkling lights spanning the port area. She pointed out other landmarks and then for a time they enjoyed the view in silence. The bay was such a familiar sight; she realized she would miss looking out across the water. For some inexplicable reason she thought of Ted, his handsome darkness, his smile, his touch...her breath caught painfully. When she left Corpus she would be leaving him as well. There would be no turning back.

Suddenly she was feeling restless—in the mood to rejoin the party, when Ralph, a social person himself, suggested that very thing. He led her back inside toward the bar where he ordered a highball for himself and a glass of Chablis for her.

The white wine relaxed her. She'd been separated from Ted for nearly a month, and this was the first time she'd felt even close to normal. Perhaps it was the wine affecting her. Perhaps it was the fact that her father had found out for certain that Ted was at his ranch and would not be returning for the party. In any event she relaxed and began to enjoy the party.

She was near the hors d'oeuvre table surveying silver dishes filled with nuts, French endive, garnished asparagus spears, avocado and chutney, crepes of all varieties, marinated carrots, and caviar. A puffy-hatted chef was cooking omelettes. She was in the process of spreading a wafer with caviar when to her horror she saw Phyllis across the room, shimmering in a gown of flowing scarlet as she stood directly beneath the floodlight at the entrance of the mansion. By her side stood Ted.

Phyllis had never looked lovelier. The red gown clung to her curves and swirled gracefully around her when she moved. Ted was casual in black slacks and a cream turtleneck.

How.... What...were they doing here?

Wafer and caviar spilled through nervous fingers to the floor, and Kit scrambled to her knees to retrieve them.

What was she going to do she wondered desperately. If only she could stay buried behind the table for the rest of the party. If only she could find some means of escape.

Her heart was thudding painfully. She was gasping as if there were no oxygen in the room. Was it always to be like this when she saw them together?

She knew suddenly that she was doing the right thing to accept the position Uncle Ralph had been kind enough to offer her. She needed to get away where there would be no danger of running into them again.

Slowly she straightened and as she did Marc Clay came to her and asked her to dance. He'd seen Ted at the door, and she knew he'd come to rescue her. The music was fast and when it stopped, they were both breathless. Marc left her safely surrounded by a cluster of friends while he went to get her a Coke.

Conversation flowed pleasantly on all sides of her. Half-listening, she nodded and murmured politely at the appropriate moments. She saw that Uncle Ralph was having the time of his life. He was on his third martini, and she knew it wasn't going to be easy to convince him to leave. And she had to convince him. She simply couldn't stay now that Ted and Phyllis were here.

Suddenly she saw Ted threading his way through the crowd and coming toward her. Smoothly he inserted himself into the conversation; just as he had smoothly inserted his own body next to hers.

Bold blue eyes fastened on her face with an intensity that she found alarming.

"Kit, would you dance this one with me?"

"Ted, I...I really don't think..." Her heart was beating so loudly and erratically she was afraid he'd hear it.

"Is it true what I just heard—that you're going to Norway to work?"

"Yes. It is."

His dark face was expressionless. "Then this might be our last chance...to dance together...to talk...."

He wouldn't take no for an answer. He gripped her shaking fingers in his warm brown ones and led her out onto the dance floor. The band played a slow number, and he pulled her slender body against his. He was a flawless dancer. He held her very close, and for a time they swirled to the music. Once his thigh brushed hers, and she felt his sharp intake of breath as he paused in the middle of a dance step. Then once more his movements were fluid although he was careful not to hold her so close.

In spite of everything it felt wonderful to be in his arms once more.

"I...I thought you were at your ranch," she whispered.

"I was, but when I found out you were going away, I had to come back...to see you."

His hand pressed hers tightly, but he did not enlighten her as to why it was so important to him to see her.

She felt strangely happy, hopeful although she knew it was unreasonable to attach any significance to what he'd said.

She wished the music would go on and on and that they could dance forever, but, of course, all too soon it stopped. He led her from the dance floor, past a clump of potted palms.

"I need some fresh air, after that," he said. He pulled her by the hand out into the terrace. Several couples had had the same idea and stood on the terrace looking out onto the bay.

"I want to talk to you," he said. "Somewhere where we can be alone..."

Again the madly hopeful thumping of her erratic pulsebeats.

"Ted...I..."

But he wasn't listening to her feeble protests. He was leading her down the stone steps of the terrace out onto the freshly mown lawn.

"Why don't we go for a walk on the beach?" he said.

"No...I really think we should go back inside."

Again he refused to listen to her protests. The lawn ended abruptly, and they stepped out onto the fifteen-foot-high seawall. Water curled and crashed beneath them. Only a few yards from them a rickety, wooden staircase descended on the beach. New lumber—doubtless intended for the construction of a new, sturdier staircase—lay in a neat pile nearby.

"Come on," he said, pulling her unresisting toward the wooden steps.

The pungent odor of salt spray and rotting sea things assailed her nostrils as she bent over and removed her green slippers. Dangling her slippers in one hand, she put a stockinged foot onto the first step of the staircase. The wind gusted and her gown was pale froth whipping around her. The step she was standing on wobbled slightly and she was glad Ted was holding her.

His eyes were again on her face; his expression was tender. His hand that was gripping hers pulled her to him tightly.

"Kit..."

Suddenly the lilting tones of a woman's voice sounded from behind him.

"There you are, Ted, dear," Phyllis said, her voice breathless from running. "I thought you might have come out here. Beautiful night, isn't it?"

"Yes, Phyllis, it is," Ted muttered, dropping Kit's hand and turning to include her.

"Whatever are the two of you talking about... and so seriously?" Phyllis queried lightly, slipping a hand through Ted's arm. Then with the savage thrust of a knife, the deceptively sweet voice continued, "Your divorce? You did say you hadn't gotten around to that yet."

Phyllis was looking directly at Kit, her gray eyes challenging, her hands clinging to Ted as if he was her exclusive property.

The horrible word so gaily spoken was pain winging swiftly and brutally through Kit. So that was why he'd wanted to see her before she left! So that was why he'd returned from his ranch! Her whole body quivered, and she lurched on the shaky staircase, losing her balance. For one horrible moment she teetered. Then she grabbed wildly for the railing, for Ted's outstretched hand, for anything that would save her from falling.

Ted was a dark blur of motion as he tried to save her, but with Phyllis clinging to him, he was not fast enough. Kit was tumbling downward. As she fell an edge of wooden stair cut into her thigh painfully. Her head hit something sharp once...twice.... Then mercifully she landed—a limp heap—on the soft, damp sand, and a wave surged and curled around her.

It seemed to her that every part of her was in pain. She was only vaguely aware of Ted rushing down the stairs after her, of him lifting her into his strong arms, of him carrying her carefully back up the stairs and into the house, of people everywhere hovering. Then there was a blackness that seemed to stretch endlessly on all sides of her.

She was aware only of a warm hand pressing hers tightly, of the comforting tones of a man's deep, resonant drawl.

Later she was still only dimly aware of being driven to the hospital emergency room, of the doctor examining her, of X-rays being taken, of a sedative to help her sleep being administered....

She awoke the next morning to the indistinct, seemingly slurred tones of her mother's voice, saying gently, "*Querida*, Ted is outside. He wants to see you."

Vaguely Kit wondered what her mother was doing home from San Antonio. Then she focused on the really important thing—Ted. She couldn't see him—not this morning—not ever.

"No.... No..."

Her throbbing mind seemed fuzzy as she sat up in bed. Every part of her was aching, but one thing was clear to her. Ted belonged to Phyllis. She'd seen that so clearly last night before she'd fallen. It was something she would never lose sight of again.

"He's been here all night, *querida*."

Kit saw him then—a lean, unshaven, dark giant standing in the doorway. Just the sight of those hard, sensually virile features was torture.

"I don't care!" Kit cried desperately, bursting into tears because she knew his interest stemmed out of kindness and not love. "Tell him he can file for divorce, he can do whatever he wants...as long as he leaves me alone. I don't want to see him again—not ever!"

When she looked toward the door again, he was gone, and she knew he was out of her life forever.

Chapter Eleven

Kit suffered surface scratches and bruises as well as a mild concussion from her fall. Two weeks later she felt strong enough to face the task of returning to Ted's townhouse to pack her things. She'd put the task off as long as she could. It was the Thursday morning before her scheduled departure Friday afternoon for Norway.

She arrived at his townhouse in the middle of the morning. She'd selected that hour because she was sure Ted would be at work. Letting herself in with her key, she paused to survey the familiar surroundings. His usually immaculate townhouse had a littered look. Beer cans were everywhere. Cigarettes overflowed from ashtrays. She remembered Ted had quit smoking when he'd been at the university.

Well, it was obvious he was enjoying himself, she thought without bitterness. She wanted his happiness more than anything. He was probably enjoying the freedom of being a bachelor again. She imagined him partying and entertaining Phyllis late into his nights.

She went to the master bedroom and began packing. He'd thoughtfully grouped all her belongings into one closet. When her suitcases were neatly packed, she closed their lids. If only she could organize her life as neatly as she'd organized her suitcases. If only she could tear the pain in her heart out and pack it away.

She sank down onto the bed. How would she ever get over him—even in Norway? Since she'd moved out, it hurt her more every day to be away from him. But she had to let him have the woman he really loved. She'd thought of calling him and trying to explain about Matt before she left, but always the thought that it was easier for Ted if she didn't, stopped her. This way, believing the worst about her, he could live his life with Phyllis free of guilt. By not calling him, she was making it easier for him to do what he really wanted to do.

She remembered the sight of him holding Phyllis in his arms on their wedding night, the sight of Phyllis on his arm, lovely in swirling red the night she herself had fallen. Phyllis and he belonged together. Above everything Kit wanted his happiness, even if his happiness could not include her.

The lock of the suitcase snapped, and Kit dragged it from the bedroom. She went back for the second suitcase.

She heard the front door open and as she stepped into the living room, her own eyes locked with the frostiest of gray eyes.

"What are you doing here?" Phyllis demanded in a possessive tone. From her attitude it was clear she felt she belonged and Kit did not.

"I was just leaving. I came for my things."

"I hope you're gone before Ted comes home. The last thing he needs is to see you again before you leave. He's been happy ever since you moved out."

"Has he?"

"Yes. I saw from the beginning that you were no good. Not for him or for Missy."

"Well, as I already know how you feel about me, I don't see any point in going over all of it again," Kit said quietly. "Whether you believe it or not I want Ted to be happy."

"I'm glad you called that night. I'm glad you found out all about . . ."

She never finished what she was going to say, for she heard a sound at the door directly behind her. She turned and stared open-mouthed at Ted, who was standing in the doorway.

His haggard features seemed chiseled from granite; his mouth was a thin, hard line. Just the sight of him was searing, bittersweet pain to Kit.

"Finish what you were going to say, Phyllis," he said in a dangerously quiet voice.

"I . . . I . . . don't know what I would have said," she stammered.

"I think you do."

"It wasn't anything important. If you don't mind I have to go now." She picked up a brown sack on the coffee table. "Missy forgot her lunch when she was over here this morning, and I promised her I'd come pick it up for her. If you don't mind," she said, edging past him, "I need to get it to her. You know how early they eat. I would hate for her to be left out."

"When you get back, Phyllis, you and I are going to have a long talk."

He turned to Kit. He was studying her with an intensity that jarred every nerve end in her slender body.

"I was just on my way out when Phyllis came in," Kit said weakly. "I didn't think you'd be home at this hour—you remember you asked me to come by when you wouldn't be here. I'm sorry if I've inconvenienced you."

She strained against the handle of the heavy suitcase, trying to pick it up. He was at her side in an instant. His long brown fingers covered hers as he took the suitcase from her. As always his touch was electric, and she jumped back.

"I'll carry this to your car in a minute," he said. "But first I'd like to talk to you."

"I can't imagine that we have anything more to say to one another," she whispered shakily.

"Perhaps we can start with what Phyllis was saying when I came in here just a minute ago. What did she mean when she said she was glad you'd called her and found about...about what?"

"It doesn't matter now, Ted. I...I have to go." The muscles of her throat constricted with the tension of being too near him. She had to get away. But that was impossible because Ted's hand was suddenly on her arm, stopping what would have been her swift retreat with the punishing grip of his strong fingers.

"If it doesn't matter then you shouldn't mind telling me," he said simply, leading her to the couch.

She sat down and he sat across from her, and she was very aware of him—so close—of the coiled strength of his powerful body which he would unleash if she tried to escape him again. She had no choice but to give him the answers he required.

"Well...the night...the night when you found me here with Matt..." she faltered. His face darkened only slightly at the mention of Matt. She thought he strained for control. "I was worried when I got home from the party and couldn't find you. I thought maybe something had happened to you, so I called Phyllis. She said you were asleep over there. I knew then for sure that what I'd suspected all along was true—that it was over between you and me, that you loved her. It was the past repeating itself."

He leaned forward in his chair, his blue eyes blazing. His dark face was amazement.

"Phyllis let you think..." She nodded mutely. "You thought I loved Phyllis...all along?" he repeated slowly, as if he needed to say it carefully to get used to the idea.

"Yes. What I don't understand is why you married me when you loved her. It really wasn't fair of you."

"And your thinking this bothered you from the start of our marriage?" His deep voice sounded suddenly eager, and an answering eagerness leaped in her.

"From the first day."

"Why didn't you tell me?"

"Because I knew you'd tell me a lie."

"Why would you think I'd lie? Did I ever lie to you before?"

"Yes, in a way."

It was strange but now that their marriage was over she could talk about hurts she'd kept bottled inside of her for a very long time.

"You said something about the past repeating itself. What did you mean by that? And I'd like to know...specifically...when I lied to you?" he said quietly.

"That night—the last night I saw you—five years ago, the night I ran out when you tried to make love to me.... Well, I called you back that night, Ted. Letitia answered the phone. She asked me if I really wanted to disturb you—that you were in bed. I knew then that you really didn't care for me in the same way that I cared for you if you could go from me to her so quickly. What you felt was merely physical. I was hurt, and I never wanted to see you again."

"Letitia!" he spoke her name in savage anger. "I can believe she did that—after living with her two and a half years. She had a vindictive streak. I only married her out of loneliness. You'd left me and she was going through a rough time herself. Dad died and I really wasn't thinking too clearly." He paused. "Kit, you can call Marc Clay and ask him to confirm what I'm going to tell you. Letitia and Marc came by after you left that night to copy my notes. Marc and I had a law class together. He'd skipped a class or something—I'm not too sure now. You'd run out on me that night and wouldn't even answer the phone when I called you. I was in no mood for company so I told them I was tired and went to bed. I'm telling you the truth, Kit. I swear it." He hesitated. "And to think...all those years I thought you'd left me for Rodney. That's why I couldn't trust you."

She knew intuitively he was telling the truth, but this knowledge gave her no joy. The past was over. He loved Phyllis now.

"I *was* asleep at Phyllis's the night you called," he continued. "But it wasn't like it sounds. I'd gotten home shortly after twelve-thirty. Her light was on. I went over and we got to talking. I must have fallen asleep—goodness, I was dead tired that night. At the party I'd tried to get your attention at midnight to tell you I felt like a walking zombie and was ready to leave. But you wouldn't speak to me. Anyway, when the phone rang, I woke up and found myself sprawled on her couch covered with blankets. I got up and came home. That's when I found you with Matt. I was hardly rational at the time."

"Why were you standing on the seawall holding Phyllis in your arms on our wedding night?" she asked, determined to know everything. "When I asked you where you'd gone you said you'd gone for a walk."

"Ah.... So you saw us then. Kit, you must have realized how much Phyllis dislikes the idea of your being married to me. She and I are extremely close. She turned to me and Missy when her sister died. She can't accept that Letitia is dead, and that I need to live my own life. That night I was trying to persuade her to give you a chance, but she wouldn't listen to me. I didn't want to discuss it with you on our wedding night. I knew you'd be upset..."

"You aren't in love with Phyllis?"

"We are close friends. That's all. Kit, you have to believe me. She dislikes you out of loyalty to her sister. That's all."

"Oh."

She'd been so wrong about him. If only she'd had the courage to ask him these things before she'd ruined her chance to be happy with him. But now he believed she was the type of woman who chased after men and brought them home to bed.

As if he read her mind: "Kit, I never did give you a chance to explain about Matt. What was he doing here at four in the morning?"

"He'd insisted on driving me home because he said I was in no condition to drive. He only stayed because I was so frantic when I couldn't find you. I was in his arms because he was comforting me after I learned you were asleep at Phyllis's."

"And that time Rodney was in the store holding you..."

"He really was getting an eyelash out of my eye. I'd been crying because I'd seen you holding Phyllis on our wedding night. I didn't want to explain that to him so I told him I had something in my eye."

"So that's what you were holding back.... It seems we've been at cross purposes, you and I. You thought I loved Phyllis, and I didn't realize you loved me. When all the time I thought you knew how much I loved you."

"What?" Her voice sounded curiously light and breathless.

"Why did you think I married you?"

"I didn't know. You certainly never said you loved me."

"Then I should have, but I was too proud, and you seemed so cold." He spanned the short distance between them, and took her in his arms. "Kit, I've been such a fool. Yes, I loved you. I always have. When I read in the newspaper about Rodney jilting you, I went over to your house hoping to see you. In spite of everything I'd never forgotten you. I hardly ever check those tents myself—you know that. Then you came out—all haughty and disdainful—and ordered me to the servants' entrance as if I weren't as good as you. I remembered all the old grievances against you. That's why I kissed you—to teach you a lesson, but the lesson backfired. You kissed me so passionately—as though you still cared. After that kiss I couldn't get you out of my mind. I went down to the club determined never to think of you again, but then you came down yourself. After you wrecked *Wild Lady*, and I saw you in the water and in danger, I knew then how much I loved you. When your father asked me to dinner, I had to come. I *had* to see you. When you weren't wearing Rodney's ring, I thought there might be a chance for us. I thought if I could persuade you to marry me, you might come to love me in time. Then you said you'd marry me on the condition that I not touch you. That month before we married was the longest in my life. I knew if I saw very much of you, I couldn't keep my promise, and you might not marry me. That's why I went out of town. Then after we got married.... Well, you know what a thorough mess I made of our marriage.... I wouldn't really blame you if you hated me."

"Oh, Ted I couldn't hate you," she said in her softest voice. "I love you. I always have."

For a long moment his eyes filled with wonder then his lips covered hers and lingered in a passionate kiss that left them both breathless. After a long time his mouth left hers.

"When I learned from your father you were going away, I drove ninety miles an hour to get to the Clays' party. I wanted to give you a chance to explain about Matt. But I never got the chance. After you fell, and you sent me away.... I thought I'd lost you."

"I only sent you away because I thought you loved Phyllis. I thought you wanted to talk about divorce."

"These past few weeks when I was sure I'd lost you have been a living nightmare for me. I even took up smoking again," he murmured. "I haven't eaten; I've hardly been able to work."

"It's been just as bad for me. I wanted to call you before I went away, but I didn't think you'd want me to."

"Kit, darling, we've been such fools."

Again his lips covered hers urgently. "But we have the rest of our lives to make up for it," he continued.

Her fingers reached up and combed his auburn hair. "Would it be too soon if we began now?" she asked tremulously.

A wicked light danced in his blue eyes and a strange rippling excitement coursed through her in response. He curved a finger under her chin and tilted her head up to his. His lips found hers again.

"I love you," she whispered against his mouth.

"And I love you, my darling *Wild Lady*, and always will."

* * * * *

Books by Ann Major

Silhouette Romance

Wild Lady #90
A Touch of Fire #150

Silhouette Special Edition

Brand of Diamonds #83
Dazzle #229
The Fairy Tale Girl #390

Silhouette Desire

Dream Come True #16
Meant to Be #35
Love Me Again #99
The Wrong Man #151
Golden Man #198
Beyond Love #229
In Every Stranger's Face #301
What This Passion Means #331
**Passion's Child* #445
**Destiny's Child* #451
**Night Child* #457
**Wilderness Child* #535
**Scandal's Child* #564

*Children of Destiny

Silhouette Intimate Moments

Seize the Moment #54

To Lynn and Lauraine,
who insisted . . .

ANNETTE BROADRICK

lives on the shores of Lake of the Ozarks in Missouri, where she spends her time doing what she loves most—reading and writing romance fiction. "For twenty-five years I lived in various large cities, working as a legal secretary, a very high-stress occupation. I never thought I was capable of making a career change at this point in my life, but thanks to Silhouette Books, I am now able to write full-time in the peaceful surroundings that have turned my life into a dream come true."

Annette's upcoming titles for Silhouette Books include: *Candlelight for Two* (July 1990, Silhouette Desire #577) and *Married?!* (September 1990, Silhouette Romance #742).

"Happy-ever-after has become a significant part of my life—and all thanks to the Silhouette Romance reader!"

—Annette Broadrick

Chapter One

Ashley Allison glanced at the digital watch on her wrist—7:15—and decided to forget about staying at the office until she cleared her desk. Her body felt as though she'd spent the day working out in a gym, rather than in court.

Her watch continued to flash other information—month, *June*; day, *Friday*; date, 28—which she ignored. She was already aware of the date. She'd spent six hours in trial at the Multnomah County courthouse in Portland, Oregon, and even the fact that she'd won couldn't compensate for the energy she'd expended.

The framed print hanging on the wall in front of her desk caught her eye as she stood up and stretched. It was a cartoonist's version of Ashley's home state, Texas. The exaggerated shape stretched as far north as the Great Lakes, east to Maine, and west to California. The print had been solemnly presented to her by the staff on her twenty-eighth birthday in November.

No one in the office allowed her to forget her origin, her southern drawl, or her nickname—"long, tall Texan." Since Ashley stood five feet eight inches in her bare feet, she couldn't argue with the nickname—or the sentiment: *If you're born a Texan, you never recover.*

Ashley pushed her shoulder-length hair behind her ear as she reached for her briefcase. Unloading papers taken to court, she glanced at the stacks of files and correspondence scattered across her desk and tried to decide what work to take home. No. She intended to forget all about the law for the next couple of days and enjoy some of the rare sunshine they'd been having. She glanced out of her window and saw Mount Hood shimmering white against the blue sky. She might even drive up into the mountains tomorrow and enjoy the fresh air.

Her thoughts turned to possible plans for the evening. She had refused an invitation to see the musical comedy at the Civic Auditorium that night. One of the new associates had invited her to go, but she didn't want to encourage his interest. How many times had she explained to various men that she had no time to devote to a relationship, that her career took too much of her time and energy? Yet there always seemed to be some egotistical male who was convinced he could change her mind and whisk her away from the drudgery of the legal world.

"There's no such critter," Ashley muttered, and her mind suddenly flashed the image of a man she'd seen that morning in the elevator. She'd never seen him before, she was certain of that. His looks were not the type a person would forget. For one thing, his size made him quite noticeable. Even in her two-inch heels Ashley found herself looking up several inches to meet his eyes. Those eyes were what had caught her attention. In a deeply bronzed face, their silver blue was striking. His ebony hair suggested that his skin tones were natural rather than the result of long exposure to the sun. So where had he gotten those eyes?

It would take more than a pair of unforgettable blue eyes, however, to cause Ashley to stray from her chosen course. She hoped to become a partner in the law firm of Begley, Henderson & Howe by the time she reached thirty, and no man, regardless of wealth, charm, or beautiful eyes, could offer anything more appealing to Ashley. Still—she'd never seen eyes quite like his before. Funny she should remember them.

As she left the office she wondered what Tasha might have in store for her that night. She loved her Siamese cat dearly but admitted that she could be a real pain. Tasha hated being left alone nights. Normally, Ashley had no problem with that idiosyncrasy since she seldom stayed out late, but that week had been an exception. Monday she'd attended an Oregon Symphony concert with a friend, and when she had arrived home she was ignored by her cat instead of being greeted with a recounting of the day's events. On Wednesday Ashley had arrived home after a long day to find her living room strewn with papers and magazines that she'd left stacked in a neat pile on the coffee table. Instead of the stack, the table held a sleek and satisfied-looking Siamese cat in the midst of intricate ablutions. Ashley dreaded to think of what Tasha might have dreamed up as punishment for that night.

As she started down the hallway to the elevators, Ashley was already planning her evening. She could hardly wait to kick off her shoes, pour herself a large glass of wine, and relax in a hot bath.

In another office on the same floor Raphael McCord had his own problems. While leaving telephone instructions with his assistant in San Francisco, he was interrupted by a strange man who burst into the office with a degree of belligerence seldom seen in the business world.

McCord kept an eye on the short, beefy man, noting the deep frown marring his face, as he continued to speak into the phone.

"That's about it, Jim. I should be arriving on the 9:05 flight on Monday, so have the car at the airport. I'll see you then." He hung up the phone and studied the man in front of him. A green and yellow plaid jacket strained across the protruding stomach and partially revealed the open collar of a dingy white shirt. Clenched fists hung below frayed cuffs. McCord cocked an eyebrow and gazed into eyes that looked like brown marbles decorated with red lace. "Is there something I can do for you?" McCord's tone implied that he doubted it.

"Your name McCord?" the man asked. Since the name on the office door read *McCord Industries*, he could be excused for jumping to conclusions.

"That's right."

A beefy hand shot out across the desk. "I'm Pete Wilson. Virgil Tysinger sent me." He waited as though he'd just explained all that was necessary.

A slight frown appeared on McCord's face. "Why?" he asked, shaking the extended paw with some reluctance.

That must have been the wrong question. Wilson's face turned a deeper shade of red and the veins in his beefy neck began to stand out. "Don't play games with me, McCord. He wants you and your wife to have dinner with him tonight. He told me to come by and pick you up." His frown deepened. "You'd never be able to find the place on your own."

McCord started at the word *wife*. His brief glance at the sofa by the windows confirmed that the infant still slept. Wilson intercepted the glance and spotted the baby.

"Where's your wife?"

McCord needed time to think, but he had none. He gave Wilson an appraising stare, then came to his feet in a lazy manner, towering over the other man. "She's shopping at the moment. We're supposed to meet later." He motioned to the baby. "As you can see, I'm baby-sitting."

"When are you supposed to meet her?"

McCord glanced down at his watch in an effort to stall for time. Seven-fifteen. Later than he thought. He shrugged as he moved toward the baby. "You know what women are like. There's no telling."

"Then we'd better locate her. It takes a while to get to Tysinger's place." He edged to the window and glanced out. "Which direction did she take?"

McCord picked up the infant and grabbed its diaper bag. "I'm not sure. I think she said she'd meet me at the car."

"Then let's get down there. The sooner we find her, the sooner we can get started." The man had a positive genius for overstating the obvious.

"Look, Mr. Wilson." McCord used his most reasonable tone. "I appreciate the invitation, but let's make it for some other time, okay?" He ushered Wilson out of the office, made sure the door locked behind him, and motioned Wilson down the hall to the elevators. He wasn't sure what he was going to do when Wilson discovered there was no wife waiting at the car. He'd think of something, he supposed. This wasn't the first time he'd managed to bluff himself out of a situation not of his making.

The sound of an angry male voice reached Ashley as she rounded the corner near the elevators. An inner alarm jangled. She knew that most people who worked in the building had gone home long before.

Two men stood near the elevators; a short, heavyset man was doing most of the talking. Her concern eased when she recognized the man listening to the tirade. He was her elevator companion of the morning, the one with the unforgettable blue eyes. Ashley watched with amusement. He seemed to have his hands full with an irate client. Then the shorter man moved a pace to the side and Ashley discovered that "Blue Eyes" literally had his hands full. He held an infant tucked into his arm much as a football player would carry a ball, and he had a diaper bag dangling from his other hand.

The business suit and diaper bag didn't blend too well, in Ashley's opinion, although the baby seemed content enough. *Better him than me. Give me a brief over a bassinet any day.*

The elevator made its appearance, and Ashley moved toward the lighted area near the men. She'd be home in a matter of minutes. It couldn't be too soon for her.

As she stepped into the elevator, Ashley nodded to the man she recognized, giving him a tentative smile. The short man spun around and saw her at the same time his companion spoke.

"Oh, there you are, love. I thought we were supposed to meet back at the car."

Ashley glanced around, wondering whom he'd addressed in such familiar terms. There was no one else in the elevator, and he was staring at her. Her smile wavered. Perhaps she had misunderstood him. There was no way she could misunderstand his next actions. He approached her and with a deft movement transferred the small infant from his arms to hers. He leaned over and kissed the side of her mouth as he murmured, "I think Josh missed you almost as much as I did."

Ashley blinked as she glanced down at the baby thrust into her arms. He returned her look with a solemn, blue-eyed inspection. The man at her side pulled her close to him.

"I want you to meet my wife, Mr. Wilson." He smiled at her and added in a warm tone, "Honey, this is Pete Wilson. He dropped in rather unexpectedly today." Ashley stared at the two men as the incredible conversation continued. "He's brought us an invitation from Virgil Tysinger for dinner tonight." His expression reflected his regret. "I explained to him that we've already made plans for the evening." In a cordial tone he addressed Wilson once again. "Maybe we can get together with Tysinger some time next week."

My God! They must be filming a television series here in the building and I got on the wrong elevator. But surely these men knew she wasn't part of the production, didn't they? The name Virgil Tysinger registered. What would the state legislator have to do with all of this?

Ashley managed to get her tongue unglued from the roof of her mouth. "I think there's been some sort of mistake—"

The man introduced as Pete Wilson interrupted. "Look here, McCord, I told you—Tysinger doesn't care what your plans are, he wants to see you—" The elevator doors opened onto the lobby.

McCord's arm clamped around Ashley's waist and he guided her into the marbled lobby. She looked around, her first thought centered on getting the guard's attention. As they reached the front door, McCord spoke to the man on duty.

"Good night, Sam. Have a good weekend."

"You too, Mr. McCord." His smile of acknowledgement did not register anything unusual in the departure of the three adults and infant.

Ashley's adrenaline managed to overcome the inertia caused by her shock. "Just a blasted minute. What do you think you're doing?" She planted her feet, determined not to move another step. The two men paused, similar expressions of impatience darting across dissimilar countenances.

"I've already explained to Wilson that we can't make the dinner tonight, honey. I don't understand his insistence any more than you do." McCord's glance at Wilson would have wilted a less determined man.

Shaking her head in an unconscious attempt to make sense out of a senseless statement, Ashley attempted her most calm, dispassionate, courtroom voice. "I don't have the faintest idea of what you're talking about. I've never seen you before in my life." Not a totally accurate statement, perhaps, but close enough to make her point.

"What do you mean, you've never seen me before? What kind of silly statement is that? You married me, didn't you, or is that up for debate as well?"

Ashley's well-ordered, uncomplicated existence began to unravel. Had she stepped into some sort of time warp?

"Married? Are you out of your mind? I certainly am not married." Her firm denunciation was made in ringing tones of sincerity that would have convinced a jury anywhere.

"I suppose you're also going to deny that Josh is our son?" He indicated the infant in her arms with all the drama of a prosecuting attorney exhibiting the murder weapon to the jury.

"Our son!" Ashley's conversation had degenerated to repeating parts of his sentences. She stared with a certain amount of horror into the eyes of the young person in her arms and was rewarded with a smile that seemed to have been produced on cue.

Wilson stepped toward them, menace in every line of his body. "Look, McCord. We don't have time for this. You and the missus can fight in the car as well as here on the steps. Get going." He spun around and started down the steps in front of them.

What an unpleasant person, Ashley thought, a faint tremor coursing through her body. Not exactly a first choice for a lighthearted companion. She had no idea what was going on, but knew darned well she wanted no part of it.

She turned to McCord and held out the baby. "I'm not going anywhere with either of you, do you understand me? If you don't leave me alone, I'll scream my head off until every policeman in downtown Portland will think a riot's taking place." She glared at him with all the anger, indignation, and fear that had been building within her.

Unfortunately McCord wasn't intimidated, nor was he accepting the baby she offered him. Instead he propelled them both down the steps and started leading Ashley past the other man with a brusque "We've got to go" to Wilson.

Ashley heard Wilson say, "Sorry, McCord, I only obey orders, and my orders was to get you and the missus and bring you to Tysinger." Then she saw two more men materialize before them, effectively blocking their path. Ashley's heart leaped from its normal position in her chest to play Ping Pong between her throat and her stomach. These men didn't have to work at looking intimidating. Almost identical in build, their arms bulged with well-developed biceps that would give the Incredible Hulk competition. She had no desire to see how they behaved when angry.

McCord's voice sent a chill through Ashley, though he never raised his tone. "I don't care for your strong-arm tactics, Wilson. I don't like threats, either against me or my family. My wife and I have other plans. Now get your playmates to move out of the way."

Once again McCord and Ashley moved forward, this time with Ashley's full consent and approval. Then she saw the long, low limousine illegally parked at the curb, a rear door open. With the three men surrounding them, McCord and Ashley had no escape route open.

One of the trained primates muttered, "Get in, McCord, we've wasted enough time. We don't want trouble, but if you're gonna insist, we'll oblige."

Ashley's ability to think on her feet, a necessary trait for a good trial lawyer, deserted her in her time of need. She'd never been physically overwhelmed before.

McCord's arm tightened and Ashley glanced up at him. He stared into her eyes as though attempting to read her thoughts. She returned his gaze, refusing to allow him to see her fear. McCord touched her cheek gently with his finger. "We might as well see what this is all about." He took the baby from her, assisted Ashley into the limousine, and climbed in behind her. The other men wasted no time; two of them leaped into the front seat, and Wilson got into the back with Ashley and McCord.

The last door slammed and the limousine pulled silently away from the curb, gathering speed as it neared the Hawthorne Bridge and crossed the Willamette River.

McCord handed the baby back to Ashley, reached into the bag he still carried, and brought out a bottle, saying, "Josh hasn't been fed." He handed her the bottle. Ashley studied his face, searching for a clue as to what was happening. Then she looked at the infant in her arms, who was already anticipating the delights of the bottle in front of him. He seemed to know what to do with it as she stuck it with some awkwardness into his mouth. What Ashley knew about babies could be inscribed on the heel of one of her two-inch pumps, with plenty of room to spare. However, the infant didn't appear to need much instruction at the moment. He grasped the bottle as though afraid she'd try to remove it.

McCord spoke to the man seated beside him. "Look, I don't know what this is all about, but I'm willing to go see Tysinger if you'll just drop my wife and son off at home."

Why did he insist on their marital relationship? Other than a rather bizarre insistence on claiming a stranger to be his wife, the man appeared strikingly normal. Ordinarily Ashley would have considered him a man who could be depended upon in any situation. She wouldn't feel in the least unsure of his ability to cope if he'd just drop the myth of their relationship. So he had made a mistake. No one was perfect. Why didn't he just admit it and get her out of this mess?

Wilson's tone reflected an unexpected apology. "I'm sorry about all of this, McCord. But the invitation was for you and your wife. Tysinger insisted on that. I'm sure this whole thing is some kind of misunderstanding he'll clear up when you see him." He drew a once white handkerchief from his back pocket and wiped away the beads of perspiration glistening on his forehead. The day wasn't particularly warm.

Ashley leaned forward. "Are you talking about Virgil Tysinger, the state representative?"

Wilson nodded with unfeigned eagerness to make amends. "That's right."

"Is this some new type of campaign strategy, dragging people off the streets for a meal? Because if it is, someone should convince him there are more subtle methods for getting reelected."

McCord covered a sudden chuckle with a cough as Wilson's flushed face turned a darker hue.

"Miz McCord, I'm sure Mr. Tysinger will be able to explain everything once we get there."

"Get where, Mr. Wilson?" Ashley's tone was deceptively gentle.

"Huh?"

"Get where, Mr. Wilson?" she repeated even more gently. "Where are you taking us?" Anyone who knew Ashley would have recognized the tone that denoted a slow rage building. Unfortunately, Wilson accepted the sweetness at its face value.

"Oh! Well, Mr. Tysinger thought you'd like to visit his mountain retreat in the Cascades. He's got a real nice place and tries to spend as much of his free time there as possible." Wilson's premature smile of relief disappeared with Ashley's next comment.

"Mr. Wilson, what you have just done constitutes kidnapping, and state representative or not, Virgil Tysinger is an accessory. Kidnapping is a federal offense, Mr. Wilson. If you're ever going to have an original thought in your head, I strongly advise you to have it now and not leave the city limits of Portland with us in this car. Federal prisons are not known for their hospitality." Her tone stayed soft, but there was no doubt in anyone's mind that she was furious.

Turning to glare at the man sitting next to her, Ashley said in the same tone, "Would you care to explain to me why you've insisted that I am your wife?"

McCord's eyes glinted in the afternoon light. "Well, for one thing, it proves Josh's legitimacy."

"Are you trying to be funny?" she demanded.

"Not particularly. I just don't know any other way to answer your question."

"My question is not that difficult, Mr. McCord. But let me rephrase it for you. I—" she pointed with some gravity to herself "—am not married. Nor do I have any children. Why, then, are you insisting that I am married to you, and that this baby is ours?"

McCord studied the young woman seated by his side. *So what do you do now, McCord? You and your sudden impulse to help others seems to have backfired.* His gaze took in Ashley's large, luminous eyes, the softness of a mouth that managed to portray sensitivity even when clamped in anger, and the cinnamon hair that fell in waves from a central part to frame her face. She ignored his inspection as he took in her tailored suit and the curving shape it covered. McCord fell back on a habit that had worked well for him in the past. If you don't know what to say to them, kiss 'em. So he did.

His movement caught her off guard and she froze as his mouth moved across hers in a warm caress. The baby in her arms prevented her from resisting the sudden move. However, the unexpectedness of the kiss wasn't the only thing that startled her into immobility. What caught Ashley completely off guard was the sudden burst of intense feeling generated within her when McCord moved his mouth lazily across hers. The kiss was almost playful—an exploration of possible joys to be found, a willingness to indulge in a get-acquainted meeting. Then his mouth settled more firmly against hers, his tongue flicking across her bottom lip in an audacious search for intimacy. Had the sensation he created not been so enticing, Ashley would have described it as almost an electrical shock, or something like the static shock one got from walking across carpeting and then touching metal. Her eyes fluttered closed in an unconscious effort to recognize and identify the reaction caused by the kiss.

Once again the technique worked for McCord. Ashley forgot her question. In fact, for a short while she forgot that she was in a large automobile with several strangers, being whisked to some unknown destination for unspecified purposes. The question that surfaced after a brief spell was even more pressing. *Who is this man and how can he have such an effect on me?*

There was no way of knowing how long Ashley would have sat there contemplating the newest discovery she'd made about herself if nature hadn't suddenly taken over. Her small charge had managed to drain his bottle and then thoroughly soak through his diaper. Ashley looked at McCord with a hint of panic in her eyes. She leaned over and spoke in a low tone. "He's wet."

McCord glanced past Ashley to the expanse of velour cushion between her and the door. "You've got room to change him, haven't you?"

Fighting to maintain her decorum, Ashley responded through clenched teeth. "He's *your* baby. You change him!"

McCord's grin was the first Ashley had seen since she'd walked up to the elevators. Only by relaxing did McCord give away how tense he'd been. For some reason her reaction to the baby's condition amused him. His amusement increased her disgust. He reached into the bag and brought out a disposable diaper while Ashley sat there, a most unfeminine glare on her face. She stared at the disposable diaper, then at him, and at last down at the helpless infant. What was she doing here? She wouldn't even have *recognized* a disposable diaper if she hadn't seen them advertised on television. Josh gazed up at her with trusting blue eyes and popped two middle fingers into his mouth as he waited with infinite patience for her help.

Setting her jaw, she snatched the offending object from McCord's grasp. Turning to the innocent baby, she mentally apologized for being so personal on such short acquaintance and managed to secure the dry diaper on him without undue awkwardness.

Baby care was not part of the law school curriculum. Just wait until she had an opportunity to give this arrogant example of macho manhood her views of the male population in general and of him in particular.

Ashley picked up the baby and laid him with some trepidation against her shoulder. Would he be willing to be this close to her? Obviously so, because he snuggled his face into her neck and relaxed. So this mixture of delicately scented powder and warm body was a baby. Such a trusting scrap of humanity. Dry clothes, full tummy, and a shoulder to sleep on—he really didn't ask for much, but she knew from her moment of panic that she'd reached her limits of adaptability. Whether he liked it or not, McCord was going to have to take over the role of parent when the baby awakened.

More than an hour had gone by since they'd left downtown Portland. They were already on the winding mountain roads, and Ashley had no idea when they'd left the main highway—her thoughts had kept her preoccupied. At the moment she conceded that she had no option but to wait until they reached Tysinger. She began to rehearse what she'd say to the man. She was determined to get back to Portland immediately, his dinner plans notwithstanding.

Her thoughts returned to Tasha and she stiffened. The thought of what she'd find when she finally managed to reach home made her shudder.

It was almost enough to make her wish she'd stayed in Texas.

Chapter Two

After they had bounced over miles of jarring roads that grew worse the higher they climbed, their automobile made a sharp turn and came to an abrupt halt in a clearing. Ashley and Josh would have been thrown forward if McCord's quick reflexes hadn't stopped them.

Ashley could see no sign of a dwelling but stepped out when the door next to her opened. McCord was right behind her, his hand resting in the small of her back. A trail disappeared around a turn at the edge of the clearing, and Wilson motioned to them to follow the men into the woods. Ashley glanced down at her shoes and shook her head. She'd be lucky not to sprain an ankle, or worse. She tried not to think about it as McCord's arm came around her waist for support. She wasn't ready to ignore his help as they followed their escorts up a steep grade.

When they reached the top of the ridge, Ashley caught her breath. On the other side the ground dropped abruptly a few hundred feet to a large lake that reflected a gleaming Mount Hood, etched in pink by the setting sun. A cedar-shake house sat on the lip of the ridge, a deck curving out over the abrupt drop. The view was spectacular.

Their guides waited with obvious impatience at the top of steps leading to a double door into the house. *Be it ever so humble,* Ashley thought with a touch of whimsy. The home would not have looked out of place nestled in the exclusive west hills of Portland.

The inside more than lived up to the promise of the outside. The entire east wall of the large area they entered was glass, so that Mount Hood appeared to be part of the room. Ashley drifted across the room full of lengthening shadows, mesmerized by the glowing mountain.

A voice from the gloom startled her and she spun around, a move that woke the baby.

"Glad you could make it this evening. I'm Virgil Tysinger." A trim man of medium height came toward them. The fading sunlight barely touched his face. He moved toward McCord with his right hand outstretched. McCord stood there staring at him without expression. Tysinger's arm dropped to his side.

McCord's voice sounded harsh after Tysinger's mellow tones. "Do you want to explain the purpose of this abduction?"

Tysinger winced. "Abduction? Good God, man, what did that idiot say to give you that idea?"

"I don't remember the exact phrases. But when two more of your men added their persuasion, I decided I'd rather not have my wife and son upset."

There he goes again. We're going to play this little melodrama out to its bitter end, it seems.

McCord continued. "I was alone when he came to my office and insisted that my wife was there somewhere. He also insisted that she be brought along. 'Abducted' pretty well describes that sort of behavior, wouldn't you say?" McCord stood with legs slightly apart, balanced on the balls of his feet, his hands resting at his waist. The word *formidable* flashed through Ashley's mind.

Tysinger attempted a laugh that didn't quite come off. "Don't be absurd. Perhaps he was a little overzealous in making my wishes known to you. I don't hire men for their gifts of perception and subtlety." He leaned over and turned on a lamp sitting on a small table. "But you see, Raul, I could never reach you by phone, you never would return my calls, and it was important that I speak with you before you left town today. Really important." The smile on his face did not reach his dark eyes. They were wary, watching for a reaction.

McCord's smile wasn't pleasant. "Then you've wasted your time and ours, Tysinger. I'm not Raul."

Tysinger gave a start. "You aren't Raul McCord?" He glanced from McCord to Ashley, then back to McCord, and smiled. "Nice try, McCord. I almost believed you, but you've been described to me." Tysinger wasn't as comfortable as he wanted them to believe. Ashley wondered if she would ever learn what was going on!

"What's that supposed to mean?" McCord strolled to one end of the room, then turned to face Tysinger. "Anyone fitting my general description has to be Raul? What's got you so uptight, Tysinger, that you start breaking some of the laws you've sworn to protect?"

Ashley watched the two men as they faced each other. Tysinger's uneasiness began to register on his face as he stared at the younger man. He seemed to take a firm grip on his temper, and his voice assumed a charming tone as he gestured to Ashley. "I invited you and your wife here, McCord, to give us all a chance to get acquainted. I want to have the opportunity to sit down with both of you and discuss your activities these last few months."

Activities? What were they supposed to have done?

"I admire your enthusiasm and your idealism, but I think you're a little misguided at the moment. I just don't want to see you rushing off with a bunch of misleading information that won't do anybody any good and could do a great deal of harm." He became more relaxed as his explanation proceeded. Ashley got the feeling that his speech had been rehearsed for just such an occasion.

"Mr. Tysinger." Ashley spoke for the first time since she'd entered the room. "I'm not quite sure how I got involved in this, but I have no idea what it's all about." She gave him her most winning smile. "I don't even know Mr. McCord. I just want to go home."

Tysinger listened to her with astonishment. When she finished he looked at McCord, then back at Ashley. "You're both good, I'll give you that. But then I already knew you were." *What was that supposed to mean?* "All right, so this is just a case of mistaken identity, is that it? Then who are you?" He waited for her response, a polite smile hovering at the edges of his thin lips.

Feeling more confident, Ashley introduced herself. "My name is Ashley Allison. I'm with the law firm of Begley, Henderson & Howe in Portland."

There was a flash of recognition on Tysinger's face; then it was gone. "Begley, Henderson & Howe. That's very interesting, Ms. Allison. You say you don't know Mr. McCord?"

She glanced over at McCord, whose intent expression indicated that he was most interested in her answer. She shook her head. "No. I've never seen him before today."

"Tell me, Ms. Allison," Tysinger asked in a satin tone, "do you usually take a baby to work with you?" His tone continued to be polite, but the smile became more of a sneer.

Ashley had gotten so accustomed to holding the baby in her arms that she'd momentarily forgotten him. She glanced down as though astounded to find him there. "Oh. Well, you see, Mr. McCord handed him to me when I got on the elevator."

"Why did he do that, Ms. Allison?"

"I haven't the faintest idea."

Tysinger stared at McCord a moment. "Perhaps you can clarify all of this, McCord."

McCord glanced at Tysinger, then at Ashley. He was quiet as he looked at the baby, who watched him with wide-eyed wonder. Shaking his head, McCord assumed a grave expression. "My wife is still not fully recovered from Josh's birth. It was a very difficult time for her and the family has been doing what it can to help her." He walked over to Ashley and placed his arm about her shoulders. "This type of incident certainly doesn't help her to deal with everything. Her weakened physical state has created some emotional problems, but nothing that can't be overcome." He smiled down at her, the picture of loving concern.

At that moment Ashley had no problem being the bewildered wife. Stunned would be a better description. Instead of explaining what sort of game he'd been playing, he'd taken the charade one step further. Not only was this man still insisting she was his wife, she had just discovered she was in delicate health. If she weren't so blasted tired at the moment she would have laughed. *Her* delicate? Her stamina had been the joke of the family for years.

Another lamp flicked on in the corner, drawing Ashley's attention away from the confrontation. She noticed a woman moving about the room, adjusting lights and shades. A rust carpet came into view, and the remaining walls, paneled in knotty pine, glinted in the lamplight.

Tysinger saw Ashley watching the other woman. "Pardon me, I neglected to introduce Mrs. Krueger. She and her husband live up here year 'round. They take care of the place for me." He turned to the other woman. "Mrs. Krueger, this is Mr. and Mrs. McCord and their young son." The woman nodded her head in silence. "Why don't you show Mrs. McCord to the guest room? Perhaps she would like to freshen up before dinner." Turning back to Ashley he continued, his charm back in place. "If there's anything you need for the baby, I'm sure Mrs. Krueger will be able to help you. She's raised several of her own."

Ashley followed Mrs. Krueger out of the room, down a short hallway and into a large bedroom that also had a glass wall on its east side. *I'll bet the sunrises are spectacular in this place.*

Mrs. Krueger gestured to a door on the other side of a large bed. "There's a private bath attached to this room. Mr. Tysinger's room has one too, and my husband and I have our own apartment downstairs."

Puzzled, Ashley asked, "Downstairs? I thought this was a single-level house."

Mrs. Krueger's eyes crinkled mischievously, giving her face a gamine appearance. "Oh, no," she said. "This place is built along the side of a ridge and goes down two stories on the east side. We like it. It gives us our privacy when Mr. Tysinger entertains guests."

Mrs. Krueger smiled with obvious pleasure at the baby watching her from the security of Ashley's shoulder. "Would you like me to take your bright-eyed young man? He hasn't taken his eyes off me since we came in here." She stroked beneath Josh's chin so that he gave a quick kick that almost caused Ashley to drop him. She wasn't used to his sudden movements.

Mrs. Krueger asked a natural question that sent Ashley into a panic. "How old is he?"

Ashley gazed at her, trying to decide how to answer. Should she be coy and ask, "How old do you think he is?" or try to guess? For the first time since she'd laid eyes on him, Ashley was glad to see McCord walk into the room. The lopsided grin acknowledged Ashley's dilemma as he commented, "He'll be four months old next week, won't he, love?"

Ashley took her cue and tried to sound calm. "That's right."

Suddenly shy, Mrs. Krueger hastened to the door. "Dinner will be ready in about fifteen minutes. If you'd like, I could feed the baby in the kitchen while you eat."

Still unsure of herself in this area, Ashley looked to McCord for the proper answer.

"That would be a big help, Mrs. Krueger. Thank you. His bottles and food are all in the case I left in the other room."

Ashley handed Josh to Mrs. Krueger and watched as he left with yet another new person. *He has no sense of discrimination, but it's just as well. What would I have done on this trip if he'd cried the entire time?* It didn't bear thinking about.

The door closed. For the first time since McCord and Ashley had met at the elevator hours ago, they were alone.

Silence stretched between them like a rubber band waiting to be released. They watched each other warily, more than the width of the room dividing them.

"I'm sorry." McCord's voice carried to Ashley in firm tones.

She continued to watch him without expression. "Just what does that mean, Mr. McCord? Are you apologizing for your atrocious behavior or just making a general statement regarding your character?"

She could tell he didn't care much for her comment, but that was all right. Ashley didn't care much for anything about him at the moment. She'd had a rough day and, thanks to him, relief was several hours away.

He moved closer, then paused. He ran his hand through his hair, causing the waves to part into a cluster of curls on his forehead. They failed to soften the tight contours of his face. Now that she thought about it, he didn't appear to have gotten much rest lately either.

"Look, Ms. Allison, you have every right to be angry." He ignored her nod of agreement. "I understand that. Believe it or not, I had no idea this plan of mine would go so far." He swung away from her, no longer able to look at the closed expression on her face. "I needed a wife to fill in just for a few minutes, or so I thought at the time. The deception wasn't going to harm anyone, and it might have helped others." He glanced over his shoulder. She hadn't moved from her position near the door. He spun around, covering the distance between them in long strides. "I'm trying to buy time for some people, Ms. Allison. By pretending to be married, you and I are assisting others who've gone to a great deal of effort and taken serious risks to obtain information. This weekend they're trying to get the information into the right hands." He wanted so much to get her to understand the importance of what was happening, but it was too complicated to explain in a few short sentences. His frustration mounted.

"I'd been stalling Wilson, trying to come up with a story, when I saw you at the elevators this evening. I made an instant decision to use your presence to help me get out of a tight spot."

She stared at him in amazement. "If you feel that getting us both abducted is getting out of a tight spot, I'm not sure I want to know what you *consider* a tight spot."

McCord's hand raked through his already mussed hair. Then he rubbed the back of his neck and let out his breath in a heavy sigh. "You're right. I didn't handle this at all well. The hell of it is that I made the biggest sales pitch of my entire career in order to talk Jeanine into leaving Josh with me. She's never gone off and left him for more than a couple of hours before." Then, as though talking more to himself than to her, he continued. "Of course, if Josh hadn't been there, it wouldn't have occurred to me to try to impersonate anyone."

She ignored his last comment to latch on to the name he'd mentioned. "Jeanine?"

"Josh's mother."

"Of course, Josh's mother. Silly of me to forget."

"It made a lot more sense for him to stay here rather than to travel with her to Washington, D.C. Who could have guessed Tysinger would go to this extreme?"

"You do realize I haven't a solitary clue as to what you're talking about. I feel like Alice attempting a conversation with the Mad Hatter."

McCord stopped pacing and stared at her as though noticing her mood for the first time. "Most women I know would have had hysterics today." He tilted his head slightly as he studied her calm demeanor. "Why haven't you been screaming and hurling accusations?" The more he thought about it, the more impressed he was with her self-control.

"It's rather trite to state the obvious. I'm not 'most women,' and my training helps me to disguise what I'm feeling." Her tone became more gentle. "Of course, if you prefer hysteria and screaming, it won't take much for me to oblige you."

His quick grin disappeared as he hastened to reassure her. "No. No, thanks. I guess what I'm trying to do is to thank you for not continuing to protest to Tysinger. You lent credibility to my story, and I want you to know how very much I appreciate it."

"Don't mention it," she replied in a disgusted tone. "I felt like an absolute fool standing there denying that I knew either one of you while I clutched your baby in my arms."

This time McCord's smile stayed in place. His hand rested lightly along her jawline as he peered down into her face. "I'll admit to counting on that when I placed him in your arms. That, and the element of surprise. I planned to use you only to get out of the building and away from Wilson." His hand slid to the back of her neck, under the long hair, and gripped. "What I wasn't counting on were the reinforcements that were used to get us into that car." His hand began to massage the tight muscles in her neck. "That's when I realized I had miscalculated, and I got angry—at myself, at Tysinger, and at the situation I'd placed us in. Quite frankly, I'm not sure how we're going to get out of it, either."

Ashley noticed the tired lines in his face. He wasn't the first person to make an impulsive decision that backfired, and there was certainly no point in her continuing to do battle with him. His long fingers were ridding her neck muscles of the stiffness caused by the long ride and the anxiety of wondering what was happening.

McCord interpreted her silence as unforgiving. Why not? Why should she forgive him for being such an idiot? She probably had a family waiting at home, frantic with worry.

"Your parents must be worried sick by now. Perhaps we can call them. I can tell Tysinger that we were supposed to be having dinner with them. Surely he'll understand that this trip wasn't in our plans."

Her parents? How old did he think she was? "I don't live with my parents, Mr. McCord."

"Rafe."

"What?"

Dark red began to seep into his face. "I'm sorry, I've never bothered to introduce myself. I'm Raphael McCord. My friends call me Rafe."

Bewilderment flashed across her face. "Who is Raul?"

"My brother."

She backed away, leaning against the door. "Somehow that doesn't clarify much for me." She held up her palm. "But I don't think I'm capable of listening to many more of your 'explanations' tonight." A slight smile hovered around her mouth, and he could sense that her mood had lightened somewhat. He was surprised at his relief. For whatever obscure reason, he didn't want this woman to stay angry with him.

He smiled. "Well, is there someone who will be upset when you're late getting home tonight?" He wondered why he cared.

She wondered why he asked. "Just my roommate. But we don't always check in with each other." She mentally apologized to Tasha for that little lie. She just wished she *could* call her to explain and perhaps prevent the destruction of her home.

He gave her a searching look, trying to understand the expression on her face. "Well, if you'd like, we can contact your roommate."

Ashley didn't care for the emphasis on the word *roommate*. What did he want to know? Whether she was involved with someone? What about him? His wife hadn't been gone very long and he was pretending to be married to someone else. Her eyes took in the picture before her. A well-developed specimen of virile manhood, convinced, no doubt, that he could have any woman he wanted, turning on the charm for her. Her encounters with the opposite sex through the years had educated her about his type of male. Well, she didn't need any of them—this one, especially.

She walked past him, moving over to watch the fading colors reflected off the snow of Mount Hood. It was almost dark. "No, I don't think I'll call my roommate. She's Oriental and not accustomed to some of our Western ways." She glanced over her shoulder at him. "She's going to be upset, but there's not much I can do about it." And that's the truth, Ashley thought with a sigh.

Once again the room was quiet, but something had happened in the past few minutes. Their awareness of each other caused a strong pull between them. Ashley refused to acknowledge the attraction. Not only was she not interested in developing a relationship with any man, she found this particular man despicable. Her disgust with amorous married males knew no bounds.

Rafe watched her straight back and wondered what he'd said or done to cause the stiffening in her manner. For a few moments she had seemed to relax somewhat. Women! There was no understanding them, and at thirty-five, he no longer made the attempt. He shrugged his shoulders. They'd have dinner with Tysinger, listen to his political propositions, then ask to be excused. He didn't want to spend any more time around this prickly female than he had to.

"Guess we'd better find Tysinger, then, and get this meal behind us." His sudden comment sliced through the silence between them, causing her to start. Her control wasn't as complete as she would have liked it to be.

She turned and, with something of an effort, forced herself to give him a polite, meaningless smile. "You're right. The sooner we eat, the sooner we return to town."

Chapter Three

Ashley shifted, burying her face in the pillow. Her internal timepiece assured her that it was Saturday and she could enjoy a few moments extra in bed. She'd slept better than she had for weeks. Smiling with contentment, she stretched her full length, tightening each and every muscle just for the pleasure of relaxing afterward. Maybe she'd run that morning. She'd missed doing that the past several mornings. At the moment, Ashley felt that all was right with her world.

"Do you intend to stay in bed all day?" a polite male voice inquired in her ear.

Ashley's eyes flew open. Silver blue eyes faced her from the adjoining pillow.

In an abrupt movement, Ashley sat up, staring around the room with bewilderment. *Where am I?* She saw Josh on a pile of blankets nearby, waving his hands and watching his fingers.

"Josh?"

"Yep, ole Josh and I have been up for hours. You must really sleep soundly to have missed all our activities this morning." Rafe watched her as their respective positions sifted through her morning fog. In a conversational tone he added, "I've managed to bathe and feed him, so he seemed content to rest for a while." He watched the look of horror grow on her face and smiled. "I've been taking it easy, waiting for you to wake up."

Ashley groaned. She wrapped her arms around her knees and rested her head on them. Events of the night before began to filter through her memory. "I'm supposed to be married."

Rafe's hand moved up the length of her back, from hips to shoulders, as he massaged the muscles along her spine. The silkiness of her slip caused a tingling everywhere he touched.

"Would you stop that!" She jerked away from him. "I distinctly remember explaining to you that I was not going to share a bed with you last night. What are you doing here?"

Rafe folded his arms behind his head and smiled. "I got cold. At these heights the nights are always cold, and Josh seemed to have the spare blankets in this room. After the noise I made looking for blankets in the closet and all the drawers I began to realize that nothing would disturb you." His arm slipped from behind his head and gestured. "As you can see, I was right. I crawled in and you never noticed."

Ashley shook her head in a flurry of waves as her soft hair settled back around her shoulders. She refused to look at him.

In a judicious tone Rafe added, "Something tells me you aren't a morning person."

Exasperated with his cheerfulness, Ashley grabbed her pillow and placed it on her knees, resting her head once again. "What was your first clue?" Her muffled voice drifted to him. She scarcely recalled going to bed the night before. The events of the day had succeeded in knocking her out as effectively as a narcotic.

Still buried in her pillow, she tried to be fair. After all, it wasn't as though there wasn't enough room for two. The bed was large enough to use for a football scrimmage. On second thought, perhaps it would be better utilized for naval maneuvers. Her recent moves had caused a gentle, undulating movement across the expanse of satin comforter. Ashley would never have considered sleeping in a water bed. She tended to get seasick crossing the Willamette River on the Ross Island Bridge.

"It doesn't slosh," she mumbled.

"It's baffled."

Unaware that she'd spoken her thought out loud, Ashley was puzzled by his remark. She raised her head and looked over at him; he was sprawled propped up against the headboard. "What did you say?"

"The bed has baffles built in to lessen the wave action."

"Oh."

"Do I take it then that you had a restful night, all things considered?"

She eyed his bland expression with suspicion. "All of *what* things considered?"

"Oh, my getting up with Josh a couple of times and cuddling to keep you warm."

"You did what?" That woke her up. "There's no way I could have slept through that," she stated in emphatic tones.

"Whatever you say, dear. I don't want to start an argument before breakfast." Rafe appeared to have a problem holding his innocent expression.

"If I'd known you were the kind of person who goes back on his word, I would have insisted that you sleep in the other room."

His eyes danced in the morning sunlight, and it was hard for Ashley to ignore the mischief in them. "There are only two bedrooms on this floor and our host is using one of them." The reasonableness of his tone further incensed Ashley. "How could I explain that my wife expected me to sleep with the host? Are you trying to destroy my reputation?"

"Isn't that exactly what you're trying to do to mine?" she snapped back. "You're enjoying this, aren't you?" she demanded.

"I could be...very much." Rafe's voice held a velvety warmth and his hand once more slid up the length of her back.

Ashley's body reacted to the caress as though independent of her. Her anger was directed as much at herself as it was at him. "Isn't one wife enough for you, or do you get some kind of pleasure out of collecting women for the weekend under false pretenses?" Everywhere his hand touched, tiny electrical impulses shot through her skin, causing it to tingle.

Rafe spoke in a confidential tone. "I wonder if Tysinger's recovered from the verbal attack you launched when he insisted that we take advantage of his hospitality and spend the weekend."

Ashley conceded, "Well, I suppose I could have been a little more tactful."

At that Rafe began to laugh.

"I'd barely accepted the idea of filling in as your wife through dinner when he suggested an overnight stay. That was just too much."

"So you told him last night. I thought your threatening to have him arrested for kidnapping added a nice touch to the dinner conversation."

"And don't think I won't, just as soon as I can get away from this place. And why weren't *you* protesting when he insisted we stay here?"

"You were doing such an excellent job of it, I felt that anything I could have added would have been redundant. Besides, I have Tysinger's full sympathy and grudging respect for tolerating a wife with a temper like yours."

"I am not your wife," Ashley stated through clenched teeth. "Please stop calling me that." Rafe's feathery caresses caused her blood to quicken as warmth began to flow through her body.

Still grinning, Rafe added, "Confiding to Tysinger that you didn't have any idea who fathered Josh certainly has him speculating on your morals."

"*My* morals! I don't go around claiming marriage ties to every stranger I meet."

"Neither do I. You happen to be the first." Changing the subject, Rafe continued. "Don't you think it's time we got out of bed?" he queried. Had he no notion of what his hand was doing to her? Apparently not, and for that small blessing she gave thanks. She kept her flushed face resolutely turned away from him.

"Yes, I would be delighted to get up, get dressed, and go home!" Ashley felt a sudden, soft movement of the bed and glanced around in time to see Rafe as he threw back the covers and stood up. She got a quick glimpse of a great expanse of dark flesh. Averting her head, she asked, "Would you mind getting out of here so I can get dressed?"

"Isn't it a little late for modesty after sleeping with me all night?" Her pillow hit the bathroom door just as he closed it behind him. She could hear his laughter.

Never had anyone dared to treat Ashley in this manner. She'd never have stood for it. But what choice did she have at the moment? Why wasn't Jeanine here where she was supposed to be? And why had she disappeared to Washington, D.C.? The mystery was beginning to bother Ashley more the longer she thought about it. She was determined to get some answers to her questions that day. She deserved that much after this disruption in her life.

Ashley came out of the shower much refreshed and ready to face the day. She picked up the wilted cream blouse she'd worn the day before just as the bedroom door swung open.

"Can't you knock?" She clutched at the large bath towel wrapped around her and glared at Rafe as he sauntered into the room.

"I suppose I could, but frankly, I didn't give it much thought. Mrs. Krueger felt sorry for you having to hobble around in your high heels and suggested that you try on some of her younger son's clothes." He handed her a bundle of clothing. "She said he left these the last time he was here."

She shook out a pair of well-worn jeans and decided that they would do nicely. A pair of sneakers appeared to be about her size. With as much dignity as possible, given that only her towel stood between modesty and embarrassment, Ashley gathered up a pullover knit shirt and the jeans and sneakers and stalked back into the bathroom.

The navy and white striped shirt clung to her curves. Ashley frowned into the mirror, then shrugged her shoulders. It couldn't be helped. The jeans were snug but the length was right. Once again she had cause to be thankful for long legs. Now she was ready to face the world and do battle, if necessary.

Ashley studied the bathroom, still unused to the luxury of her surroundings. Had she given much thought to the idea, she would have imagined that kidnap victims would be forced to endure privation and severe discomfort, not to mention starvation. If the previous night's meal was any indication, severe dieting would be a necessity after a lengthy captivity around Mrs. Krueger.

Ashley faced an empty bedroom when she came out of the bathroom, and she set off in search of her new family.

She heard Tysinger's voice and halted. "I realize you young people plan to save the world, and I admire that. Why, I'm well known for my interest in the environment and the preservation of our natural resources." Ashley stepped to the door of the living room. Tysinger paced in front of the fireplace as Rafe sat on the sofa bouncing Josh in a gentle rhythm on his knee. "I'm not against what you're doing and what you stand for. I want you to understand that. I admire you tremendously." Ashley's movement at the door caught the pacing man's notice and he stopped abruptly. She walked into the room, her eyes trained on Tysinger's face.

"Good morning." She stopped behind the sofa, her hand resting lightly upon Rafe's shoulder. Rafe reached up and pulled her hand against his cheek. *We can't look any more domestic than this,* she thought. She was weary of the role playing, regardless of how helpful it was supposed to be to Rafe. She just wanted to go home.

Tysinger stared at her with a hint of surprise and she acknowledged to herself that her casual outfit gave an entirely different impression from the business attire of the evening before. "Good morning, Mrs. McCord. I trust you spent a pleasant night."

She stared back at him, her eyes blue in the morning light. "Yes, Mr. Tysinger, I did. However, I do want you to understand that I don't intend to stay here any longer. I didn't appreciate your high-handed attitude last night, but you got your way. Hopefully, that's satisfied whatever quirk caused you to drag us up here in the first place."

Tysinger's glance veered to Rafe with what could have been sympathy in his eyes. "As I attempted to explain last night, Mrs. McCord, I've been trying for some time to meet with you and your husband and discuss his recent activities. The matter was too important to postpone any longer. I thought I made that quite plain."

What was the use in trying to make him understand that she wasn't Mrs. McCord? And did she even want to at this point? After all, she'd just spent the night with the man. Ashley attempted a smile. "Well, then, why don't I leave you two men to discuss whatever, and I'll just get back to town." She smiled down at the top of Rafe's head in what she hoped was a wifely expression of encouragement.

As Rafe moved to stand up, Tysinger exploded his next little bombshell. "Unfortunately, I'm a little short on transportation at the moment, Mrs. McCord. Mrs. Krueger sent for some supplies, and I'm not sure when the car will be returning."

"Well, then, call a cab or something," Ashley suggested, trying to hang on to her hard-won composure. "I can't believe we're just stranded up here."

A wary smile appeared as Tysinger explained. "I don't have phone service up here. I don't want to be bothered by all the so-called emergency interruptions when I manage to get away." Rafe walked around the sofa and placed his hand at Ashley's waist. He had a pretty good idea how she was taking this latest piece of news. Tysinger continued. "I sincerely thought you and your husband would enjoy being up here."

The man was incredible, Ashley thought with amazement. He actually looked and sounded offended. The stage had lost out when he chose politics.

Rafe pulled her closer to him. "Tysinger mentioned that some of the trails around here have spectacular views. He thought we might want to go for a walk—enjoy the sunshine and get a little exercise." He squeezed her waist as she looked up at him. "Perhaps by the time we get back, the car will be here and we can get back to town." Glancing back at Tysinger, Rafe continued. "My wife still gets upset rather easily. You have my word that we won't be flying East if you'll just get us back to Portland."

The two men stood there in silent communication. Then Tysinger smiled. "Fine, McCord. I knew you'd see things a little more clearly if I just had a chance to discuss them with you. The car should be back in a couple of hours, so why don't you take that walk you mentioned? I know you'll both enjoy it." He left the room with a definite bounce to his step.

Ashley noticed that the baby in Rafe's arms had fallen asleep. "What about Josh? We can't just go off and leave him."

"I suppose we could, but I don't intend to. I'll take him with us, but let's get you some coffee and a piece of Mrs. Krueger's coffee cake. You'll need strength for that hike." He took her by the hand and led her into the kitchen.

Rafe was right, she decided as she viewed the glistening day from the kitchen window. She might as well relax and enjoy the next few hours, since there was little else she could do.

After a generous helping of coffee cake and several cups of coffee, Ashley felt ready to hike back to town, but decided she might be a little overambitious. She went looking for Rafe and found him dressing the baby for the outdoors. When Josh saw her he gave her one of his exuberant smiles.

"What a flirt you are. Almost as bad as your father."

Rafe ignored her comment. Not that he didn't deserve it, she decided some time later as she set off behind him on one of the trails. However, she couldn't fault him as a father. Rafe appeared familiar with Josh's routine and made sure all his needs were met.

In the serenity of the mountain forest, Ashley began to relax. The scent of cedar pleased her. Whenever she smelled cedar she thought of her mother and her treasured mementos stored in an old cedar chest.

A ground squirrel caught her eye, and she stopped to watch his antics as he flitted around, then paused to scold her. Somehow she lost track of Rafe. When she glanced back at the trail he was no longer in sight. She stopped, concerned; the trail branched off and she was unsure which direction he'd taken. Eventually she chose to follow the trail going downward, hoping he'd opted for the same one. Ashley had no desire to try to find her way out of there on her own. She quickened her steps in hopes of catching up with him.

The trail made a sharp turn, and Ashley gave a quick sigh of relief. Rafe stood on a ledge overlooking the lake.

The sun had burned off the early morning haze and left the air clear. A windfall tree, no doubt a casualty of the winter, lay alongside the trail. Rafe sat down and propped Josh up against him. Josh found his favorite fingers and enjoyed the view from the security of Rafe's arms.

Ashley noticed that Rafe's shoes were not the handmade Italian leather shoes he'd worn the day before. "Where did you get your sneakers?"

He glanced down at his feet and smiled. "Tysinger had several pairs in his closet for 'drop-ins' and suggested that I make use of them. These aren't climbing shoes, but they beat the ones I wore yesterday."

Ashley had already noticed the snug-fitting jeans he wore with a yellow knit pullover shirt. The color enhanced his dark attractiveness.

She turned away from him to explore the edge of the bluff. The ground dropped about five feet to the edge of the water. She knelt at the edge and watched tiny fish feeding along the top of the water.

Rafe cleared his throat. "I thought if we could get away from Tysinger I'd try to fill you in on why Tysinger wants us here." He watched her as she peered over the side of the ledge, her profile defined by the thick shrubs bordering the path.

She made a gentle correction. "Why Tysinger wants *you* here, not me."

"Actually, it isn't me he wants, it's Raul."

She turned to look at him, then sat back on her heels. "That's right. He called you Raul last night, didn't he? So he really wants your brother?"

"Yes, my brother and his wife, Jeanine."

Her eyes widened. "You mean Jeanine is married to Raul, not to you?"

He was amused at her reaction. "That's correct. And Josh is their son. I'm just baby-sitting for the weekend."

She tried to sort through the confusion in her mind.

"I wanted you to understand that I wasn't trying to play some kind of game with you this morning. I'm not married."

She schooled her face to show no reaction to his news. "The whole story was sheer fabrication, wasn't it?"

He nodded. "As I explained last night, it wasn't one of my better ideas."

She shook her head in confusion. "Okay, so Tysinger thinks you and I are Raul and Jeanine, and he wanted to talk to them before they went to D.C." She looked up at him. "Do I understand so far?" She was more curious than angry at this point.

"Yes. Jeanine and Raul arranged to fly to Washington to meet with Senator Hensley this weekend. Tysinger made it obvious yesterday that he didn't want them to contact Hensley until he talked to them."

Ashley moved from her position on the ground and joined Rafe on the fallen log. "Where does Senator Hensley fit into all of this?"

"Raul and Jeanine became friends with W.A. Hensley when they helped with his campaign for the senate a few years ago. When they stumbled onto some unexpected information during a recent survey they were doing, Raul wasn't sure who to talk to about it. It touched several people involved in Oregon politics, and he decided to talk to someone he could trust."

Ashley waited for him to continue. She noticed Josh draped across Rafe's arm, fast asleep. When Rafe glanced down he smiled and placed the sleeping infant on his shoulder.

"Raul and Jeanine were helping a group of conservationists with a survey in southern Oregon designed to determine the effect of the herbicide sprays being used in that area."

"Now that's one controversy I've heard of. The media mentions it on a regular basis."

"I know. While in the midst of the survey, Raul and Jeanine discovered a group within the conservationist movement that had strong reason to fight the use of herbicides. It killed their prolific crops of marijuana."

Ashley sat next to Rafe, contemplating the tranquil scene before them and trying to understand how the growing of marijuana in southern Oregon was responsible for her spending the weekend with Raphael McCord.

"Does Tysinger have something to do with the marijuana?" She watched the shifting leaves shadow Rafe's face as he admired the view.

"From his actions this weekend, I'm very much afraid that Tysinger is up to his neck in the mess. Otherwise, why would he take such drastic action to stop Raul and Jeanine from taking their information to Hensley?"

"Why would a politician jeopardize his career like that?"

Rafe stood up and began to follow the trail that paralleled the lake. Ashley wandered along beside him as he pondered her question. Eventually he shook his head. "I don't know. There could be several motives: greed, the desire for even more power, who knows?" He paused as they reached a clearing and looked around. From this view they could see Tysinger's home perched on the ridge above them; the Kruegers' quarters were clearly visible. "Maybe he needs money to support some of his more expensive habits, such as his home up there."

"I wonder what Tysinger is going to do when he finds out that he didn't stop them from going to Washington."

Rafe's eyes reminded Ashley of arctic glaciers as he continued to stare at the house on the ridge. "That's what concerns me at the moment. Why don't we head back? The car should have returned by now, and I'd prefer to be away from here when Tysinger gets that piece of news."

"Do you think he's going to let us go?"

"He's an intelligent man. If he's thinking at all, he knows he can't keep us." He put his arm around her shoulders and pulled her toward him. "I can't get too angry at the man. Because of his little plot, I had this chance to meet you."

Ashley started at the personal turn of the conversation. Why had she thought his eyes looked cold? At the moment, the warm regard in his eyes caused a definite skip in her steady pulse. His lips touched hers with gentle pressure, giving her the opportunity to pull away. She had no intention of getting involved with this man, but inertia seemed to have set in. It was far easier to stay in the circle of his arm. As he felt her relax, his arm tightened, pulling her hard against his chest. Her hand came up to rest against Josh's back as he lay curled on Rafe's shoulder. Somehow it felt right to be in the circle of his arms with the baby. Rafe deepened the kiss and Ashley could no longer think. His gentle insistence as he explored her soft lips affected her more deeply than a passionate kiss could have done. This man was rapidly reaching a part of Ashley that she had never known existed, and she wasn't at all sure she could handle the emotions he was provoking.

Chapter Four

Their return to Tysinger's home took place in silence. Mrs. Krueger met them at the door. "Why don't I take this young man and let you enjoy some time alone together?" She took the slumbering baby from Rafe's shoulder with a smile. "My supplies arrived. I ordered more baby food to be on the safe side. I also had them bring more disposable diapers. That's something they didn't have when I was raising mine, and I have to admit they're convenient."

Ashley followed Mrs. Krueger into the house. "You shouldn't have gone to so much trouble, Mrs. Krueger. Now that the car is back, we'll be leaving."

Mrs. Krueger turned a puzzled face to Rafe and Ashley. "I didn't realize you planned to leave so soon. Mr. Tysinger must have forgotten. When the men came back they brought him a message that caused him to rush right out of here. He didn't say when he'd be back."

"They left?" Ashley repeated in disbelief. "But they couldn't have!"

"It looks as if we're stranded for a while, Ashley." Rafe's voice held a warning note in it.

Mrs. Krueger nodded uncertainly. "Let me put this little fella down. Lunch is ready whenever you are." She disappeared with Josh.

Ashley whirled to face Rafe. "Do you think they learned something about Raul and Jeanine?"

Rafe seemed to ignore the urgent question for a moment; then he spoke. "It's a possibility. I don't particularly want to face him if that's the news." He crossed to the front door and stepped through, eyeing the trail they'd taken the day before.

"Is there any way we can follow that trail back down to the highway?" Ashley peered around his shoulder.

Rafe's hands rested on his slim hips as he stared out over the thousands of acres around them, the dense forest covering the mountains with a mantle of green velvet.

"I probably could, but not with you and Josh along." He turned to her and noticed her expression. "Look, I don't intend to go anywhere and leave you or Josh, so quit looking at me like that. I got you into this mess and I intend to get you out." He leaned against the rail for a few moments in deep thought.

Mrs. Krueger appeared at the door. "I have lunch set up for you on the deck. The weather's too nice to waste inside." Ashley responded to her thoughtfulness with a smile, then turned to Rafe.

"Let's get something to eat. This mountain air has made me ravenous—you'll think of something." She heard her reassurance with some astonishment. *She* had no idea what to do, so why did she feel confident he'd find a solution? It was certainly out of character for Ashley to rely on anyone but herself.

They ate lunch in silence. Ashley's few attempts at conversation were answered with absentminded replies, and she soon gave up. Besides, when had she ever had a better opportunity to enjoy the Cascade Mountains? When she moved to Oregon one of her first plans had been to join a hiking club and enjoy the outdoors that were such a contrast to the ranch she had called home. Instead she became absorbed in trial work and the weeks, months, and eventually years slipped away unnoticed as she began to make a name for herself in the legal field. She learned to accept that a woman in the profession had to work twice as hard as a man in order to prove herself capable.

Watching the silent Rafe methodically eat his fresh fruit salad and man-sized sandwich, Ashley recognized with some surprise that she'd spent more consecutive time with this man than she'd spent with any man since she had left Texas. She had dated occasionally at first, but then found she didn't have time even for that. She had given up dating with no regret. She could not ask for more from life than to pursue the career that fulfilled and sustained her.

Early in her life, Ashley had come to believe that love for a man became a sort of bondage for a woman. Her father and her four older brothers had run the family cattle ranch and, while there was no doubt in Ashley's mind that her dad loved her mother dearly, he gave no thought to the countless demands ranch life made on her, trying to keep five hungry males fed and clothed and cared for. Ashley grew up with the belief that love and marriage, for a woman, meant never having any time for herself and her own needs.

The piano had always been her mother's escape, but Ashley was in her teens before she discovered that her mother had once been offered a scholarship to the Fort Worth Conservatory of Music. Ashley's father, afraid he would lose her mother if she went away to school, had convinced her to marry him instead of going to the conservatory. When Ashley learned of this, she decided that *she* would never make that mistake. She had her mother's support when she decided to study law. Marriage would never hold any appeal for Ashley!

"What a ferocious expression you have on your face." Rafe must have been watching her for some time. She flushed with embarrassment.

"Well, did you come up with a solution in all of this quiet?" She hoped her change of subject would allow her to avoid having to explain her thoughts.

"I guess I've been thinking more about what Tysinger is going to do when he finds out this visit didn't accomplish what he'd hoped it would."

"He'd better not try anything else. He's already in enough trouble because of kidnapping us. That's certainly not going to increase his political popularity."

"In the first place, he's going to deny any accusation of kidnapping; he made that clear last night. His story is going to be that it was all a misunderstanding, and how do we disprove that? Have we been threatened, mistreated, abandoned? We're going to look foolish accusing him of forcing us to have a luxurious and secluded weekend together in the mountains."

Ashley began to laugh at the word picture Rafe painted. "You know, I'll bet that's exactly what he'll say. Can't you just hear him now? Here he has Mrs. Krueger busy taking care of us and preparing her scrumptious meals, and we sit plotting ways to escape. The whole thing's a farce."

"That's what I've been thinking. Another is, how long do we have before we *must* get back. I presume you need to be at work on Monday." She nodded in agreement. "I have to be back in San Francisco for a ten o'clock appointment on Monday." She looked startled and he stopped. "What's wrong?"

"You don't live in Oregon?"

"No. Most of my business interests are located in California. Raul opened the plastics plant here in Oregon a few years ago, but I have no connection with it."

She began to smile. "For a man with whom I've spent almost twenty-four hours of uninterrupted time, you're still very much a mystery to me." Her eyes lit with humor and caught Rafe's attention. He lost the thread of their conversation as he admired her animated face. With reluctance he forced his mind back to what they had been saying.

"You're as much a mystery to me. We haven't had much time to get acquainted, but we can always remedy that, you know." She didn't trust the gleam that appeared in his eyes.

"That's all right." She refused to meet his eyes. "We probably won't ever see each other after this weekend."

He reached over and took her hand, waiting until she raised her eyes to meet his. "Ashley, I come up to visit Raul and Jeanine frequently. There's no reason why you and I shouldn't see each other, is there?"

He wanted to know whether she was involved with someone else. If only it were that simple. "I'm pretty well tied up with my practice, Rafe. I don't have much time for socializing."

"Your practice?" Her statement disconcerted him; she could tell by his startled expression.

"I told you last night that I'm an attorney. At least, I told Tysinger."

He sat there staring at her as though she'd whipped out a baseball bat and thumped him over the head.

"You're a lawyer?" he repeated, convinced he'd misunderstood.

She nodded. "Yes, I'm with the law firm of Begley, Henderson & Howe." Why did he seem so shocked?

His next question surprised her. "How old are you, anyway?"

"Twenty-eight. Why?"

He leaned back in his chair, his hands resting on the table, and shook his head. "I feel like a complete fool," he admitted with a shrug. "I thought you were a college student working during the summer. I didn't think you were more than twenty-one years old."

"Thank you very much, I think. I wondered what made you think I lived with my parents, but it never dawned on me that you didn't understand I've got a law practice."

"Wouldn't you know," he muttered.

She could feel tension begin to tickle her neck like hackles rising on a dog. "What do you mean?" Once again she felt defensive about her choice of career.

Rafe gave her a rueful grin. "Nothing, really. Lawyers don't happen to be my favorite brand of people, and it never occurred to me that you were one of them." His grin broadened. "Now that I think about it, your attack on Tysinger last night was more in the way of a professional performance. I guess I should have realized that at the time."

"What do you have against lawyers?"

"I don't think the majority of them have enough business sense to set themselves up as soothsayers, but that hasn't stopped them as far as my business is concerned. They're an unmitigated nuisance to have around, but a necessary evil."

"What exactly is your business, Mr. McCord?" She found his amusement offensive.

"I buy into ailing companies and try to turn them into profitable businesses. Many times a business will fail because legal advisors are allowed to make business decisions."

"I take it that you've made the right decisions and saved your ailing companies."

"Most of them."

"A real knight in shining armor, is that right?" Her sarcasm touched a nerve: his jaw clenched as he stared at her.

"Obviously, I'm not *your* knight unless I can come up with a way to rescue you from your dragon—Tysinger." He pushed back his chair and stood up. "If you'll excuse me."

Ashley sat at the table long after she heard the front door close behind Rafe. Why had she baited him like that? He'd shown her nothing but courtesy and kindness since she'd met him. Why did she feel the need to ridicule him? Her behavior since she had met Rafe continued to confuse her.

Hours later, Ashley sat once again on the deck, waiting for Rafe to reappear. Patience had never been one of her virtues. She'd had plenty of time to review the events leading up to his disappearance and had even framed several apologies during the three hours he'd been gone.

She'd finally faced the fact that her reaction to Raphael McCord was more violent than any she'd experienced in the past. His sudden appearance anywhere around her set her nerves on edge, but why couldn't she at least be polite to him, even if friendliness seemed to be beyond her? Her puzzling seesaw of emotions was causing her a great deal of distress. She hated to admit to herself that her usual friendly and outgoing disposition had gone into hibernation during the past two days. If she didn't watch it she'd turn into a crotchety caricature of spinsterhood.

She blamed part of her confusion on the romantic surroundings of the Mount Hood National Forest in the summertime. It was easy to forget the real world and bask in the lazy warmth of the sunshine. Ashley had spent the earlier part of the afternoon getting acquainted with Josh. She'd found him quite amazing and wondered whether all babies were so smart. He'd spotted her good-luck pendant, which hung from a gold chain at her throat, and managed to grab it as it swung past his waving arms. His tenacious grip caused quite a tussle before she managed to free herself without hurting him.

Ashley admitted to herself that she was enjoying her acquaintance with Josh, which surprised her. She wasn't a domesticated woman. Perhaps an unconscious desire to escape the role of her mother had caused the younger Ashley to refuse to learn the housewifely arts. As a result she could neither cook nor sew.

She was satisfied with her life and would never have given the matter a thought if she hadn't met Raphael McCord. She jumped up and walked over to the railing. There was no reason to let him upset her life any more than he'd already done.

The lake looked inviting, but even if she'd had a swimsuit she wouldn't have gone in; she knew the water was close to freezing. Melting snow kept the lake at a high level. As she stood there admiring the scenery she heard whistling down below.

Leaning over the railing, Ashley peered in the direction of the sound and saw Rafe move out of the trees. The sight of him caused her heart to lurch in her chest and she forgot to breathe.

He didn't see her watching him as he strode across the clearing, his movements like those of a big cat silently stalking. The memory of his kisses leaped into her mind. Ashley gave herself a shake, resenting her purely physical response to him. *I wonder if there's a pill to take to counteract my reactions*?

"Did you find a way out of here?" she called to get his attention. Rafe saw her and turned toward her. He stood below, hands resting on his hips, his chest moving visibly in his effort to breathe more easily in the thin air. His smile erased the earlier hostility between them.

"I think so. We can get away, but I'm not sure when."

Ashley gave no thought to why she felt relief that he was no longer angry. She returned his smile. "So what do we do?"

"Hang on. I've got to get cleaned up a bit. I must have hiked five miles since I last saw you." He looked over his shoulder at the lake and back at her. Then he waved and disappeared around the corner of the house.

Ashley started to dash back into the house but decided to show a little more dignity by strolling into the kitchen. Mrs. Krueger looked up from cutting salad vegetables and smiled. "How is your son?"

"Oh, I put him down after his bottle and he conked out in no time. He's probably awake by now—maybe I should check on him."

As she turned toward the hallway, Mrs. Krueger asked, "Is there anything in particular you would like to have for dinner?"

"Anything sounds fine to me so long as I don't have to make it. Cooking is not one of my skills."

Mrs. Krueger's face lit up with astonishment. "You mean you don't cook for Mr. McCord?"

I've done it again, she scolded herself. "Of course I cook for him, but I don't go to a lot of trouble." That didn't sound any better. "What I mean is, I, uh, I think I hear Josh." Ashley escaped down the hallway. In her need to make a hasty retreat she burst into the bedroom, where she came to an abrupt halt.

Rafe was walking out of the bathroom toweling his hair and wearing the smallest pair of briefs Ashley had ever seen. Her mouth dropped open.

"Don't you ever knock?" he asked in a fair imitation of her tone of voice earlier in the day.

She realized where she was staring and spun around toward Josh. "I thought I heard Josh."

"Obviously not, if our voices haven't disturbed him. You must have worn him out today."

She thought back over her afternoon with Josh and grinned. When she heard the zip of Rafe's pants, Ashley figured he was decently covered and turned back around. His bare chest tugged at her attention, and she studied the thick mat of fur spread across it as though she'd be tested on it the next day. She managed to bring her eyes up to meet his and nodded, intent on concealing her reactions.

"Yes, Josh and I spent quite a time together. I've discovered that he loves to pull hair and is fascinated by my pendant. Do you realize he can move himself? He gets his knees under him, then lunges and scoots on his stomach.'' Rafe watched her as her eyes sparkled with the description.

''What color are your eyes?'' he asked, interrupting her.

The change of subject surprised her, and she stood there for a moment in confusion. ''My driver's license says blue. Why?''

''Because when I first saw you in the elevator they appeared to be gray. Today on our hike they were more of a jade green, and now they have a misty blue look about them.'' He walked to where she stood as though to examine them closer.

His proximity unnerved her. She wished he'd put on a shirt.

''My mom used to tease me about my eyes. She said they're like a mood ring.''

Rafe pulled her to him and she looked up. The expression on his face caused her knees to turn to jelly. He lowered his head as he murmured, ''What mood are you in at the moment?'' His breath caressed her mouth as his lips touched hers in a tentative manner. Without thought Ashley relaxed in his arms and offered him her mouth, which he took with a sudden possession that seared through her. His mouth began to mold hers as his tongue touched her upper lip, then slipped into her mouth. She reached up to him, her arms sliding behind his head in an effort to get closer.

His hands moved along her back, continuing the exploration they had begun that morning, and discovered the indentation at her waist as well as the flare of her rounded hips. He pressed her body closer, showing her the effect she had on him.

Her hands had not been still. She brought them back to his chest and touched all the places her eyes had feasted upon earlier.

The sounds of Josh stirring from his nap began to seep into Ashley's consciousness, and she fought to regain control of herself. She managed to pull away from Rafe and opened her eyes. He looked at her hungrily, making no effort to hide his desire for her.

She turned away from him, struggling for composure. "What did you find out this afternoon?" she asked in an attempt to sound casual as she moved over to Josh and picked him up. She kept her head down as she sorted through the baby's clothing for something dry to put on him.

The amusement in Rafe's voice acknowledged the reason for her change of subject. "I found out that Tysinger isn't without communication here. He's got a shortwave unit somewhere, according to one of his neighbors." Rafe walked over and grabbed a fresh knit shirt from the bed, slipping it over his head. Ashley wondered where he kept getting all the shirts.

"You mean they have neighbors here?"

"Everyone has his own idea of what a neighbor is. I found a small cabin located on one of the tributaries that feeds into the Clackamas River." He sat down on the edge of the bed and pulled on his sneakers. "The man who lives there is probably in his late sixties. He was pleased to pass the time with me and share some of his fishing and hunting yarns." He watched her as she laid the baby down on the bed beside him. She refused to look at him as he continued. "He lives up here year 'round and said there are several families scattered around the area who stay in touch with each other to make sure everything is all right."

Ashley managed to change Josh's diaper and attempted a glance at Rafe as she picked up the baby. He was watching her intently and she could feel her color rise. In a lazy movement he stood up and placed his arms around her waist, Josh cuddled close between them. Ashley had trouble concentrating on his words.

"In the course of our conversation I asked how anyone managed to communicate with the outside world, and he told me about the Kruegers. He didn't know Tysinger's name and didn't seem all that interested in who I was, so I didn't bother to explain. The Kruegers seem to be well liked in the area and are known to be willing to help out whenever needed."

Ashley tried to withstand the heat of his stare as she asked, "Where is Mr. Krueger? I haven't seen anyone by that name, now that you mention it."

"I wondered the same thing. It seems that one of their sons is a logger and asked his dad to help with one of his rigs for a few weeks. He's been gone for a couple of weeks now. I was amazed at how much the man knew about what was going on with everyone." He paused, then added with a thoughtful expression, "He may already have known who I was, for that matter."

"You mean he may have thought you were Raul."

The mischievous grin Ashley found so attractive stole across Rafe's face. "Yes, I guess you're right. I never realized just how much I might enjoy playing house."

Her back stiffened. "I don't know what you have in mind, Rafe, but I don't intend to play house. Not with you—not with anyone."

She stepped away from his loose grasp and smiled. "You should wipe the lipstick off. Something tells me Mrs. Krueger might wonder why you're wearing that particular shade."

He grinned. "Do you really think so? For some reason I feel certain she'd understand exactly why I'm wearing it." He reached into a back pocket for his handkerchief.

Ashley was thankful that Josh was there at the moment. She needed some breathing space. One kiss and her knees gave way. For the first time in her life, Ashley began to appreciate how easy it would be to get carried away by a sensual response. She found it most irritating to discover a passionate nature behind her no-nonsense outlook on life. She consoled herself with the thought that the particular circumstances were far from normal, so she intended to ignore her reactions.

When she entered the living room, Ashley discovered that Mrs. Krueger had been busy. A small table containing two place settings and a flower centerpiece sat before the glass wall. A pair of candles shone in the early evening light.

"Mrs. Krueger, you're a magician. Everything is beautiful." Mrs. Krueger beamed her pleasure at Ashley's approval. "Aren't you going to join us?"

"Oh, no! This is your weekend to be alone and enjoy each other. If you don't mind, I'll take your young man and keep him entertained while the two of you enjoy some privacy."

That's all I need, Ashley thought in mounting frustration. *Everybody's determined to put us in a romantic setting.*

Rafe followed her into the room, and she waited for his comments. Instead, the room echoed with the unspoken thoughts and undercurrents Ashley had tried to leave in the bedroom. She shrugged and decided she might as well enjoy the evening.

She did. The dinner of broiled steaks, baked potatoes, and tossed salad was delicious. A light rosé wine glinted in the candlelight as they sipped from tulip glasses. They relaxed and chatted easily.

Rafe shared a little of his childhood. "Raul and I are less than two years apart in age and looked enough alike to be twins. Somehow we managed to keep our neighborhood in an uproar during our early years."

"There were just the two of you in the family?"

"Yes, much to Mom's shame. She'd come from a large family and felt she hadn't done her part to repopulate the Ramirez family."

"Ramirez?"

"My mother's family. She was a fourth-generation Californian. The family owns a fair amount of land in the north central part of the state."

"McCord doesn't have much of a Spanish sound to it."

"So I've been told. My father is of Scottish descent—and a quiet, introverted sort. He and Mom made quite a pair." He shook his head at some of his memories. "Mom had a very fiery temperament, while Dad always tried to look at things from a reasonable, rational, logical viewpoint. When he and Mom had an argument he would give her all the numerous reasons why he was right and then fall apart when she broke down and cried. He loved her very much. We all did."

Ashley watched his face gentle with memories from his past. She had trouble seeing him as a little boy—he must have been a handful.

Rafe glanced up and caught her smiling at him. He picked up his glass of wine, tipped it against hers, and said, "When do I get a chance to meet the Allison tribe?

Will they give me a hard time because I want to run off with their only sister and daughter?"

The sudden change in subject, together with his careless remark, caused Ashley to choke on her wine. Trying to look and sound composed, she responded: "I'm afraid all of this is news to me. Has your role-playing gotten out of hand?"

"Not exactly. I suppose now that I've found you I don't intend to lose track of you." The smile that accompanied his statement did not lessen the seriousness of the expression in his eyes.

Ignoring the sudden increase in her pulse rate, Ashley spoke carefully. "I thought I made myself clear earlier. I don't have any serious relationships because I don't choose to have them."

"What makes you think I'm serious?" he retorted.

"Let me rephrase my remark. I'm not interested in having affairs. They only complicate matters, and someone always gets hurt." Her eyes glowed in the candlelight as she stared across the small table at him. "We're in a freakish situation this weekend; we've been thrown together under intimate circumstances that most newly acquainted people don't have to face."

"Are you referring to our impetuous marriage?"

"Our what?"

"Wouldn't you consider a marriage that took place as two people stepped into an elevator together rather impetuous?" His dancing eyes urged her to share his amusement at their predicament.

"I'd call it insanity. Whatever you label it, I'm not interested." She stood up from the table and took her wineglass into the shadows of the room. "So these elaborate scenes are being wasted, as far as I'm concerned."

He followed her and found her seated at the end of the sofa. He switched on a lamp as he sat at the other end. "Do you think I've set all this up as some sort of seduction scene?" His voice sounded almost angry.

"No, I don't think you've had to do anything but go along with Tysinger's plans. If we were married I could see what a nice weekend this would be. I'm sure Raul and Jeanine would have enjoyed it." Her tone stayed calm. Only she saw the slight tremor in her hand. When he made no comment she went on. "How do you propose to get us down from here?"

His eyes darted to hers in surprise. His mind had not been on leaving as much as on wondering what had caused such an attractive woman to cut out an entire side of her personality.

"I really haven't given it much thought," he admitted. "My mind's been on other things since I returned." The look he gave Ashley let her know where his mind had been.

"Do you think we can contact anyone tonight?"

"I have no doubt I can reach someone. The question is, can I give directions specific enough to enable someone to find this place? The roads up here don't seem to have many street signs." Ashley recalled the many roads they had passed and knew that without a map, a person unfamiliar with the area would only get lost.

Rafe leaned back in his chair. "I have a suggestion to make. Why don't we wait another night before doing anything? If we haven't heard from Tysinger by, say, noon tomorrow, I'll confront Mrs. Krueger about getting a message out." He glanced at her sitting there looking so aloof, making no comment. He shrugged. "At least then we'll be moving around in daylight hours, which would be much more sensible than feeling our way along at night. How do you feel about spending another night up here?"

Ashley had expected the suggestion. Waiting for daylight made a lot more sense. "I don't see that we have much choice."

"Then I'm glad to know we've managed to find some subject on which we agree."

She lifted her head from staring into her wineglass. "Do you find me that difficult to get along with?" She sounded almost shocked.

His lazy grin caused her stomach to do a sudden flip. "I refuse to answer on the grounds that whatever I say will no doubt start another argument, and I'm feeling too peaceful at the moment." He lounged there looking for all the world as though his only concern was how to spend the evening. As a matter of fact, that was her concern as well. Something told Ashley they might have opposing views on the subject.

She glanced at her watch. "I realize it's rather early, but I think I'll go on to bed."

"Suit yourself." He sounded bored. "I think I'll build a fire and enjoy the atmosphere for a while." He rolled his head against the sofa so that she was in his line of vision. "You're welcome to join me if you'd like."

She sat there wavering. To be honest, and she was forcing herself to at least be *that*, she wasn't ready for bed. But then, she wasn't ready to continue a romantic evening in front of a fire with Rafe, either. "Well, maybe I'll stay for a while longer."

She noted that he didn't stand up and cheer, but what had she expected? She'd made her message clear, and he no doubt felt that the matter was closed.

Ashley was annoyed that her nerves seemed to be on edge, her skin was flushed, and her pulse was racing. Perhaps another glass of wine would help to relax her.

Chapter Five

Ashley was amazed to find how much the wine had relaxed her. She lay on her stomach, stretched full length on the sofa with her shoes off and an empty wineglass dangling from one hand. She had been listening to Rafe's anecdotes about his past.

"You mean you actually jumped a freighter at sixteen to prove to your father that you were a man?"

"Yep. I figured he was too old and stodgy to understand what life was all about, so after one of our many verbal battles I slammed out of the house, hitchhiked to San Francisco, lied about my age, and headed for Japan on a freighter." Rafe was stretched out on the hearth rug, propped up on an elbow, dividing his time between watching Ashley and watching the fire as it began to settle into a glow of hot ashes.

"Weren't you scared?"

"If I was, I wouldn't admit it to anyone, especially not to myself. Hell, I was convinced I knew all there was to know. I didn't need to finish school." He paused. "Come to think of it, I think that's what started that particular argument. My dad had found out I'd been skipping some of my more boring classes." He grinned at the memory.

"What did your mother do?"

"What could she do? She tried to get us both to calm down and be reasonable. Coming from my mother, that should have broken us both up right there. However, my sense of humor hadn't reached the point where I could laugh at myself."

"But now it has?" Ashley asked with a smile.

Rafe's eyes rested on her face as the dying firelight created multicolored patterns across its surface. "I think so, yes." He continued to study her, and the thought came to him that he'd rarely seen a lovelier woman. She seemed to be unaware of the beauty that radiated from her. He felt his body reacting to her presence and admitted to himself that he wanted to make love to her.

"You're staring."

"I know."

"Do I have soot on my face?" She laughed softly, her earlier feelings of unease forgotten in the camaraderie of the evening. Why hadn't she liked this man, she wondered in surprise? She found him delightful. He'd allowed her to see his vulnerability, perhaps because he was comfortable with who he was. Funny, she'd noticed that only this evening.

A big yawn overtook her. She looked at her watch and laughed. "It's after midnight, and I'd planned to go to bed at nine."

He watched her mouth as it turned up in a soft smile. "I'm glad you didn't."

Her smile widened. "Me too, but I really do need to get some sleep. You were right when you pointed out that I'm not a morning person. But I want to get up early in case we have a day of hiking ahead of us."

Rafe groaned at the thought and rolled over onto his back. His shirt crept up on his stomach so that dark hair showed as it swirled into a T-shape and disappeared into his jeans. The snug pants outlined his shape. Ashley's eyes jerked back to his waist, but that didn't help much. She had an almost irresistible impulse to place her lips along that bared portion of his anatomy and plant kisses across the brown expanse. She eyed her empty wineglass with disfavor.

"How long was it before you went back home?" she asked, attempting to distract her mind from its erotic wandering.

"I was gone for two years before I had the guts to face my dad and admit I'd been wrong. That was the hardest thing I've ever had to do in my life." He shook his head. "I'll never forget it."

"Was he surprised?"

"Shocked, actually. I've never been one who could admit to being wrong, you see. That was the day I took my first step toward maturity." He was silent for a moment, lost in his memories. "Somehow I always knew he was there with me every step of the way."

Ashley's eyes drifted shut, then popped open. She sat up and stretched. "I think I'll go on to bed." She waited for his comment, but he was silent. She looked down at him lying at her feet and poked a bare toe into his ribs. "What are you going to do?"

The look he gave her made a mockery of the question, but she was determined not to be the one to break eye contact. She was a novice at the badinage they'd enjoyed all evening, but she'd discovered she liked it and refused to back down.

"Oh, I'll probably go to sleep shortly. I think that sofa is long enough to hold me—unless you have a better suggestion." His eyes dared her to comment.

She looked at him, then at the sofa. "I'm sure you'll be quite comfortable. I'll even find you some extra blankets so you don't get too cold tonight." As she turned to leave the room, she heard his soft "Good night, Ms. Allison" and turned back. He hadn't changed position, but he was watching her with a grin. She made a formal curtsy.

"Good night, Mr. McCord," she replied, and disappeared down the hallway.

Moonlight glowed through the glass wall in the guest bedroom. Ashley didn't need a lamp as she removed her clothes and hung them in the closet. They would probably have to be worn again tomorrow. She drifted into the bathroom, smiling to herself as she remembered some of Rafe's tales. She felt too keyed up to sleep and had decided that a nice, hot bath was just what she needed to relax her.

She piled her hair on top of her head and haphazardly stuck pins she'd found in her purse into various curls. Oh, how she wished for some moisturizing cream. Her face felt like sandpaper. Next kidnapping, she'd insist on it.

While rummaging in the bathroom cabinet for a face cloth, Ashley found a large container of bath oil and ended up dumping most of it into the hot water filling the tub. At that rate she'd slide right into bed and promptly slide right off it again. *Ashley*—she stared at herself in the mirror—*you never do anything in moderation.* Her image solemnly stared back. *You wait until you're twenty-eight years old before developing your very first crush. You idiot.*

I wonder if I'd be as attracted to him if I'd just met him in the normal course of events? Who knows? But he's managed to break through more of my defenses than anyone before.

The warm water caressed Ashley's skin, the oil causing the water to feel like liquid silk. She was aware of her body, as though Rafe's hands touched her everywhere the water lapped.

Enough of that! Much more and not only will you not be getting any sleep tonight, you'll be begging him not to sleep on the couch—and that would never do. Thank God he was self-assured enough not to feel threatened just because she'd made it clear that she had no intention of playing house. She nodded firmly and several curls slipped down onto her face.

As she stepped out of the cooling water, she noticed her small stack of underwear. It had to be rinsed out, but that would leave her with nothing to sleep in. Shrugging her shoulders, she filled the sink, added some face soap to the water and washed and rinsed her underthings. As she draped her lingerie over one of the towel racks, she smiled at the thought of Rafe coming in to wash and dry his face and grabbing a handful of slip. He wanted to experience marriage, did he?

Ashley wrapped a towel around herself, turned off the light, and opened the bathroom door with caution. The room was still moonlit, although the moon had moved higher in the sky. She glanced over at the undisturbed bed. What had she expected?

Ashley searched through the dresser for a suitable garment to sleep in. She pulled out a soft T-shirt, glad to see that it fell modestly to her thighs. The rest of the pins tumbled out of her hair as she flicked her small hairbrush through it. She could hardly hold her eyes open as she pulled back the covers and crawled into bed. She was sound asleep before her head hit the pillow.

The room was in dark shadow when Rafe came silently into the bedroom. He moved over to the bed of blankets and checked Josh. There was still enough light to show him Ashley's face as she slept, and he moved to the side of the bed as though drawn by an invisible cord.

She slept on her side with one hand tucked under her cheek, her hair in disarray on the pillow. He could feel deep within him the painful desire that he'd fought all evening. He couldn't understand his reaction to her—she wasn't the type of woman he admired. She was too independent, too opinionated and, if he were honest with himself, too virginal for his taste.

His women had several things in common. They were beautiful, eager to please, and understood their place in his life. Ashley certainly met the first criterion, but after that, she totally missed the mark. *So why do I have this irresistible desire to take her in my arms and coax from her the passion I've seen hints of?*

He sat down on the side of the bed and with a light touch brushed the hair from her ear. *An irresistible desire...* Rafe leaned over and kissed her softly just below her ear. Ashley murmured something and turned her head, her mouth a hairbreadth from his. He settled his lips on hers with a delicate touch, no longer thinking about his actions.

Ashley's mouth moved against his. She lifted her arms languidly to his shoulders as he deepened the kiss. His tongue sought the entrance it wanted and Ashley accommodated, her mouth shaping itself to his, her arms tightening around his shoulders. Without loosening his hold, Rafe shifted on the bed until he lay beside her, his arm slipping under her as he began to stroke her body.

Her response sent electrical impulses throughout his system. The pounding of his pulse shook his body. His hand explored her sweet curves, finally settling on her breast, chastely covered by the T-shirt. He knew he must stop—he'd never intended to take advantage of her, but her lips were sweet—so sweet. Just a moment more, then he would leave her.

The spicy scent of Rafe's aftershave lotion stole into Ashley's dream. She was back in the forest, following the long, tunneled trail, trying to find her way. She was lost and panic began to overwhelm her attempts to be rational. Where was Rafe? He was supposed to be up ahead. How would she get out from among the endless trees?

Then she saw him. She'd been frightened and felt abandoned, and he'd come to find her. Unhindered by shyness, she ran toward him, acknowledging her need for him. She threw herself into his arms and pressed her head against his chest, loving the closeness of his body, wanting to absorb him through her very pores. She never wanted to be alone again.

He lifted her face with gentle hands and fit his mouth to hers. His fingers danced lightly across her face, soft touches upon her closed eyelids, over her cheeks and down to her shoulders.

He needed her as well. He told her that by the way he held her, kissed her, and stroked her. Ashley wrapped her arms around him as she melted against him, opening her mouth to his invasion.

The cedar-touched air and his spicy scent intermingled. His hands moved with more urgent caresses, outlining the curve of her hips—pulling her closer to his male need. Ashley drifted with him into the soft, silent night of sensations and physical yearnings she'd never before experienced.

He turned her in a gentle movement, his feather touch exploring the shape of her breast.

Her breast!

Ashley realized that she was no longer dreaming. Rafe was in bed with her, his arms wrapped around her, his mouth moving with heart-stopping touches along her throat, down the V-neck of her shirt. And she wasn't stopping him! In fact, her hands were exploring the rugged strength of his shoulders, exulting in the feel of his body.

"No!" She shoved him away from her.

Rafe had forgotten how the kiss had started. He only remembered her response—the warm, passionate response that he had known was there. He'd found it. Her sudden withdrawal left him stunned.

"Get out of this bed!" she demanded in a whispered hiss.

Rafe sat up, trying to gain control of his runaway emotions.

"What's your excuse this time, Mr. McCord? Didn't I bring you enough blankets, or did you need your mommy's good-night kiss before you could sleep?" she demanded, her anger intensified by the knowledge of her own arousal. How *dare* he do this to her!

Her words stung and he stood up, pulling his shirt down to his waist. "My mother never gave me a kiss like that! That must have been some dream you were having, lady."

Remembering her dream, she was further incensed. "Get out of here, do you hear me?"

"Oh, I hear you, all right. It's a wonder Josh hasn't."

She clamped her hand over her mouth but her eyes continued to scream at him. She sat there until he left the room, then fell back on her pillow.

Her body still quivered from his touch. She ached with the needs he had aroused in her. Damn him! What kind of man would take advantage of a sleeping woman, regardless of what she was dreaming? It was a long time before Ashley fell asleep again.

What kind of man would take advantage of a sleeping woman? Rafe paced the living-room floor, disgusted with his actions, tied in knots with unsatisfied needs. *My God, she might have had to add rape to her list of outrages for the weekend if she hadn't realized what was happening.* Rafe knew he wouldn't be able to forgive himself for his loss of control. But more important to him at the moment was whether *she* would forgive him. He wouldn't have admitted it, but that question was more important to him than their need to leave the mountain retreat.

Ashley's eyes fluttered open and she saw daybreak. Mount Hood was a black silhouette, but the sky behind it changed from gray to pink as she lay there watching. Her eyes wandered to the recliner near the window, then blinked in surprise. Rafe sat there in profile, giving Josh his bottle.

The light filtering in was harsh on his face, showing heavy lines and deep circles under his eyes. He looked as though he hadn't slept at all. *I hope his conscience kept him awake!*

She continued to watch him, the knot in her chest dissolving as she noticed the loving way he held Josh. His expression was tender as he studied the tiny face of the baby energetically working on his first meal of the day.

Ashley had never seen her father or brothers hold or feed a baby. They loved their children—she knew that—but they would no more offer to help look after them, or nurture them, than they would expect one of the women to help brand cattle. Yet Rafe did it so naturally, as though he enjoyed it.

He's going to be a very handy father to have around.

Now where had that thought come from? He probably *would* be a good father, of course, with all the practice he was getting, but it certainly had nothing to do with her. She drifted off to sleep and dreamed of little boys with black curls and light blue eyes calling to her.

The next time she awoke, she was alone. Subdued, she crawled out of bed and took her shower. She leaned into the water as it began to run warm, then hot, unconscious of the luxury of hot water that far from civilization. She stood there with eyes closed, sudsing her hair, wishing she could return home and forget the weekend.

Rafe was standing looking out of the window and holding a cup of coffee when Ashley walked into the kitchen. He turned, his face an impersonal mask. "Coffee's ready. Mrs. Krueger has Josh. I thought that would give us a chance to discuss a few things."

Ashley's heart started pounding. What could they possibly have to discuss at this point? Hadn't they said it all the night before? She poured a cup of coffee and glanced out of the window. The view was unbelievable.

"I know it doesn't erase what happened, but I want to apologize for my behavior last night." His voice was low, as though he found the words painful.

She turned away from the window and realized that Rafe had moved closer. She felt drawn to him and wanted nothing more than to rest her head on his shoulder. She found the thought annoying and straightened to her full height, determined to face the situation in an objective manner.

"Apology accepted. Can we talk about something else?"

"Dammit, Ashley, I mean it. I don't want you to think I'm the kind of guy who waits until his victim is asleep and then has his sinister way with her pure and innocent body!"

His tone of disgust was too much. She started laughing. "Believe me, Rafe, that isn't what I was thinking. As a matter of fact, that *was* some dream you interrupted." Her cheeks flushed at the memory.

She really wasn't angry. He couldn't believe it. Most women would have had his hide tacked to the barn door by now. Or at the very least had their fathers out looking for him.

"I'm sure it's obvious to you that I'm not very experienced in these matters," Ashley said. "I've never reacted to a man as I have to you, and I don't understand it." She managed to raise her eyes and face him, only to lose her train of thought when she saw the warmth and tenderness in his.

A smile began in his incredibly silver blue eyes and spread to his lips, curling them in an endearing way. "Does this mean I haven't totally turned you off men forever?"

"Not exactly. It means that I will be in better control of my reactions in the future. I don't intend to get carried away again—with you or anyone."

"But Ashley, what happened last night wasn't wrong. Premature, perhaps, but our reactions to each other are natural and normal."

She moved away from him. In crisp tones she answered, "I'm sorry, but I don't buy that rationale." She waved her hand as he started to speak. "I appreciate your trying to smooth things over, though. I'm sure you're not used to getting this kind of reaction the morning after. It must be hard on your ego."

His eyes hardened as he clamped down on a retort. Taking a deep breath, he spoke in a slow, clear voice. "Let's just leave my ego out of the discussion, if you don't mind. All I'm saying is that you don't have to go into a convent or do penance for the rest of your life." He stood up and moved to the door of the kitchen. "You managed to prove you're like the rest of us. Welcome to the human race!"

"I *know* that. I told you I'm not blaming you, so why are you getting so angry?"

"I don't know!" he shouted. "You manage to get under my skin quicker than anybody I've ever known!" They glared at each other across the room, tension stretched taut between them.

The sound of car doors slamming broke the tension and Rafe spun around, heading for the window overlooking the trail.

"It's Tysinger and his companions. He doesn't look very happy."

Rafe and Ashley were in the living room when Tysinger entered the house. He was very quiet. They heard the muffled click of the door as it closed, then silence.

He walked into the room and stood there looking at them. The dapper man they had met on Friday was gone. This man had aged twenty years. His eyes burned with a rage that caused a quiver to shoot down Ashley's spine.

He looked at Rafe. "Who are you?" Never had a soft tone been so menacing.

"Raphael McCord."

"Are you Raul's brother?"

"Yes."

"I see." Tysinger moved away from them toward the sliding glass doors. He stood there for a moment, staring, then turned back to them. "You will no doubt be pleased to learn that your brother and his wife—" his eyes cut to Ashley, then back to Rafe "—managed to meet with Senator Hensley this weekend. So your little game was successful."

His eyes touched Ashley once again, the rage barely under control. "I happen to know Ralph Begley very well, Ms. Allison." A feeling of foreboding began to stir within Ashley. "We go back a long way together, so when you told me you worked with him I decided to give him a call. He passed on some very interesting information."

Ashley knew what was coming. Ralph Begley was one of the most conservative attorneys in the state—in his practice, his politics, and his personal beliefs. He was the one who had kept the firm from hiring women attorneys for years. Ashley knew he was her biggest hurdle to becoming a partner in the firm. And he was a friend of Tysinger's!

"Begley tells me you are known for your cool head and sharp wit. He also informs me that as far as he knows you are not married and have never been married. He was quite interested to hear the details of your romantic weekend with Mr. McCord."

Chapter Six

The ride back to town was completed in silence. Tysinger had made no objection to their leaving immediately, for which Rafe was thankful. He had a feeling they hadn't heard the last of Tysinger. He kept an eye on Ashley as she gazed out of the window. She had lost all color when Tysinger mentioned discussing her with her boss. Surely in this day and age nobody cared about an employee's personal life, but why else would she have shown such a reaction? She had handled the weekend so well, never breaking down, ready with a snappy retort, but Tysinger's news seemed to throw her.

He had no one but himself to blame. *Yes, McCord, you've managed to create quite a lot of havoc in people's lives, including your own, in one short weekend.*

What did he intend to do about it? He couldn't leave her to face the situation alone. She'd already explained that her law practice was her life. Could her career really be in jeopardy? He was going to have to get some answers from her.

They were dropped off in front of their office building, and Rafe spoke for the first time since they'd left the mountain.

"Where's your car?"

"At home. I rode the bus on Friday."

"I'll take you home."

"That's all right—"

"Ashley, it really isn't necessary to argue about *everything*. I said I'd take you home." He grasped her forearm in a firm grip as they walked to his car.

Other than giving directions, Ashley said nothing more on the way. When they had pulled into the driveway of her remodeled Victorian house and stopped, she started to hand Josh to Rafe.

"I want to go in with you to make certain everything is all right."

"Why shouldn't everything be all right? I've only been gone a couple of days."

"Indulge me, will you? Besides, we didn't finish our earlier discussion."

She stepped out of the car, careful not to awaken the sleeping baby. Rafe slid Josh from her shoulder, then followed her up the steps.

"I can't think of a thing that needs to be discussed at this point. I'm just glad the weekend is behind us and can be forgotten." She unlocked the door and swung it open, then came to an abrupt halt just inside the doorway.

The living room was a shambles. A lamp was overturned on one of the end tables. The oil painting over the fireplace hung at an angle. Papers, magazines, and a couple of figurines that had been sitting on Ashley's rosewood desk littered the floor.

Rafe acted first. "Let's report this to the police right away. Can you tell what's missing?" He started searching for her phone.

Ashley stopped him. "Don't call the police. There isn't anything missing." How was she ever going to explain?

"Dammit, Ashley, how can you be so blasted calm? Your house has either been burglarized, vandalized, or both, and you don't even want to let the police know?" Rafe looked at her as though she'd suddenly sprouted another head.

"Tasha did this, Rafe. She doesn't like to be left alone."

"Well, in that case my friend, it's my strong suggestion that you find some sort of treatment or counseling for your roommate." He waved his hand at the room for emphasis. "This is obviously the result of a very sick mind." Rafe pushed his hand through his hair as he gazed around in disbelief. "Why do you put up with it, for God's sake? If she's this violent now, there's no telling when she might turn on you." Josh had long since been awakened by Rafe's tirade as he stalked about the room, inspecting the damage. The baby's sleepy expression of puzzlement was almost more than Ashley could handle.

"Rafe." She tried to keep a straight face. "Tasha is my Siamese cat. She's really very gentle and lovable, but she just doesn't like staying alone." His eyes narrowed as he listened to her explanation. "She's grown used to being here all day by herself, but if I'm not home in the evening she gets upset. When she gets upset she likes to tear through the house. I've never left her on her own for a weekend before." She glanced around the room. "She's probably waiting in my bedroom right now expecting me to coax her out of her mood."

Rafe stared at her in disbelief. "Tasha is a cat?"

"That's what I said, Rafe."

"Your Oriental roommate is a cat?" he repeated, his voice climbing slightly.

A slight quiver in her voice gave Ashley's amusement away. "Well, I didn't know why you wanted to know who I lived with, and I thought it'd be safer if you thought there was someone who might worry."

Rafe might have been able to accept her explanation at another time, but he'd just had one hell of a scare. In fact, he had discovered that he wanted the right to protect this woman, and she found the whole scene hilariously funny! "Well, Ms. Allison, you must have gotten your fair share of laughs this weekend, all at my expense. I've spent the weekend worrying about how to protect you from the situation I'd gotten us into. Now that's the laugh of the week—"

For the first time since Ashley had met him, Josh let out a wail. The loud voices were too much for him. His angry face so resembled the flushed countenance of his uncle that Ashley could no longer contain herself. She collapsed into a chair, laughing.

Even Rafe's anger couldn't hold out against her infectious laughter and, as he hastily patted the sobbing infant, his grin began to appear. Before long he was laughing with her, the subdued baby totally bewildered by the incomprehensible behavior of the adults around him.

"I'm so sorry for laughing, Rafe—I know it isn't funny," Ashley finally managed to say. She wiped the tears from her eyes as she sat up. "Part of it is just being so glad that the only casualty of the weekend was my living room." She sobered as she stared at him. "It could have been much worse."

"Yes, I know. But I'm not convinced the house is the only casualty. That's what I think we need to discuss." He took the blanket from around Josh and spread it on the area rug in front of Ashley's fireplace, then placed the baby on his stomach on the blanket.

"What do you mean?"

"What is Ralph Begley's reaction going to be concerning Tysinger's attempt to embarrass you?" He watched her closely and noticed how quickly she schooled her face to a bland expression.

"It's hard to say at this point, but I'm sure I'll find out tomorrow. It's nothing to concern you, though."

"Wrong. It directly concerns me. I caused the problem in the first place."

"Okay. I'll explain that to Mr. Begley. I'm sure he'll understand." She smiled brightly and stood up. "I know you're as anxious as I was to get home. Don't let me keep you."

Frustrated, Rafe got to his feet. "Look, why don't we have dinner together tonight. I've got a glimmer of an idea how we can resolve the problem so that Begley is satisfied." He leaned over and picked up Josh. "I want to think it through a little more before I let a cross-examining attorney get hold of it." He smiled, his eyes filled with a warmth that suddenly reminded Ashley of the night before.

"What will you do with Josh?"

"Jeanine's mom will keep him. She plans to take care of him when I leave for California." He waited. "What do you say?"

She didn't want to see him walk out of her life. In three days he had managed to turn her sane and sensible world into a whirling mass of emotions she never knew existed. She would be much better off never seeing him again. "Dinner sounds fine. What time?"

Rafe opened the front door, then paused. "I'll be here around seven—see you then." The door closed quietly behind him.

Ashley stood staring at the door for long minutes after he left. What was happening to her? She felt as though she'd visited another planet and had just been beamed back to earth. Wandering into her bedroom she was greeted by an outraged cat. Tasha met her, tail high in the air, indignation in every line of her feline body.

"I know, Tasha. I abandoned you and I'm sorry." Ashley peeled off her clothes and padded barefoot into the bathroom where she began to fill the tub. Tasha followed, detailing her list of complaints and emphasizing them with sweeping exclamations of her tail.

"Quit throwing me those obscene gestures, if you don't mind," Ashley added as she slipped into the heated water. As she lay there soaking, her mind wandered back to all that had happened since Friday night. Discovering that she was capable of the passion Rafe had aroused in her had come as a distinct shock. She wasn't at all sure she was capable of forgetting the experience and continuing her life as though she'd never met him.

She knew she had to try.

"Get married!" Ashley's startled exclamation caused several heads to turn in the dimly lit dining room of one of Portland's finest hotels. Her face flamed as she watched the amused expression on Rafe's face. He wasn't even embarrassed by everyone looking in their direction.

"You don't have to act as though I just made an indecent suggestion, Ashley. Marriage is a perfectly respectable institution."

"That's not funny, Rafe."

"I don't mean it to be funny, Ashley. I'm serious."

"But why?" Ashley wailed.

"Come on, counselor, surely the reasons are obvious."

Ashley fumbled for her wineglass, took a hasty sip, then returned the glass to the table with careful deliberation. "Perhaps you should explain them to me anyway."

Rafe had spent the afternoon planning how best to approach the subject. The idea had first come to him during a sleepless night and he had pushed it from him, convinced that his guilty conscience was overreacting. But the more he thought about it, the better he liked the idea. They didn't have to enter into any "death-do-us-part" relationship, but it would give Ashley credibility with her boss, and her job was her first priority, it seemed. He ignored the fact that he would also be able to enjoy all her delectable attributes without apology once they were married.

"All right. I postponed my meeting in San Francisco tomorrow. I could meet you at the courthouse as soon as it opens in the morning. We could get our license and find a judge to marry us. Then if Begley tries to give you a hard time, you can tell him we're married. He doesn't need to know for how long."

He was serious. Ashley studied the intent expression on Rafe's face as he explained his plan. This must be what he's like in a board room. Serious, concise, and devastating. No one had warned her how lethal to her sensible life the charm of a dynamic man could be. She felt like a drowning person going down for the third time.

"But, Rafe, I don't want to be married. I've never had any desire to be married. I've seen what it does to a woman. She spends all her time providing for everyone else's needs, with no life of her own. I can't be that way." Her eyes met his in a steady gaze. "I could never make such a commitment to anyone. Call me selfish—or self-centered—or too ambitious. Call it whatever you want, but I can't be that way. I don't even want to try."

"Does it have to be a permanent arrangement with you?"

"You mean marriage?"

"Yes. We'd only have to stay married long enough to protect your position at your office." He watched the emotions reflected in her expression and waited. He knew the importance of timing, and he used the knowledge with consummate skill.

"Let's dance while you think about it," he said as he took her hand and led her to the dance floor. Ashley had never danced much, but within moments she found herself following Rafe's strong lead, and she began to relax against his lean, muscular body.

Rafe's gaze lingered on her face as her eyes refused to meet his. It took all his restraint not to drag her to a secluded corner and kiss her until she agreed to marry him. Although the idea of marriage was new, he was eager to experience it with Ashley. It never occurred to him to wonder why.

When they returned to their table in silence, Rafe suggested that they leave. He wanted privacy to discuss the matter. When they walked into Ashley's house, Rafe paused in the doorway of the living room, taking in the total picture. "I must admit I prefer your decorating to

Tasha's. She may be exotic, but a trifle wild with some of her ideas."

Ashley smiled, but her mind was obviously on other things.

"Where is Tasha, by the way?"

"In the bedroom, probably."

"I really think she and I ought to get acquainted." He wandered into the room and slid out of the soft blue suede jacket he wore. Loosening his tie, he opened the first few buttons of his shirt. "Ahhh, that's much better. Hope you don't mind my getting comfortable."

Ashley waved a hand. "Be my guest."

"So what do you think of my suggestion?"

"I don't think it would work."

"Why?"

"Do we have time to go into all the reasons or shall I skim over the top?"

Rafe sat down in a large, overstuffed chair and grinned. "If it's going to take a while, would you mind if I had a drink as . . . uh . . . fortification, perhaps?"

"Certainly. What would you like?"

"Do you have any brandy? I have a feeling I'll also need something reviving."

She disappeared into the kitchen. A few minutes later she returned holding two brandy snifters with generous measures of brandy in each.

He glanced at the amounts in each glass. "I said reviving, Ashley, not embalming." He shrugged his shoulders and settled back into his comfortable pose, sipping his drink.

Ashley took a rather large gulp of brandy and choked. Maybe she should have chosen something a little milder, but it was too late now. She began to pace.

"All the reasons I gave at the restaurant are valid. I am not a homemaker. I have no desire to become a homemaker." She spun around. "I can't even cook, and believe me, in this day and age, it takes a tremendous amount of skill to avoid learning how to cook."

He started laughing.

"It isn't funny. Besides that, we don't even know each other. This is only the second time we've been together."

"That's true, but our first meeting was a blockbuster." He stood up, gently pulling her into his arms. "I'm not going to ask you for anything you don't want to give me, Ashley. I thought you knew me well enough by now to understand that. If you really hate the relationship, we can call it off with no hard feelings. Surely you don't find an offer like that threatening, do you?"

She was so confused. Everything he said made sense. Without the protection of a marriage, she might very well lose her chance to move up in the firm. She was making it sound as though marriage would be a real sacrifice for her. Then she remembered how this man could affect her and she stiffened. If she were ever to experience his lovemaking, she knew she'd never be able to end the relationship.

Finally, she nodded. Before she could say a word Rafe tightened his arms around her, giving her a kiss that claimed his possession of her. "Then you'll marry me?" he murmured, his hands smoothing the silky material covering her back.

She pulled back from him, determined to be honest with him. "I know what you're doing, Rafe, and I really appreciate it. You're determined to play the role of my knight come to rescue me."

His face flushed. He wasn't that saintly.

"Because it's so very important for me not to jeopardize my job, I'll marry you on a temporary basis." He started to pull her to him once more but she resisted. "But it will have to be a marriage in name only."

Chapter Seven

Ashley glanced at her watch as she left her office. It was a few minutes after five. She smiled. Leaving on time had become a habit since Rafe McCord had entered her life. Nothing had been the same since the weekend she'd spent on the mountain six weeks earlier.

They had followed Rafe's plan and gotten married the Monday after they met. Rafe's instincts had been sound. Ashley had no sooner arrived in her office that Monday than the phone rang.

"Ashley," a male voice intoned, "this is Ralph Begley. If you have a few minutes, I'd like to see you."

"Certainly, sir. I'll be right there." She flicked a comb through her hair, straightened the bow on her blouse, and walked to Ralph Begley's corner office.

Tapping on the door, she entered dutifully at his command. Two walls of glass provided views of Mount Hood and Mount Saint Helens and, in the foreground, the

Willamette River curving around the downtown area like a snake.

"Ashley, come in. I appreciate your taking the time to see me." He motioned to one of the chairs. She took a seat and waited.

Ralph Begley looked larger than life. White wavy hair framed his aristocratic face. A heavy jawline gave him something of the look of a bulldog, and from his reputation Ashley understood him to be as tenacious as one.

"You may not be aware that Virgil Tysinger and I are close personal friends."

Here it comes. She attempted a smile. "So he mentioned this weekend, sir."

He looked startled at her easy admission. "Then you admit to being at his mountain retreat this weekend."

Ashley feigned a puzzled expression. "Why yes, sir. My husband and I had the pleasure of being Mr. Tysinger's guests. He has a beautiful place, but then I'm sure you know that."

The conversation was obviously not progressing along the lines Begley had planned. "Uh, no, as a matter of fact, I've never been there. Uh, Ashley, I wasn't aware you were married."

She smiled. "Oh, yes, but we haven't mentioned it to many people, and I intend to continue using my maiden name professionally."

"I see. Is there a particular reason you don't want it known, Ashley?"

Hang on to the ole temper, girl. He's trying to bait you, and you're too smart for that. "No. As a matter of fact, as soon as Rafe finishes his business in California we intend to have a reception for all our friends and family." Smile firmly in place, she added, "You'll receive one of the first invitations." If only he were aware of his role as Cupid in their hasty merger!

Begley reminded Ashley of a clipper ship sailing before a wind that has suddenly failed, leaving it becalmed on a motionless sea. She returned to her office mentally praising Rafe for his foresight.

When Rafe called that evening he seemed pleased that his tactics had been effective, and they discussed their next step. To be convincing, Rafe would need to spend some time with Ashley, and she agreed it was only sensible that he move in with her—on a temporary basis, of course. He had accepted her decision not to consummate the marriage, but Ashley was nervous at the thought of sharing her home with him.

She needn't have worried. Rafe arrived and good-naturedly moved into her guest room, then set about showing Ashley that her ideas of marriage needed revising. For one thing, Rafe was used to living alone and taking care of himself. Wonder of wonders, he didn't suddenly develop a helplessness that Ashley had always suspected occurred in the male promptly upon repeating his marriage vows.

He shared chores in the kitchen and other domestic duties with no hint of complaint and, once again, she tried unsuccessfully to picture her father or brothers doing a load of laundry or drying dishes.

Most important to Ashley, she was given the privacy she needed. She had trouble at first adjusting to his affectionate nature—his need to touch, his habit of hugging her to him, of stroking her shoulder whenever he walked by—but within a few short weeks she discovered how much she looked forward to his demonstrative behavior and tentatively began to respond.

So why was she beginning to feel on edge whenever Rafe was around and restless when he was gone? During the six weeks they'd been together, he'd flown to California once, for four days, and she and Tasha had wandered around the house as though lost.

Tasha had adopted Rafe within days of his arrival, much to Ashley's chagrin. She had explained to Rafe that Tasha did not take to strangers, that she carried aloofness to an extreme, and cautioned him not to be hurt when she ignored him. Hah! Tasha followed him everywhere he went, and Ashley suspected that she slept with him since she no longer turned up in Ashley's room at night.

Yes, Rafe had turned Ashley's sane and sensible world upside down, and she hesitated to think what adjustments she would have to make once the need for their marriage was past.

An unexpected bonus of her marriage was the acquisition of Raul and Jeanine as family. Once Ashley met Raul she could better understand the confusion that first weekend—the two men looked very much alike. However, in Ashley's opinion, Rafe had a compelling sensuality that was missing in Raul. Ashley felt comfortable and relaxed around Raul, restless and disturbed around Rafe. Jeanine reminded Ashley of Tinkerbell with short, black curls. She would never forget Jeanine's explanation of how she and Raul had met....

"We met at Stanford University," Jeanine explained in her ebullient fashion. "I'm the world's greatest crusader for hopeless, helpless causes. Raul managed to extricate me from one that was about to be hit with a big scandal." She grinned, not at all repentant. "It did, too. My family was so grateful to him for running interference for me that they welcomed him into the fold." Her large, black eyes rolled. "For my family, that's really something." In a confiding tone, she whispered, "They were convinced that the only reason anyone would want to marry me was for my money."

The women had met for lunch, and Ashley almost choked on her iced tea. "Your money?"

"Yes. I come from a long line of moneyed Oregonians who believe in intermarriage with other moneyed Oregonians. It almost becomes incestuous after a while." Her eyes danced as she watched the expression on Ashley's face. "They recognized that Raul was different. We've laughed about it several times since then. The McCords could buy and sell our family out of their miscellaneous fund."

Nor would she forget Jeanine's explanation of how she had become involved in the southern Oregon investigation....

"In my normal crusading spirit I got involved in the fight against the use of herbicides and volunteered to help gather data. You can imagine how surprised I was to discover that some of those anxious to fight the use of herbicides were growing marijuana. However, they weren't letting themselves be known and we needed specific information about them." She paused and took a drink of her coffee. "So I got this idea about going 'underground.'"

Ashley groaned.

"That was exactly Raul's reaction! But by the time he found out what I'd done, it was too late to back out." She shrugged her shoulders. "As long as I was involved, I stayed to find out what I could."

"But weren't you pregnant during that time?"

"Of course. That's what made my idea work. You see, I pretended my boyfriend had dumped me when I told him I was pregnant. The guy I named had been a dealer and was in jail awaiting trial on drug charges. I figured they wouldn't check up on my story—" she paused, her twinkling eyes sharing her amusement "—and I was right. I managed to find out quite a lot...."

Ashley had never known anyone quite like Jeanine, but she enjoyed her enormously, and they became friends.

Rafe rapidly became the focal point of Ashley's daily routine. He never crowded her, but he was there when she needed him. When things were hectic for her, she enjoyed sharing her day with him while she unwound. One of his most endearing traits was his ability to plan sudden trips to the coast or the mountains whenever she had free time. They spent a great deal of time laughing together; their sense of the ridiculous was a bond they shared.

However, the nights were becoming more difficult for Ashley. Knowing he was in the next room kept her tossing restlessly each night. He never suggested that he was dissatisfied with their arrangement, and she was embarrassed by her increased arousal whenever he was near. If Rafe was similarly afflicted, he hid it well.

She entered the front door and heard his voice, and her stomach began to quiver in anticipation. "Rafe?"

"In here, love," he called from the kitchen. His casual use of endearments had been something else she had grown accustomed to. "Tasha's just been filling me in on your outrageous behavior."

Ashley stopped in the doorway of the kitchen and surveyed the scene. Rafe stood with one foot negligently crossed over the other as he leaned against the cabinet, arms folded over his chest. Tasha sat on one of the chairs facing him.

"What outrageous behavior?" Ashley demanded to know.

"She won't say," he admitted, his tone grave. "She just looks at me with a knowing expression and blinks when I ask for specifics."

"Don't fall for that—she practices her inscrutable expression before the mirror. Doesn't mean a thing."

He moved over to her, slipping his arms around her waist. As his lips moved toward hers, he whispered, "I've missed you today." His mouth found hers with unerring precision. As he fitted her snugly against his taut body, Ashley relaxed, enjoying the haven of his arms. Her mouth opened in unconscious invitation and his tongue took advantage, moving across her teeth and touching her with an intimacy that hinted of further delights, if she only dared to accept them. She could feel the acceleration of his heart under her palm. At least she was consoled to know she affected him too.

With reluctance he drew away. "We're invited to Raul and Jeanine's for dinner. I told them I'd let them know if you wanted to go out tonight—that it would depend on the kind of day you've had."

It wasn't fair. It wasn't enough that he was handsome and sexy, he had to be sensitive and understanding too. Ashley knew that she had never stood a chance of resisting this man. If he only knew, she'd given up the struggle weeks ago.

"I'd enjoy dinner with them," Ashley murmured. "We haven't seen them in a while."

Rafe chuckled. "That's because I explained that since we're on our honeymoon, we prefer to keep to ourselves."

Ashley could feel the warmth move into her cheeks. "I'm sure this hasn't been quite your idea of a honeymoon." He continued to hold her closely against him, and she knew he was not unaffected by her nearness.

"Oh, I don't know," he said, mischief dancing in his incredibly blue eyes. "It certainly has had its moments."

Slowly disengaging herself from his arms, she tried for a casual tone. "Let me shower and change and I'll be ready to go."

Rafe watched her walk away, then went and poured himself a drink. *Much more of this frustration and I'm either going to turn into an alcoholic or a human prune from all the cold showers I've taken during the past six weeks.*

He had understood her reservations about their union. In fact, he agreed with them. They needed to get to know each other; that was why he had canceled the delicate negotiations he'd been involved with in California. Since meeting Ashley, Rafe's priorities had undergone a subtle shift.

The most important task he had now was to win her trust. He was reminded of the summer he and Raul had managed to tame a young doe their grandfather had caught and penned. As long as they allowed her to make the approaches, they made progress. Eventually she would come and eat from their hands but continued to shy away whenever they attempted to touch her. Ashley was the same way. She was skittish whenever he attempted more than a casual embrace, and he patiently waited for her to come to him. The toll on his restraint had been tremendous.

Is it even worth it? he muttered to himself as he took a large swallow of bourbon and water. *All it would take is a phone call, and there would be someone waiting by the time my flight arrived in California tomorrow.* The imminent trip ate at him. The call had come that afternoon, and he knew he couldn't ignore it. How long did he intend to stay up here like a lovesick schoolboy waiting to be noticed? He had his own life to live, and from all indications Ashley was content to live hers without him.

His gamble of moving in with her had not paid off and he might as well accept it. He wondered whether she would even care that he had to return to his business interests. Finishing his drink, he set his glass down with deliberation. He didn't want another woman; he wanted Ashley. Somehow he'd pictured himself falling for a docile, homemaker type who would be content to raise his children and spend his money. Who would ever have believed that he'd fall for an independent, sassy-tongued witch who had the ability to turn him inside out with a flash of her smile or the sound of her laughter.

The ride to Raul and Jeanine's was quiet; each was lost in his or her own thoughts.

Ashley was listening to Jeanine describe Josh's latest feat when she heard a sentence of Rafe's conversation with Raul that caused her to hold her breath.

"I'm going to have to go back down there and see what I can save of the fiasco. It may already be too late, but I have to try." Rafe's voice was low, but Ashley caught every word.

So did Jeanine. "I didn't know you were going to have to return to California, Rafe. I thought your move up here was permanent."

Rafe's eyes found Ashley's trained on him, a question in their depths. He smiled at his sister-in-law. "Sounds great in theory, Jeanine, but unfortunately, all my investments are in California."

Raul caught the strain in Ashley's face. "Will you be able to go with him, Ashley?"

Three pairs of eyes speared her with their intentness. Why hadn't he mentioned that he was leaving? How long had he known? She shook her head. "No, I'm afraid there's no way I can leave right now. My court docket is filled for the next several weeks." She attempted a smile. "Of course, Rafe knows where to find me when he finishes his business in California."

"Well, the honeymoon had to end some time, I suppose," Raul offered with a grin. Unfortunately, his brother didn't find the remark amusing.

Jeanine was quick to change the subject and during the rest of the evening the conversation was light, for which Ashley was thankful. She had known that her relationship with Rafe had to end, but somehow she hadn't expected it to be over so soon. However, she had no intention of letting the others know how the news had affected her.

The tension between them was almost visible when Rafe and Ashley returned home. There was nothing to say, but Ashley made the attempt.

"When do you have to leave?"

Rafe was silent for so long that she thought he was going to ignore her question. At last he cleared his throat. "There's an eight-thirty flight in the morning that would put me into San Francisco in time for a meeting scheduled at ten."

They entered the house and Ashley absently went about the routine of feeding Tasha. Since Rafe's advent into their lives, Tasha had seemed to accept their occasional evenings away. Somehow Rafe had managed to hypnotize the cat into more civilized behavior.

When she returned to the living room, Ashley found Rafe staring out of the front window. A light from the hall was the only illumination.

Determined to get a grip on her emotions, Ashley decided to confront their situation. "I suppose our marriage has been accepted by now, so there's really no reason to prolong it, is there?"

She saw Rafe stiffen as she began to speak. He turned slowly, the light slanting across his face, leaving his eyes in shadow.

"What marriage?" he asked, his tone harsh.

"Rafe?" She was bewildered. "What's wrong?"

"I just find it amazing that you can discuss so unemotionally the end of something that never had a proper beginning."

"But Rafe, the whole idea was to protect my job, and our marriage accomplished that. I thought you'd be eager to resume your life in California by now."

In rapid strides Rafe moved to where she stood and clamped his arms on her shoulders. "You really do see me as some self-sacrificing knight who came to your rescue, don't you?"

Confused by the anger she could hear in his voice, she attempted to step back, and his hold tightened. "What other reason was there?"

"This!" He took her in his arms, his mouth taking hers in fierce possession. Ashley's arms locked behind his head and she returned his kiss passionately, running her hands through the curls at the nape of his neck, and loving the feel of her breasts pressed against him.

They were both breathless when Rafe broke their contact. In a tortured voice, Rafe spoke. "I made a promise to myself that night I almost took you that I would never make love to you unless you invited me to. That was the only way I knew to show you that you could trust me." He groaned as he nuzzled her neck. "But it's been hell living with you every day, seeing you, wanting you, and not being able to have you." He stopped and kissed her again as though starved for the taste of her. "I can't take any more of it, Ashley. I've got to get away from you before I break that promise and end up causing both of us to hate me."

Ashley's arms slid around Rafe's waist and she reveled in the feel of him. "Rafe, all you needed to do was tell me how you felt. I've lain there night after night fantasizing about what would happen if I were to get up and go to your room and beg you to love me." She placed quick kisses along his jaw line and his hands explored her spine, caressing the curves of her hips as though he planned to sculpt them. "I couldn't do it. As much as I wanted you, I couldn't ignore the ingrained inhibitions. I couldn't be so brazen as to force myself on you."

"*Force* yourself." He groaned. "Oh, Ashley, we've both been so ridiculous and wasted an unbelievable amount of time." Rafe scooped her into his arms, carrying her easily, and moved down the hallway to her room.

As he placed her on the bed, Ashley was certain that she smelled the soft scent of cedar intermingled with Rafe's aftershave lotion. She watched him as he removed his clothes down to his briefs, those incredibly tiny briefs that could not conceal the effect she had on him. Then he joined her on the bed.

She tensed as he touched her, unsure of the next step. "It's all right, love, I'm not going to rush you," he murmured as he slipped her blouse and skirt from her. He paused when scraps of lace were all that covered her and began to kiss her with long, drugging kisses. Her trembling ceased and she began to respond to his caresses. A slow fire started deep within her and she began to imitate his movements.

"Oh, yes, Ashley, touch me, love—I want to feel your hands on me."

His encouragement led her to further exploration and by the time he shifted his weight over her, she ached for his possession. She had never thought herself capable of experiencing the emotions Rafe stirred within her. His possession appeased a need that had been growing in her since their first weekend together. She gloried in the tremor she felt course through him, reassured that the overwhelming response she felt was shared. Ashley felt that nothing could equal the emotional high his love-making created until she heard Rafe murmur, "Dear God, how I love you, Ashley Allison McCord," and her heart overflowed.

After twenty-eight years, Ashley had found her home in Rafe's arms.

Chapter Eight

Autumn had left its calling card wherever Ashley looked; the yellow leaves of the sycamores and the red of the sumac dressed up lawns and parks. Brisk mornings warned that winter was beginning to stir from its summer hibernation.

Ashley had gotten into the habit of walking to work. She needed the exercise, and it gave her time to make the transition from her personal to her professional life. Not that there was much happening in her personal life at the moment. Rafe had been back to Oregon only twice since the night they had made their marriage a reality more than two months earlier. She lived on the memories of those visits, waiting for his return.

Rafe had called several times to see whether she could fly down to him, but she had always had to refuse. She was too close to making partner now to risk taking time to travel south. More than one partner had met with her during the past few weeks to discuss her feelings toward her practice and the firm, and to ask her about her goals. She was excited about her career, and only the knowledge that Rafe would arrive the next day gave her more pleasure than her job.

One more day. They'd been apart for more than three weeks. Something was going to have to give in their schedules soon.

About midmorning her phone rang. It was Raul. He had never called her at the office before, and her first thought was something had happened to Rafe.

Ashley's heart leaped, then started pounding. "Raul? Is something wrong?"

"Well, let's put it this way. I'm calling you in your professional capacity. I think I've been framed."

"Why? What's happened?"

"There was a chemical spill at the plant last week under rather peculiar circumstances. Today I've been served with papers from the Department of Environmental Quality asking that the court shut McCord Industries down." His voice sounded grim. "Since you happen to be my favorite lawyer, I wondered if I could make an appointment to see you and discuss the matter." He paused. "Will it hurt your feelings to know that you're also the *only* lawyer I know?"

Ashley laughed, relieved to know that Rafe was all right. "No, Raul, that doesn't hurt my feelings." She glanced at her calendar. "As a matter of fact, I've got a cancellation at eleven this morning. Why don't you bring the papers around and let me look at them?"

"That'll be great. I'll see you at eleven. Oh, and Ashley?"

"Yes?"

"Thanks." The receiver clicked.

Raul watched Ashley's face as she read the summons, complaint, and motion for temporary injunction. If granted, McCord Industries would have to shut down immediately, perhaps on a permanent basis.

"What can you tell me about the spill?" Ashley said, glancing up from the documents.

"Well, we have a number of drains that allow chemical waste to run off into holding tanks. The spill occurred because one of those drains was plugged."

"You think it was deliberate?"

"I know it was. I found a large piece of wood stuck in the drain. There's no way that piece of wood could have gotten in there accidentally."

"Have you talked with the employees who were at the plant when the spill happened?"

"More than once, and no one seems to know anything or to have seen anything. I'm completely baffled."

"It looks as if Tysinger's still at work, Raul."

"How could he be behind this, Ashley? He and several others have been indicted and are awaiting trial. What could he hope to gain?"

"Nothing. It's what he hopes you lose. He's obviously vindictive and could easily have bribed someone in your plant to cause the trouble. I think you're right. You've been framed."

"So what do I do about it?"

"We fight it, that's what."

Raul took in the picture Ashley made. She looked as though she'd been energized, ready to go into orbit, to move mountains and leap rivers. She suddenly broke the silence. "The hardest part of all of this is the hearing for the injunction. That's only a week away, and we'll need as much time as possible to investigate your employees."

"What does the temporary injunction mean?"

"It means they think your business is a menace and so dangerous that the court should shut it down immediately until such time as a trial can be held so that a judge can hear the arguments and decide whether—" she ticked off on one finger "—you reopen the business, or—" she touched another finger "—you stay closed permanently."

"If we should get closed down, how long before a trial?"

"A good question. It could be months. I don't think any business could stand that."

Raul's face blanched. "No. I'd miss too many contract deadlines. That would ruin me."

"And that, dear brother," she said with a wink, "is why I don't intend to let them win on their motion next week. So we've got a busy time ahead of us." She smiled, her air of confidence creating a feeling of confidence in him that she could do what she set out to do. For the first time since he'd been served with the papers that morning, Raul managed to take a deep breath and relax.

Ashley was relieved to see the tension ease in his face. She walked him to the door. "See what kind of information you can get for us, then quit worrying about it. Remember, you've turned it over to your lawyer now, so let me do the worrying. That's what you pay me for."

Raul stepped out of the office, then turned back to say, "Now I can see the advantages of having a lawyer in the family, Ashley. You're going to be one of our greatest assets." Ashley could feel her face flush. What a thing to say in front of her secretary. He was almost as bad as Rafe. "And you turn such pretty colors too. A really unusual addition, that's for sure." He walked down the hall laughing as Ashley smiled sheepishly at her secretary and dived for her office.

By the time Ashley got home that evening she was too excited to sleep. Rafe would be flying in sometime the next day. She decided to start reading the Robert Ludlum book she'd purchased some time ago. She would probably be sleepy after a couple of chapters. Wrong! Midnight found her in bed, propped up with pillows, avidly turning pages. Tasha perched herself on the pillow next to Ashley. The predicted rain had started in the afternoon, which had made her walk home a little damp but sounded very soothing as it tapped a merry rhythm on her bedroom windows.

The book had her total concentration, so she didn't hear the car drive up the rain-slicked street until it pulled into her drive and stopped. She lowered the book and checked the clock. It was after midnight.

The doorbell rang as she tugged on her warm housecoat and fished for her slippers. It rang again as she trotted down the hall. "Who is it?"

"Rafe."

She fumbled for the chain, yanking it away as she turned the handle of the door. She threw open the door and flew into his arms. "What are you doing here?"

The impact of her body knocked him back a pace or two, his arms instinctively holding her to him. "I thought I'd find you asleep this late at night. Is something wrong?"

She grabbed his hand and pulled him into the darkened house, the glow of the lamp from her bedroom providing enough light for them to see.

"I'm all right," she said with a hint of impatience, "but how come you're here early?" She led him into the bedroom, turned, and for the first time saw him in full light. Lines of weariness were etched across his face. "Rafe! What's happened?"

"Nothing's happened." He shrugged out of his jacket and pulled her back into his arms. "I just couldn't stand not seeing you for another day. I was in another interminable meeting today, listening as they cussed and discussed, and I realized that I no longer cared what happened." He pulled her closer, his hands wandering up and down her back, hungry for the feel of her. "So I got up, told them politely that I had to leave but would be in touch, then walked out to the car and started driving."

"You *drove* up here?" She couldn't believe it. "That's a good twelve-hour drive."

He gave her an endearing grin. "Well, I made it in better time than that, but you're right, it's a long drive." He started kissing her cheek and ear. "And I haven't been able to sleep for wanting you." His kiss left her in no doubt that she'd been needed. She felt so complete when he was holding her. The past few weeks had been tough for her and obviously for Rafe too. She'd never seen him look so drawn. He'd lost weight and there were deep circles under his eyes. "Oh, Rafe, what have you been doing to yourself?"

"Just trying to get back up here to you," he murmured, his hands finding the tie of her housecoat and pulling it open. He couldn't seem to touch her enough.

She pulled away from him. "Are you hungry? Can I fix you something to eat?"

His eyes seemed to be almost glazed. "I'm more thirsty than anything."

"Let me get you something, then. Are you sure you don't want a sandwich?" She unbuttoned his shirt and pulled it off his shoulders, then pushed him onto the bed.

"I don't care. A sandwich is fine." He lay back across the bed with a luxurious sigh. "I never knew a bed could feel so good." He lay there with his eyes closed.

Ashley rushed into the kitchen, prepared a sandwich in record time, poured a large glass of milk, put them on a tray, and dashed into the bedroom with the tray. Rafe was sprawled across the bed, asleep. He'd taken his socks and shoes off, but his pants were only unsnapped at the waist. Tasha sat next to his shoulder, studying him with feline interest.

"So what do you think? Shall we keep him?" she asked Tasha. She set the tray down and worked his pants down his hips and legs. Rafe was a dead weight as she pushed and pulled him over to one side of the bed, then managed to pull the covers up over him.

She looked at the glass of milk, the sandwich, and the book on the bedside table. Then she looked at Rafe. He'd been trying to kill himself, she thought. Nothing was worth that.

She crawled back into bed with a smile, picked up the book, and continued to read, this time eating Rafe's sandwich and sipping his glass of milk.

Ashley finished the book a little after two. During that time, Rafe had not moved. She'd never seen a person sleep so soundly. *He must be exhausted.* For that matter, so was she. She glared at the book resting on the nightstand. She should have known better! Turning off the light, she curled up to Rafe's back. He was home at last.

Sometime during the night Rafe turned over and pulled Ashley into the curl of his body. He woke up and found her in his arms. She looked like a young girl, her hair spread across the pillows, a contented smile on her face.

Should he wake her? He knew she needed her rest, but the temptation was more than he could resist.

With a very light touch, Rafe ran his hand down her side from her ribs to the hollow of her waist, then over the curve of her hip. His hand slowed as it reached her thigh and began to drift inward. She leaned back into his warm body, then turned her head. Slowly lifting heavy eyelids, she murmured, "Good morning."

"It certainly is," he whispered and turned her more completely toward him. Her silken skin caused his hand to tremble as he caressed the hills and valleys of her body, warm from the covers. Her hands began their own exploration, reacquainting themselves with his body, which she was beginning to know as well as her own.

Rafe pulled the covers from her, wanting to enjoy the sight of her lying there waiting for him. He started placing kisses on her shoulder, then slid his mouth down to the breast waiting for his possession. His mouth covered the tip and he began to tease the nipple until Ashley could feel the reaction in her innermost body.

She reached for him but he resisted the pull of her arms as he began to taste her body. She remembered several ways to get his attention. Her hand softly stroked him, causing his flesh to quiver.

"Ashley," he groaned. As she continued to glide her hands over him, Rafe pulled her to him roughly. Their need proved greater than their patience, their merging more volcanic than gentle, more intense than pleasurable, their striving for unity more necessary than the ultimate fulfillment, but in that striving and seeking they were fortunate, and found it all.

The persistent ringing of the phone cut through the mists of sleep and Ashley felt for the phone by the bed.

"Hello?" Her voice sounded groggy.

"Good afternoon!" Jeanine bubbled. "Something tells me that Rafe has arrived. Sorry if I woke you from your nap." She didn't sound in the least sorry. She sounded more as though she were trying not to laugh.

Rafe stirred, then opened one eye.

"I'm calling to see if you and Rafe would like to come over for dinner."

"I'm not sure what this fireball of energy has planned, if anything. Shall I ask him?"

Jeanine chuckled. "By all means."

Turning to Rafe, Ashley explained. "Jeanine wants to know if we'd like to come over for dinner. She probably thinks I haven't planned much." She'd be right, for that matter. Eating was not on her list of priorities when Rafe was home. She reached over and brushed the hair away from his forehead.

He groaned and closed his eye. Ashley ran a hand through her hair and looked at the clock. It was after one o'clock. She spoke into the phone. "I'm not sure I can interpret his groan right now, Jeanine. Why don't I call you back in a little while?" Rafe's head nodded into the pillow.

"No problem. We're going to be here and if you show up, I'll just throw on two more steaks."

Ashley placed the phone back on its stand. Rafe's hand began to move along her ribcage and over her stomach.

"I thought you were asleep." They were still in the same position they'd been in when they fell asleep, legs intertwined, Rafe's arm under her neck.

"I am." His eyes remained closed.

"At least I'll bet your arm is asleep. I must have cut off the circulation." She sat up and gingerly moved his arm.

"Ow! You're right. My fingers are numb." He moved them tentatively; one eye opened to watch.

Ashley managed to prop herself up on a pillow. She couldn't remember when she'd last slept so well. Rafe was much better than a sleeping pill.

She glanced down at the man lying beside her. "So what do you want to do?"

Both eyes opened and watched her for a moment. "I'm not sure. What sort of entertainment can you provide if we stay here?" His mouth turned up at the corners. She got off the bed, then glanced back at the sprawled male in her bed.

"Darned if I know. My entertainment director took the weekend off." She wandered into the bathroom and turned on the shower.

By the time she'd pinned up her hair, Rafe was already in the shower yelping as he tried to adjust the water flow. "My God, woman, doesn't this place run to hot water?"

Peeking into the shower, she laughed and said, "I knew I forgot to pay something. Must have been one of the utilities." The water was pleasantly warm when Ashley stepped in and grabbed the soap. Filling the washcloth with suds, she began to scrub the wide back before her. She heard a purr of pleasure. Then she stroked down over the startling white skin on his slim hips. "When I first met you I wondered if you were naturally bronzed all over." He turned around and tugged the washcloth from her hand.

"Disappointed?" His voice roughened as he began to cover her breasts and shoulders with soap.

"Nope. I'm rather impressed, actually." Her eyes were twinkling as she looked at him demurely from beneath her lashes.

He handed her back the soap and washcloth. "Since you started this, you might as well do my front, too." A definite gleam appeared in his eyes. From this angle Ashley noted that his body had been stimulated by the shower—or something.

"Maybe I'd better let you do your own washing," she muttered as she vigorously soaped his chest and shoulders. "Here, you do the rest." She handed the cloth back to him and grabbed for the soap.

"Oh, no, that's not fair. You got to wash me, now it's my turn." He began to ease the washcloth over her body in long, nerve-tingling strokes, starting at her shoulders and slowly sliding down to her thighs. Ashley's response was all Rafe could have wanted. She gazed up at him, her eyelids heavy with desire, then she reached up to kiss him as his arms came around her.

"Oh, Rafe—"

It was several hours before she returned Jeanine's call to tell her that they would be over.

The rain that had started on Friday continued through the weekend. It was the steady, soaking rain that was so much a part of the fall and winter months in the Pacific Northwest. The rain tapping on the windowpanes provided a counterpoint to the spirited conversation around the dining table at Raul and Jeanine's. The impending lawsuit was the topic.

Raul told Rafe and Ashley the results of the investigation of his employees.

"I'm very much afraid James Jackson is involved in the accident," Raul said.

Rafe looked up from his plate. "But James has been your plant manager for the past five years. What would make you suspect him, of all people?"

"Nothing concrete, I'm afraid. Just a general attitude of surliness where there hadn't been one before—a defensiveness that seems out of character."

"Do you think he's the one who set up the accident, or that he knows who did?"

"I haven't a clue. Either way, it would end his career with us." He glanced at Ashley. "My counselor keeps telling me not to worry—that's what I pay her to do." He grinned, his resemblance to Rafe intensifying.

Rafe's eyes rested on Ashley with a warmth that caused her to shift in her chair. "So what do you think, counselor? Can we win this one?"

"We're going to do our best. The company's clean record over the past several years is a point in our favor. What we really need to do is to prove that the spill was, in fact, engineered. Why would one of your employees sabotage you like that?"

"That's what I can't figure out." Raul refilled their wineglasses as Jeanine took their plates into the kitchen. "I can't figure the motive. If we're forced to shut down, who would benefit from it? Certainly not the employees."

Ashley spoke thoughtfully. "Who *would* benefit if you were shut down?"

Jeanine returned to the room and volunteered, "Well, Tysinger probably wouldn't benefit from it, but he would certainly be glad to hear that we lost our business."

As a result of their report, Tysinger had been indicted along with several others and was awaiting trial for taking bribes to protect the marijuana growers. The investigation had uncovered several million dollars worth of marijuana.

"Could Tysinger be behind something like this, Ashley?" Jeanine asked.

"If he is, it would be tough to prove. I'm sure he wouldn't allow himself to be directly involved."

Rafe mentioned a possibility. "It might be worth checking out the activities of that guy Tysinger sent to get Raul—you remember, Pete Wilson. What do you think?"

"I think any idea is worth pursuing at this point," Ashley responded. "The hearing is set for this coming Friday. We don't have much time."

"Will you be here on Friday, Rafe?" Raul's question was one Ashley had wanted to ask, but she wasn't sure she wanted to hear his answer.

Rafe sat there for a moment, mentally reviewing his schedule. "There's a possibility I could get away Thursday night, but I'd have to turn around and go back on Saturday." He looked over at Ashley with a question in his eyes. She smiled her response. Whenever he could make it would be fine. "I've never seen Ashley in action. This should prove interesting."

Ashley overslept the next morning, having forgotten to set her alarm. If Tasha hadn't awakened her by sitting on her chest and licking her nose, she might have spent the day asleep.

My hectic weeks and sleepless weekends are beginning to catch up with me, she decided as she forced herself out of bed and under the shower. She smiled as she remembered that she and Rafe had managed to get some sleep over the weekend, but at rather odd hours. By the time she arrived in the kitchen, Rafe had coffee made and was carrying on one of his many conversations with Tasha, who sat on a chair next to him and listened while he kept an eye on the frying bacon.

Without a word Ashley padded over, sat down on his lap, and buried her head in his neck. He smelled so good. His aftershave lotion should be banned from the market, she thought. It was alluring enough to create riots. Rafe took the opportunity to kiss her exposed neck, which caused chills to run down her body. They smelled the burning bacon at the same time. Rafe jumped to his feet, almost causing Ashley to fall flat on her bottom. As she scrambled to get her balance, he attempted to rescue their breakfast.

"I wish you'd warn me when you're going to make sudden moves like that," she complained.

He was busy placing fresh strips of bacon in the skillet and gave her a brief glance over his shoulder. "Sorry, I seem to be out of practice on how to treat a woman." His grin contradicted the serious tone of voice.

She decided to ignore the comment and began to prepare orange juice and toast. She tried not to cling to him when he was ready to leave, and her only comfort was the work waiting for her when he was gone. She hoped he would be able to make it back on Thursday. As the days went by Ashley had the same thought more than once.

The investigator's supplemental report on James Jackson turned up some interesting news about his son that Ashley thought might be the clue they were looking for, but it was a long shot. As the week progressed, it became obvious to her that it was the only chance they had. If she could prove in court that the suit had been filed in order to strike back at the McCords, she had a good chance of getting the case dismissed. Unfortunately, the burden of proof for that allegation fell on her. The only way she could prove it would be to get Jackson on the stand and force him to admit that he had deliberately caused the spill. Could she do it? Would the judge allow it? Would opposing counsel stand for it? She didn't know, but she could see no other way to win Raul the time needed to fulfill his company's contracts.

At that point in her hectic week, Ashley received a phone call that wiped all thoughts of her profession from her mind. Her doctor's office was calling to report on the tests they'd run the week before. "Your test was positive," a nurse told her cheerfully. "You're pregnant."

Ashley replaced the phone in a state of shock. Pregnant. Of course they had done nothing to prevent it from happening, but somehow she hadn't expected it. Once more she wished for Rafe's presence. This was one piece of news she couldn't tell him over the phone. They had never discussed a family, but she knew he would make an excellent father. It was herself that she was unsure of. What did she know about babies? Could she cope with a family and a career? She really needed Rafe's comforting at the moment.

When the phone rang the second time, Ashley felt immune to any further shocks.

It was Ralph Begley and he wanted to see her. Mystified—she hadn't talked with him since their meeting months before—she waited to hear what was on his mind. It wasn't long in coming.

"I understand that you agreed to represent a new client for us: McCord Industries?"

Puzzled, Ashley replied, "That's right, sir. They were served with papers last week and asked me to represent them."

"I see." Begley sat back in his large overstuffed chair, his fingers drumming on the arm. "Isn't that your husband's name?"

"Yes, sir." She smiled pleasantly.

"Does he hold some interest in the company?" Begley's eyes were cold.

"No, he doesn't. The firm is owned and operated by Raul McCord, my husband's brother." She waited, knowing he'd get to the purpose of his questions sooner or later.

A sigh escaped Begley, and his jaw seemed to set. "You know, Ashley, I recognize that you're a relative newcomer to this area." He paused, making sure he had her undivided attention. "Maybe you aren't aware of just how high feelings run against these big companies that have pushed their way into our area from California. It's not enough that they've destroyed the air and water down there so nobody can live in it." Once again he paused as though keeping a tight rein on his emotions. "Now they're trying to turn Oregon into the same kind of wasteland." His look dared Ashley to refute his statements.

She sat quietly, waiting for him to continue.

"Our firm has been very careful not to support any particular faction involved in the environmental dispute. We have to be nonpartisan. We're here to provide a service to our clients, but we, ourselves, don't take sides. But then, you already know that, don't you?"

"Yes, sir."

He leaned forward in his chair, his expression hard.

"I don't want you handling the case."

A tiny gasp escaped from Ashley. "Mr. Begley, the hearing is set to take place in two days."

"Yes, well, I want you to tell McCord you can't represent him, that this firm cannot represent him." His statement rang with finality.

"But what reason can I possibly give for doing that, sir?" she asked.

"Conflict of interest."

"What conflict of interest, Mr. Begley?"

Astonishment rolled across Begley's face like a cloud crossing the sun. Nobody argued with this man, not members of the firm, anyway. "I just explained to you, Ashley. We do not represent any California companies that move up here and pollute our air and water supplies."

"Mr. Begley, sir... In the first place, no one has proved that that's what McCord Industries is doing. After going into all the facts during the past few days, I have found no evidence to support the charges against them. There has been only one incident of contamination since they opened, and I don't think it was an accident."

"Fine. Then let someone else represent them. They shouldn't have any trouble finding legal representation elsewhere."

"But, Mr. Begley," she implored, "I've already accepted the case and prepared for it. No one else could possibly give adequate representation with less than two days to prepare." She could not believe that he would close his mind to the ethical considerations involved in suddenly refusing to represent a client without adequate cause.

Begley's expression pinned Ashley to her chair much like a butterfly to a board. "You are too closely involved to give objective counseling. You should never have accepted the case in the first place." He glanced at his watch. "I have an appointment now, Ashley. I'm afraid I don't have time for further discussion."

Ashley nodded and stood up, staring at Ralph Begley as though she'd never seen him before. She had her orders. It was up to her to carry them out.

Chapter Nine

By the time Ashley reached her office she was shaking so much she could barely stand. Withdraw from the case. How simple that sounded. Such an easy command to make, but how could she drop Raul's case two days before trial? Her integrity was at stake.

She needed to get away, to come to grips with the pain she was feeling. Thank God she'd kept her afternoon clear of appointments.

Ashley escaped from the office and drove to Washington Park. Perched high on one of the western hills, the park directly overlooked Portland. Its rose garden was one of her favorite places in the city. Although the air was cool there was no wind, and she found the garden deserted.

She wandered through the roses and finally settled on a bench that gave a clear view of the city. Images from the past began to drift across her mind. She remembered her father's shock when she first informed him that she wanted to become a lawyer and her mother's quiet support of Ashley's desire to go out in the world. She remembered the hours of study during her pre-law courses, the grueling hours spent in law school, and her single-minded efforts to build a career during the past five years. How ironic that the career she sought to save by a hasty marriage now threatened that same marriage.

Ashley had reached a point in her life when she had to make a choice. The news of her pregnancy caused an upsurge of unfamiliar feelings. She had never given much thought to having a family. If she had, she would have pictured herself in the role her mother had chosen, but Rafe had taught her so much about relationships. She and Rafe were entirely different from her own parents, and in her heart Ashley knew that she could depend on Rafe's loving support to help raise their child. Now that the shock had worn off, she was becoming excited about her pregnancy, wondering whether she would have a miniature Rafe, knowing she would love his child.

Over the months, Ashley's life had moved into a new dimension of love and fulfillment. Rafe had given her so much and had asked for so little in return.

She also acknowledged that, regardless of who a client was, she could not in clear conscience refuse to represent that client so close to the date of the hearing. It was not fair to the client or to the attorney who would attempt to replace her. Her professional integrity was now on the line.

As she began to weigh her options she knew she had no choice, professionally or personally. Ralph Begley had delivered his ultimatum. By ignoring it, she knew she forfeited all chances of being made a partner. Her very job would be at stake.

A cool breeze finally interrupted Ashley's concentration, and she realized that she'd been sitting in one position for hours. It was time to go home. The phone was ringing when she walked into her house. Throwing her coat and purse at a chair, she grabbed the receiver.

"Hello?" she said in a breathless voice.

"Ashley? What's wrong?" Rafe sounded so close that he could have been in the next room. Oh, how she wished he were. Unexpected tears flowed. She bit her lip, trying to regain control of herself.

"Nothing's wrong, Rafe. I just rushed to get the phone." Her voice had a definite wobble in it, but perhaps he would attribute the sound to the long-distance line.

"I thought I'd let you know I'm going to be able to manage that quick trip to Oregon. Can you pick me up at the airport Thursday night at nine?"

"You know better than to ask that question. You'll recognize me when you get off the plane. I'll be the one doing handsprings along the concourse."

He was still laughing when they hung up. Rafe was coming. Life suddenly looked a great deal brighter. She wasn't sure how she'd broach the subject of her pregnancy. Perhaps she would wait until the hearing was behind her. She might have to tell him she was not only pregnant but metaphorically barefoot, or at least unemployed. She was already recovering from the shock of Begley's demand and realized she wasn't as upset as she would have been a year earlier. Begley, Henderson & Howe wasn't the only law office in town. She had built a reputation that would enable her to find another position. Rafe and the baby were more important concerns in her life at the moment.

She could hardly wait to see Rafe's reaction to the news of the impending arrival.

Flight 287 from San Francisco arrived on time. Ashley felt certain she couldn't have survived the wait much longer. Her face glowing, she watched as each person stepped through the door of the plane. Rafe's face lit up when he spotted her. When he reached her he pulled her into his arms, kissing her passionately as he crushed her body against his.

She managed to pull away from him, her face flushed and her eyes sparkling. "Rafe—" she glanced around quickly "—everybody's watching! Despite rumor to the contrary, not *every* trial lawyer is an exhibitionist." The look he gave her caused her color to turn a deeper shade of pink. He'd mentally stripped her and made love to her with his eyes. She found him irresistible when he was in this mood, and she had trouble keeping her hands away from him until they could reach the car.

He'd carried one bag on the plane, so they went directly to the car in the parking lot. After throwing the bag in the back, Rafe slid into the front seat next to her and then turned to her. "I don't dare start kissing you here, or we'll get arrested before I finish."

She leaned over and kissed him on the cheek. "There. Hopefully that will hold you until we get home." She batted her eyelashes with coy bashfulness.

"Not very likely, but I'll try to contain myself."

As Rafe found change to pay the parking fee, Ashley managed to move a little closer to him and rested her hand on his thigh. She could feel his muscles flex while he tried to ignore her. She didn't help matters by stroking his leg with a feather touch.

"Enough!" he growled as he grabbed her hand. He moved it back to her lap, where his hand lingered, finding that he had access to various areas belonging to Ashley.

"Not fair, Rafe," she remonstrated as she wriggled in her seat.

"I'm glad to know you agree with me. Now behave yourself." He flashed her a smile that reminded her of why she'd married him in the first place. *They were worse than a couple of teenagers who couldn't keep their hands away from each other.* Ashley grinned at the thought. Somehow she had missed that part of growing up, but she was glad she had waited to share it with Rafe.

Tasha greeted them at the door and, when she saw Rafe, marched over to him and welcomed him with a purr and a soft caress of her back against his leg. Tasha never did that to anyone, not even Ashley.

"I don't believe this. What have you done to my cat?"

He carried his bag into the bedroom. "I haven't done anything."

Ashley watched as Tasha followed him into the room and jumped onto his suitcase. He reached down and massaged behind her ears and under her chin. "She's just being sociable."

"I find it disgusting. Why, she's practically slobbering all over you."

He grinned. "Yes, she is, isn't she?"

"You insufferable egotist." She grabbed him around his neck, pulling herself up so that her mouth could meet his. She put all the endless longing she'd felt since he'd left three days before into her kiss. He was most cooperative in returning her offering. At last Ashley managed to pull away from him and rubbed her head under his chin. "I'm forced to admit that I admire her taste," she said with a defeated sigh.

Rafe had eaten on the plane, so they wasted no time in going to bed. As Rafe pulled her into his arms, he asked, "Should I call Raul and let him know I'm here?"

"I told him you would be. He seemed relieved." They lay there in contented silence for a moment; then Rafe whispered, "Are you going to sleep?" The soft words tickled her ear.

"Not very likely, with you lying next to me in 'that' condition," she pointed out as her hand gently touched him.

"I can't tell from that comment whether you're bragging or complaining." His tongue touched her ear, causing her to shiver.

She moved so that she was above him, her hair falling around her shoulders and brushing against his chest. She began to kiss him just under his jaw—soft little kisses that caused the surface of his skin to quiver. She moved down his chest, kissing first one nipple, which hardened as she lingered to stroke it with her tongue, then moving lazily across his broad chest to the other one.

Rafe's groan was music to her ears. Between her hair brushing against his sensitive skin and her mouth and tongue touching him with delicate skill, his body began to tremble. So much for bragging or complaining. Her tongue darted along his ribs, tracing them faithfully, then it paused for further exploration around his navel.

"Ashley!" Rafe's hands came up and encircled her waist. He lifted her so that her hips came down upon him in perfect symmetry. She could feel the tremor through him as their bodies and spirits intermingled in an embrace, forming a unity and a communion.

She began to move on him, accelerating the pace until both of them became caught up in the rhythm and flow of their lovemaking. His hands reached to restrain her abandoned movements, but it was too late—the force of their tempestuous pace swept them both far out from shore, and the frenzied and frantic feeling of moments before rolled and tossed them on sensuous waves, until they once again were washed up on the shore of fulfillment.

Both were damp from their loving exertions, and Ashley's hair clung to her brow and across one cheek. Rafe clutched her in his arms, reluctant to allow her to pull away from him in this moment of total sharing and undiminished joy. Never had she responded to him with such openness and abandonment.

Rafe could feel her heart fluttering like a bird captured and afraid. He began to soothe her overheated body with his hand, easing down the length of her back and up over her derriere. Ashley had become the focal point of his existence—his love was almost frightening in its intensity. He drifted off to sleep, a smile hovering on his face.

When Rafe's eyes opened it was daylight, and Ashley stood by the bed watching him. He was startled to find her dressed and ready to leave. She bent over the bed and kissed him.

"I've got to go, love. There's coffee and fresh orange juice made." She smiled as she witnessed his bewilderment. "I need to get to the office early—there's so much to be done." She cocked her head. "You know, I rather like to see you asleep in my bed. It's seldom I'm ever awake before you," she added with an impish smile.

Turning to go, she paused. "The hearing starts at ten, so if I don't see you before—" she gave a half salute "—I'll see you in court."

Rafe looked at the clock by the bed. Seven-thirty. He hadn't heard the alarm or felt her stir—he'd been more tired than he realized. Maybe it had something to do with coming home to relax. He didn't sleep as well anymore in his comfortable condominium in San Francisco, although he'd been quite pleased with all it had to offer until he met Ashley. She'd managed to ruin his sleeping habits as well as disturb the even tenor of his bachelor existence. She had a lot to answer for, that woman!

He felt a movement on the bed and watched Tasha as she picked her way across to the pillow Ashley had deserted.

"I'm sorry, Tash, ole girl, you'll never be able to take her place, but I suppose you can stay." The cat gave him a lazy stare, then sat down and proceeded to bathe. "You're not easily intimidated, are you?" His rhetorical question remained unanswered as he headed for the shower.

Around nine-thirty Ashley developed an unexpected case of nerves, a problem she'd overcome early in her career. But then this case wasn't typical. And she wasn't at all confident that she could win it. It would be bad enough to lose her job; to lose the hearing as well would be a double blow.

She was glad of the interruption when her secretary buzzed to say that Raul had arrived. As they walked to the courthouse he teased Ashley about Rafe using the hearing as an excuse to come back to see her.

"He doesn't need an excuse, you idiot," she said, laughing at the idea.

"He says he's afraid you'll get tired of him hanging around all the time if he visits too frequently." He shook his head. "I've never known Rafe to be as unsure of himself as he is with you. A lesser man would probably be intimidated."

"Now that I will never believe." She smiled up at the man walking alongside her. "You won't ever convince me that Rafe doesn't recognize his own worth."

They made their way through the echoing halls of the marble courthouse and entered the empty courtroom. Ashley wasn't surprised—they were a few minutes early.

The opposing counsel appeared and, nodding to Ashley, began to lay his papers out on the desk. She and Raul moved to the defense table and she began to arrange her papers for presentation. Neither attorney had requested a jury trial, and there were no visitors to the courtroom. Ashley kept glancing over her shoulder, watching for Rafe. He had not yet arrived when the bailiff stepped into the room from the judge's chambers and announced, "All rise as the Multnomah County Circuit Court is called to order, the Honorable Jed Downing presiding."

With no fanfare and in a steady voice, the plaintiff's attorney presented his client's case to the judge. The man knew what he was doing. He had constructed a tight case from circumstantial evidence. She had to convince the judge there were other, more reasonable ways to view the issue.

The plaintiff's attorney presented dates, figures, and diagrams that, according to him, proved the case against McCord Industries. Then he called several witnesses who were employees of the company. Ashley noted their restlessness on the stand and their uneasiness whenever they were forced to answer questions they were afraid were harmful to the company. With each witness she limited her cross-examination to how they felt about working at the plant. Did they feel it was safe? Did they consider the way in which waste materials were handled a hazard? She waited for Jackson to be called as a witness and was not disappointed.

Jackson appeared to be in his late forties. He was a tall, stoop-shouldered man with a receding hairline. He sat quietly in the witness chair, his eyes trained on the plaintiff's attorney.

When her turn came to cross-examine, Ashley took her time approaching the witness. After the opposing attorney had sat down, Jackson seemed to have trouble knowing what to do with his hands. His demeanor was similar to that of a penitent schoolboy having to face the principal.

At that point, Rafe entered the courtroom and slipped into the last row of visitors' chairs, but Ashley was unaware of his arrival. Rafe recognized Jackson, having seen him at the plant, but the man had aged considerably since then. A likable man, but at the moment he appeared ill at ease. Rafe didn't imagine anyone would feel comfortable on the witness stand, regardless of the person's guilt or innocence. He found the courtroom atmosphere stifling.

Ashley proceeded with her cross-examination as Rafe sat back to watch.

"Mr. Jackson." Ashley spoke in a low, clear voice. "You have stated that you were in charge of the production line at the time the spill in question took place, is that correct?"

His eyes flickered to the other attorney, then to her. "Yes." His answer was scarcely audible.

The judge leaned forward from his position above the witness. "You will have to speak up, Mr. Jackson, so that the court reporter can hear you." The judge gave the witness a reassuring smile.

Jackson cleared his throat and nodded. Raising his voice, he repeated: "Yes."

"Who besides yourself had authority to enter the area where the spill occurred, Mr. Jackson?"

He mumbled an answer.

The judge spoke once again. "Mr. Jackson, you must speak up. None of us can hear you." His voice was not quite as pleasant as it had been.

"The two floor supervisors."

"I see." Ashley paused, wondering how to get the next question answered without opposing counsel raising an objection.

"How well do you know Pete Wilson, Mr. Jackson?" She watched as the color faded from Jackson's face, leaving him parchment white. Whether he answered the question or not, she knew she had him!

"Objection, Your Honor. The question is irrelevant to the proceedings."

The judge eyed Ashley. "Does Pete Wilson have some connection to the spill being discussed, Ms. Allison?"

"It is my strong belief that he does, sir." The opposing counsel looked bewildered, and she knew the Department of Environmental Quality had no idea what was involved in the case.

"Objection overruled. The witness may answer the question," the judge stated.

Jackson looked ill; his skin had turned a pasty color. Perspiration dotted his forehead. He looked at the other attorney, then back to Ashley. With head bowed and shoulders slumped, he said, "I hardly know him at all."

"But he knew about your son, didn't he, Mr. Jackson?"

"Objection, Your Honor," came from the other attorney. "This is the most irregular line of questioning I've ever witnessed in a courtroom."

"Ms. Allison," the judge stated in a weary tone, "I hardly see that Mr. Jackson's son has anything to do with the matter presented for hearing today. What is your point?"

"My point, Your Honor, is that I believe Mr. Jackson knows more about the spill than he has admitted. I believe that he can explain why it happened and that his involvement is the result of pressure brought to bear on him. I believe Mr. Jackson's actions on the day of the spill are directly related to an attempt to protect his son."

The other attorney watched Ashley with amazement. When he could speak, he said, "Your Honor, I believe Ms. Allison is the victim of too much late-night television, sir. That has to be the most ridiculous plot anyone could have dreamed up. Creative, perhaps, but it has no place in a court of law."

The judge sat with bowed head for a moment, then nodded. "Continue with your cross-examination."

Ashley felt relief seeping through her system. One hurdle passed. Now, if she could get the answers she needed... She returned to the witness. "Mr. Jackson, is your twenty-five-year-old son presently employed?"

"Yes."

"Where?"

"The Port of Portland."

"When your son filled out his job application at the Port of Portland, did he report his drug conviction on the application?"

Jackson paled. She knew he had tried to protect his son, but at the expense of McCord Industries. She felt sorry for him, but her feelings did not stop her from trying to get the information she needed. "No."

"If the Port knew about the false application, he'd lose his job, wouldn't he, Mr. Jackson?"

"Yes." Once again his answers were almost inaudible but, because of the silence in the courtroom, his words rang out clearly.

In a very gentle tone Ashley asked, "What did Pete Wilson say to you, Mr. Jackson, when he approached you about causing an accident in the plant?"

"Objection, Your Honor!" The opposing counsel's face glowed with anger. "Counsel is leading the witness. There is absolutely no evidence in this hearing that anyone approached anyone to cause the spill in question."

"Sustained. Please rephrase the question."

"What did Pete Wilson say to you when he first approached you, Mr. Jackson?"

"He said he knew my son had straightened himself out. He knew he was married and they were expecting a baby, and he was sure I wouldn't want to see him lose his new position."

"That was all?"

He looked at her with something like pity at her naive question.

"That was enough."

"What did you do to cause the spill, Mr. Jackson?"

In a trembling voice, Jackson told the court that he had slipped into the production area and wedged a piece of wood in one of the ducts that drained waste chemicals, knowing the flow would hit the wood and begin to splash over the drain. By the time anyone noticed, the chemicals were pouring onto the floor and draining away through the outside doorways. The spill succeeded in reaching the Sandy River, contaminating it; the incident was immediately reported to the Department of Environmental Quality.

"Did Mr. Wilson tell you why he wanted you to cause the spill?"

"No. I didn't ask."

"Thank you, Mr. Jackson." She looked at the judge. "No further questions, Your Honor."

The judge nodded. "The witness is excused."

The plaintiff's counsel approached the bench. "Your Honor, the Department of Environmental Quality does not use intimidation, blackmail, or other coercion to get evidence of the nature presented in this law suit." He paused and glanced at the defense table where Ashley and Raul sat, then back to the judge. "We have more reports of violations each day than we can possibly investigate. We are not out to persecute, Your Honor; we're here to protect."

He walked to his table, picked up some papers, and walked back to the bench. "The exhibit that has been entered into the record states on its face that McCord Industries has not met the standards set to contain and control contaminating waste products. I feel we have proven that today. No one has denied the spill in question. The contaminants that polluted the Sandy River destroyed fish, polluted the water supply of a rather large area, and caused injury to undetermined numbers of wildlife and game. As stated in my motion, I believe McCord Industries should be shut down immediately, and upon trial of this matter, we will prove that the plant constitutes a threat to its environmental surroundings and should be closed on a permanent basis." He moved to his table and sat down.

Ashley approached the bench. "Your Honor, I believe there has been enough testimony to show a preponderance of evidence that one violation of murky origin is not sufficient reason to warrant closing the McCord Industries plant, either on a temporary or on a permanent basis. We respectfully request that the motion be denied and the case dismissed." Ashley returned to her chair.

The judge spoke to the plaintiff's counsel. "Am I correct in assuming that you have no evidence that might support your allegations that McCord Industries is hazardous to the environment other than the one incident discussed today?"

"That's correct, sir."

"In that case I see no reason to prolong a decision on this matter. I find for the defendant. Case dismissed."

The judge stood as the bailiff intoned, "All rise. The Multnomah County Circuit Court, the Honorable Jed Downing presiding, is dismissed."

Raul turned around and grabbed Ashley in a bear hug. "You did it! You cleared us! You were fantastic!"

Ashley blushed at Raul's affectionate enthusiasm but shared his relief that matters had turned out so well. Raul added, "I've got to call Jeanine and tell her the news. I'll talk to you later." She watched him rush down the aisle—and spotted Rafe. He was sitting in the back row next to the door, but Raul dashed by without noticing him. Ashley made quick work of placing papers back in her briefcase and hurried to Rafe, who stood up at her approach.

"I didn't see you come in, Rafe. I'm glad you made it. Did you see the whole hearing?"

Rafe's face masked his thoughts. "I came in just as Jackson took the stand." He paused, an inscrutable expression in his eyes. "Congratulations."

"Is something wrong, Rafe?"

"Wrong? Of course not. You won your case, and as far as I can judge, you did an excellent job." Ashley could not tell anything from his expression. Whatever he thought, she wasn't going to find out now. She took his arm and started out the door. "Do you want to get a bite to eat?" Ashley led the way to the stairway and started down the steps; Rafe kept pace with her.

"I can't. I have to call California as soon as I get back to the house. I had to cut a call short or I wouldn't have made it when I did." He stopped as they reached the sidewalk. "I'll see you when you get home."

Ashley found it difficult to respond in a natural voice. "Fine, I shouldn't be late." She watched him stride down the street as though eager to leave. *Don't be silly,* she admonished herself. *Just because he didn't grab you and kiss you passionately the way he did at the airport, you think your marriage is failing!*

She discovered that her instincts had been right when she arrived home. Rafe was waiting in the living room, his bag sitting near the door.

"I thought you weren't leaving until the morning?"

"I had to change my reservations. We've called an emergency meeting first thing tomorrow. I need to be there." He stood across the room from her, his body tense.

"It's more than a sudden business meeting, isn't it, Rafe?" she asked softly.

He looked at her as though he'd never seen her before, as though he was seeing a stranger who didn't impress him. Finally he answered, "Yes." He moved to the window and looked out, and she waited. A fluttering had begun in her stomach. "I've been thinking all afternoon about how slim the chances were that I'd ever see you in action, but the fact remains that I have."

"And?"

"And today, watching you excel in your profession, I realized that I don't even know the woman I married. It's quite possible that the woman I thought I married exists only in my imagination." He turned away from the window and moved back to her, studying her intently.

Ashley shook her head in confusion. "I'm afraid I don't understand."

He continued to study her. "It hit me today, Ashley, what it means—your being an attorney—a highly skilled trial lawyer with all the necessary killer instincts. I can understand your success—you go straight for the jugular."

The words he spoke spilled out into the quiet room and bounced around her. Ashley heard the sounds but had difficulty absorbing their meaning. Rafe continued to speak as though thinking aloud. "When I first met you I saw an attractive woman who stirred me as no other woman I'd ever met had, and I wanted you. I took unfair advantage of your lack of experience and caused you to want me." He moved toward her as though to touch her, then dropped his hand. "I had no concept of what the other part of you was like until today. I sat there and watched you, wondering what it would be like to have those skills turned against me. For a moment the thought shook me." His gaze wandered over her face and he frowned, noticing her lack of color for the first time.

Moving to the door, he leaned over and picked up his bag. "I'm hurting you, and God knows I don't want to do that. I think I'd better leave before I say any more."

She was surprised at how calm she sounded as she asked, "Would you like me to take you to the airport?"

He hesitated, glancing at his watch. "I'm afraid I've left it a little late to call a cab. Would you mind?" How polite he sounded.

"No. I had planned to, anyway."

Rafe drove. They were almost at the airport when he spoke.

"Ashley, I've got a lot of thinking to do, and I need some time. I've been driving myself—" he paused "—just as you have. I can see what it's doing to us. You shouldn't have to justify who and what you are to me. It's just that I'm not sure I can accept who you are at the moment."

"Do you want a divorce?"

"No!" Then he qualified the statement. "At least, not necessarily. I'm just facing the fact that marriage means more than legalizing our right to make love. I thought we had a similar value system, a similar outlook—"

"When did you decide that we don't?"

His face reflected the agony his thoughts were causing him as he pulled up in front of the airport. "When I saw you tear apart a man whose folly was in attempting to protect his son. Why, Ashley?" He was almost pleading. "Why was it so important to the case? Couldn't you have made the same point without dragging that poor man's most private pain out for everyone to see?"

"Rafe, I conducted the case in the only way I could if I wanted to win it." Her gaze remained steady. "I think you'd better catch your plane." One part of her noted his face go pale at her unemotional tone, and anguish showed in the blue depths of his eyes.

He got out of the car, and she moved over and looked at him for a moment through the open window. "Goodbye, Rafe." She then released the hand brake and drove off, refusing to glance into her rear-view mirror. The pain began to grow and spread through her body like flood water inching across a dam. "I mustn't think of him right now." Her voice sounded loud in the quiet car. "Think of other things, Ashley. You won the case. That was the important thing. You mustn't lose sight of your priorities. At least Raul was pleased with the outcome." She knew she'd done the only thing she could. "I wonder if winning will justify my ignoring Begley's orders."

Ashley knew that an attorney never entered a courtroom to lose, not if that attorney wanted a career as a trial attorney. She'd never faced how painful winning could be.

Chapter Ten

Ashley returned home. The house had never seemed so empty. She sat down on the sofa and stared into the cold fireplace, remembering the plans she'd made for the evening. She'd intended to prepare the only casserole she'd ever learned to make. The wine waited in the refrigerator. That, along with the candlelight and a small fire in the fireplace were to help set the mood for her news. Her sudden choked laugh sounded more like a sob.

Not telling him doesn't make him less a father, she reminded herself, *but for some reason I don't think the news would have helped matters tonight.* The awful thing, the thought that kept eating away at her, was that she couldn't blame Rafe for his reaction. Knowing his attitude toward attorneys, she should have been better prepared for it. As he had pointed out, he might never have seen her in a courtroom. With her career as uncertain as it was at the moment, and the added advent of motherhood, Ashley might have managed to practice on a limited basis and been the woman Rafe thought she was.

He was right. She wasn't that woman, but he'd made the woman he saw come alive within her, to begin to have meaning and substance to Ashley so that she wanted to become that warm, loving creature. She wanted to develop the emotional and loving side of her nature that had lain dormant within her.

Ashley began to notice the chill in the room. As she stood up, Tasha reminded her that she hadn't been fed but for once didn't make a federal case out of it. She followed Ashley into the kitchen and waited patiently for her meal. Rafe had even managed to transform Tasha.

As she climbed into bed, Ashley admitted to herself that she had reason to be exhausted. Her pregnancy notwithstanding, she'd had a traumatic day. Word would have reached Begley that Ashley had not withdrawn from representing McCord Industries. He would probably consider her win a final insult to his authority.

At long last her body's needs overcame her and she fell into a restless sleep, the scent of cedar haunting her dreams.

Ashley managed to retain a blessed feeling of numbness during the next few weeks. She waited for some word from Begley, but heard nothing.

One day at the office, when she'd been involved in depositions and had escaped to the restroom, she returned to hear a conversation between one of the attorneys of her firm and one of the opposing attorneys there for the depositions. She heard her name mentioned and paused. The opposing attorney was saying, "My God, Fred, that woman was a barracuda in depositions today. I've seen some aggressive women lawyers, but Allison is something else."

She waited, unsure of how to get past the door to the conference room without being seen when she heard the reply. "Oh, don't mind her, Jim. You know how these women lawyers are. They think they have to look tougher, act meaner, and hit harder than any man. She's a good lawyer, though. We're pleased to have her in the firm."

Their voices faded as they left the room through another door. She went into her office, ostensibly to check phone messages but in reality to regain her composure. Was that how others saw her? She'd been too busy learning how to practice law to be concerned about her image. She tried to shrug off the comments. They weren't all bad—more like backhanded compliments. It was good to hear that at least one member of the firm considered her an asset.

The following morning she woke up sobbing. Her dream still floated in her mind like a shroud. She'd been with Rafe and it was just like the first time she had awakened and found him kissing her. She'd been holding him close, stroking his face and shoulders, when in the dream he became Virgil Tysinger. He was saying, "So you're a lawyer, huh? You really know how to pick the barracudas, Rafe." She'd glanced behind her and saw Rafe standing there watching her, a look of disgust and distaste on his face. Her sobbing had followed her out of the dream and she woke up, facing the loneliness of her life. She cried until she was limp. Then she lay exhausted, her chest hurting from the great gulps of air she'd taken in an attempt to quell the dry sobs.

One morning in late November Ashley received an interoffice envelope marked "Confidential"—which could only mean its contents concerned an administrative matter. The wheels of justice might turn exceedingly slowly, but she knew they'd caught up with her. The message was a request that Ashley attend a partners' meeting scheduled for the following Tuesday at five-thirty.

Ashley arrived on time but was the last one to come into the room. She glanced around the conference table at the eleven men. *I wonder if this is how a condemned criminal feels,* she thought as they watched her take a seat. She placed her hands loosely in her lap and waited.

Ralph Begley spoke. "Thank you for joining us today, Ashley." He refused to meet her eyes, a sure sign that his news wasn't pleasant. "There are some matters we wish to discuss with you. We've been going over your record." He paused, looking down at his notes as if to confirm his facts. "Five years now, isn't it?"

Ashley nodded.

"We've been quite pleased with your contribution to the firm, Ashley."

Then why can't you look me in the eye when you speak to me? she wondered.

"You've been honest and straightforward with us," Begley continued, "and we've tried to work with you on the same level." He paused, then cleared his throat. He glanced around at the other men seated at the table. "A few weeks ago I had occasion to speak to you on a matter regarding what I felt to be a conflict of interest within our firm."

Ashley wondered why he was prolonging the meeting. Perhaps he derived some sort of pleasure from pointing out to his more liberal partners that he had been right in his reluctance to hire a woman attorney. *I've probably set the cause of hiring female attorneys in this firm back fifty years.* She mentally apologized to any would-be successors who would not understand the reason for their rejection.

"At that time—" Begley's voice began to sound hoarse as though he had to force his speech "—I strongly advised Ashley to turn her case over to someone else."

"Advised"? "Ordered" would be more accurate. She waited with no expression on her face.

"She did not do so."

Eleven pairs of eyes turned on Ashley as she sat there. *You would think I'd stolen the key to the executive men's room.*

"Our firm has never been faced with a situation quite like this one, and we've spent several weeks discussing what, if anything, should be done."

Ashley forced herself to meet his eyes, but he was having trouble sustaining the contact.

"Out of the several meetings that have been held regarding this issue, one point seems to remain outstanding. To be a part of the firm, it is necessary that each of us recognize the team effort it takes to make the firm successful. If we each start pulling in a different direction, we'll never move forward."

All right. The verdict was in—and she was out.

Begley paused and poured himself a glass of water from the decanter at his elbow. She was surprised to see how difficult he was finding it to tell her she was fired. She had an insane desire to do it for him, but she managed to restrain herself.

"Ashley." He paused, then cleared his throat. "It is my rather unpleasant task to inform you that in a unanimous vote the partnership has decided to request that you seek employment elsewhere."

There, that wasn't so bad, was it? She wanted to console him, then forced herself to face the fact that she'd just been fired from her first and only position as a lawyer. *Is this how shock feels?* She felt so differently than she had when Rafe left, perhaps because she'd already come to terms with this eventuality. At the moment all she could feel was a sense of relief that something definite had taken place. Now she could pick up the pieces and go on with her life.

All eyes were trained on her, and she realized with a start that they were waiting for her to say something. *Like what? Oh well, here goes....*

"Thank you, Mr. Begley, for taking the time to explain your position. I was aware at the time I made the decision to attend the hearing that there was a possibility my employment with the firm would be terminated." She glanced around the table with a pleasant smile. "I can't say that I'm surprised, because I'm not. I'm very sorry that the situation arose, but I would be less than honest if I didn't tell you that given the same set of circumstances, and knowing what I know now—" her smile grew "—I would make exactly the same decision," she finished in a soft, firm voice.

Glancing back at Begley, she asked, "When would you like me to leave?"

The men continued to stare at her with varying degrees of puzzlement, and she realized that none of them had expected her reaction. *They probably expected tears and hysteria. Well, sorry to disappoint you, fellas, but if I didn't do that when I was kidnapped, you won't catch me doing it over a job.*

"There's no rush, of course," Begley said to reassure her—unnecessarily, as it happened. Her savings account and severance pay would see her through several months, if not a couple of years. She wouldn't be without work that long, she knew. "We would appreciate your handling any cases pending during the next four or five weeks. As for the rest, if you could work with the other attorneys so that they can pick up from there, it should make the transition easier for the clients involved."

She nodded. "Of course. Then the end of the year would probably be a suitable time for me to leave."

"Oh, it doesn't have to be that soon, Ashley. If you'd like to stay on until, say, March or so, that's perfectly satisfactory with us."

Once again she smiled, finding it hard to hide her amusement. She was still refusing to play by the old school rules the men seemed to understand so well. "My January calendar is almost empty, as I had intended to take some time off and spend a few weeks in California with my husband." No one knew that those plans had been abandoned some time ago. She had continued to keep the time open, knowing that she would need a break from her work at the office.

In the end, it was very simple to start severing her ties with the office, and she found herself looking forward to the first break in her routine since she had left law school. She needed some time to herself.

During the week between Christmas and New Year's an ice storm hit Portland, paralyzing traffic and causing most people to stay home. Eager to finish clearing out her desk, Ashley chose to leave her car at home and walk to work. Her boots had nonskid soles that made it easy enough to walk, and the exercise was welcome.

She took a shortcut to save time and distance and marveled at the beauty of the ice-weighted trees. Portland had become an artist's paradise, but the damage to utility lines created chaos for the crews in charge of them. Her office building had escaped the loss of electricity, for which Ashley was thankful after hiking that far.

Once she was in her office, her day became predictable; by the time she was ready to leave, each pending file had full notations of what had been done and what still needed to be done to prepare for trial. She left content with the work she'd accomplished.

The transit mall appeared deserted as Ashley stepped out of the building. The winter light had faded, and she was glad she had decided to leave a little early. She was watching where she walked and didn't notice anyone until a hand touched her arm. She jumped, startled, and glanced up. Rafe stood there, his heavy coat adding to his size. The collar was turned up to protect his neck and ears. No cap covered his thick, wind-ruffled hair. It fell across his forehead in a familiar fashion. Ashley felt as though someone had squeezed her heart. She raised her frightened face to meet Rafe's gaze.

"I'm sorry I startled you, Ashley. I was just on my way upstairs to try to see you." She continued to stare at him, watching his lips as though he were a puppet mouthing words. His face looked as though he'd forgotten how to smile. "I'm glad I didn't miss you."

Trying to regain some self-control, she attempted to joke. "Don't tell me this is another kidnapping attempt?"

She saw the expression in his eyes change as her whimsical response registered. "Is your car here downtown?" he asked.

She shook her head.

"May I give you a ride home?"

Her mouth lifted in an attempt to smile. He sounded so polite, like a little boy properly trained. "That would be very nice, thank you." *You see, I can be polite too.*

She noted the changes in his face since she'd last seen him. He looked older, much older. She couldn't quite decide why that was. Perhaps "defeated" better described his appearance. He stood there, his broad shoulders slumped, his head not quite erect. His eyes reflected the cold surrounding them.

Rafe led her down the steps and to the street where his car waited by the curb. He had driven to Oregon, hoping he'd make it before the bad weather hit. The roads could be treacherous in the border area between the two states.

They were both silent as he helped her into the car and then hurried around to the driver's side and got in. The car's warmth felt good to Ashley's already chilled legs and feet. Rafe drove with care, taking no chances.

Ashley turned her head toward Rafe, rolling it in a lazy movement against the headrest. Her body felt limp, like a stuffed doll that had suddenly lost all its filling. Her mind was blank; not even fragments of thought interfered with the gray expanse of nothingness.

"How are Raul and Jeanine?"

His eyes flicked to her, then returned to watch the street. "They're fine. I drove up for Christmas. Thank God I managed to miss all of this mess on the road." He was quiet for several moments. "They asked me about you."

"Did they? What did you tell them?"

"Very little. They knew something was wrong when you began to refuse their invitations to visit. Raul called me to find out what was going on, and in my usual subtle fashion I told him it was none of his damned business and to butt out." His voice sounded fierce; as was his expression.

Ashley could think of nothing to say, and they lapsed into silence once more. The drive home seemed interminable—tree limbs were down everywhere. City and utility trucks were the only vehicles to be seen except for an occasional Tri-Met Transit bus.

When they had parked in front of her house, he helped her out of the car. Then he took the keys from her and opened the door to the house. Tasha greeted them as though they'd left together that morning. She pressed against Rafe's leg as he hung his heavy coat in the hall closet, then followed as he knelt before the fireplace and began to build a fire. Ashley could hear her purr from across the room. At least he knew Tasha was glad to see him. Ashley had no feelings at all at the moment. She hoped she could maintain the numbness until after he left. She wasn't up to discussing divorce arrangements at the moment.

"Would you like some coffee?" she asked in her polite hostess manner.

"That sounds great. Do you have any Kahlua?"

She had started for the kitchen and stopped at his question. "I think so."

"Good. Some of that in the coffee would help to warm us up." The half smile he gave her was well remembered, and she moved away from him and his attractiveness. As she prepared the coffee she hoped Rafe hadn't seen her pain.

By the time she returned to the living room, Rafe had a blazing fire going, had pulled one of the pillows off the couch onto the floor, and lay propped up on the rug before the fire. Tasha was stretched out beside him, still purring. He stood up when she entered the room and took the tray she carried. Ashley had sliced some banana nut bread left over from a weekend spree of baking. He smiled, but made no comment.

"The fire feels good from here. Why don't you join me?" he asked as he settled on the rug and patted the place beside him.

"I think I'd like to change into something more comfortable first." She indicated her suit. Ashley had never seen Rafe in winter clothes and her eyes lingered on the woolen pullover sweater he wore.

Several pieces of the bread were missing when Ashley returned. Since her waistline had begun to spread she'd been forced to purchase some elastic-waisted woolen slacks. Her matching sweater fell in loose folds around her middle, making an effective camouflage.

"Thank you for the ride home," she said matter-of-factly. "I wasn't looking forward to the walk." She sat down beside him and poured herself a cup of coffee. Taking Rafe's advice, she measured a small amount of Kahlua into the steaming cup. She took a small sip and smiled. He was right—it was delicious.

"How did you get to work this morning? Did you ride the bus?" He sounded genuinely interested.

"No, I walked. It really isn't too far if I cut through a couple of parks." They both looked at the flames as though wary of facing each other. They sat there in silence, sipping their coffee, aware of the unmistakable vibrations that occurred whenever they were in the same room. She wondered whether he felt them as strongly as she did.

Rafe turned around to pour himself another cup. "Thank you for allowing me back in the house. I wouldn't have blamed you if you'd thrown a rock and chased me away."

A dart of pain ran through her. "Rafe, don't." Her hand darted out, paused, then touched his. "There's no need for recriminations, you know. Believe me, I understand."

"I'm glad *you* do," he responded with bitterness, "because I left here wondering if I was going out of my mind. It has taken me this long to come to grips with my feelings." He settled back on the rug and faced her. "What I said to you that day was the truth as I saw it then."

"I know. I accepted it then and I have no reason not to accept it now." She sounded calm because that was the way she felt. She loved this man, the father of the child she was carrying, the lover she'd never dreamed existed before the past summer. Whatever his decision for them, she would accept it.

Rafe made an impatient gesture, running his hand through his hair. "I've tried to understand and, although it's no excuse, I recognize that I'd been pushing myself hard for several months." His smile flashed for a moment, then disappeared. "I was putting in very long hours in order to be able to return to Oregon. Even when I wasn't working, I couldn't sleep for thinking about you, wanting you."

Ashley could feel the pain awakening within her, and she felt she had to get him to stop. She couldn't bear hearing that. "Please, Rafe—"

His hand reached out and touched one of the curls lying on her shoulder. He picked it up as though measuring its weight, bounced it in his hand, then moved on to touch her shoulder.

She became very still at his touch, afraid that if she moved she'd throw herself into his arms. His nearness had started up all the old sensations once more. He had always affected her that way—she had no reason to believe it would ever change.

She started to remove his hand from her shoulder, when he suddenly grabbed her hand and carried it to his lips. He placed light, gentle kisses at the base of each finger, the thumb, and in the palm itself. He carefully folded her fingers over and placed her hand on the rug between them.

She turned her head away from the hypnotic flickering of the flames and watched as shadows danced across his face. Some of his color had faded, as though he'd spent the last months indoors.

"I knew I had to come and talk to you, share with you some of what I've discovered about myself these last few weeks."

"I'm glad."

"You don't even know what I have to say," he said with a hint of confusion.

"That's true. I'm just glad that, whatever you have to say, you feel able to share it with me. I would like to think we might continue the friendship we began."

Pain shot across his face for a moment, then was gone. "I'm not surprised you feel that way, Ashley. As a husband and a lover I might manage to make a halfway decent friend."

"That isn't what I meant, Rafe, and you know it." She reached for his hand. "There's no reason for you to try to shoulder all the blame for the failure of our marriage. I'm willing to accept my part of it. Why should you feel guilty because it didn't work out?"

Rafe sat there watching her as the flames from the fireplace cast a gentle glow over her cheeks. She seemed so serene, somehow. Less tense, more content with her life. He had no reason to suppose she'd want him to step back into her life, but he had to find out. He couldn't continue wondering whether they might have had a chance together. "I wanted to talk to you tonight, Ashley, not about any mistake we made by getting married, but about my mistake in walking out."

Had she heard him right? What was he saying?

"I don't want to be just a friend of yours. I want to live here with you and love you, take care of you. I don't ever want to be separated from you again."

Her heart was hammering so loudly she was certain Rafe must hear it. How many nights had she dreamed that he had returned and was telling her just what she was hearing now? Surely she wasn't dreaming once again!

"But, Rafe, I'm still a lawyer. I can't change that, as much as I might want to try."

"I know that!" He started to reach for her, then stopped. "I discovered that we don't choose the person we fall in love with. We may think we do. We may think we know why we fell in love with that particular person. We can find all sorts of reasons to explain it." He raised her hand to his mouth and placed a feather kiss on her knuckles. "I had to face the fact that love wasn't something I could order about. When I fell in love with you, I didn't fall in love with just the indignant lady I first met or the passionate woman I came to know. I fell for the total person, everything that makes you what you are, and that includes your training and skill as a lawyer."

He stopped speaking, watching her face as she listened to him. Then he went on. "I can't sit here and apologize for what I said, because I meant it when I said it. I'm apologizing for being the kind of person who could set himself up to judge your behavior, to decide what kind of person you should be." He turned back to the fire. "I began to realize what kind of person *I* was and despised myself. I'll understand if you despise me as well."

"That isn't true, Rafe." She reached out and rested her hand on his sweater. She could feel his heart thudding.

"You threw all your time and energy into saving Raul's business while I stood on the sidelines condemning your methods." Ashley noted a roughness in his voice and glanced up in time to see a sheen of moisture in his eyes. She could feel his chest rise as he took a deep breath. "You gave me everything you had to give—your friendship, your love, your passion—and I threw it all back in your face and demanded more." The pain he felt broke through in his voice, and she could no longer stay silent.

"Rafe, we may not have any control over whom we love, but we can choose how we allow that love to affect us. I never wanted my love for you to form a cage to hold you against your will."

Tentatively Rafe placed his arm around Ashley's shoulders and pulled her against him. It felt so good to be close to him again. He kissed her just under her ear and muttered, "All I ever want is to be able to find myself snug within the confines of your love. That isn't a cage, dear heart; that would be heaven."

She turned her lips to his and gave him the answer he was almost afraid to expect. Finally, she pulled back and said, "I love you, Rafe. There's nothing you can do to stop me from loving you."

A shudder went through him and his arms tightened around her as he began to kiss her again. She pulled away once more, breathless, and laughed. "If you don't stop hugging me quite so fiercely, your son or daughter is going to punch you." Her face radiated the love she felt for him.

Rafe sat up, his face reflecting the emotions hitting him as her statement registered.

"Ashley?" He pushed her away and looked down at her body. His hand moved from her back to her stomach, where it rested on the slight protuberance. "You're pregnant," he announced in cautious tones.

"The doctor assures me that's the correct term for my condition."

"But, Ashley, why didn't you mention it? When did you—How—"

"Don't you dare ask me how it happened, or I'll show you just what kind of temper your wife has." Her glare didn't seem to intimidate him.

"When will it be here?"

"The doctor thinks the early part of May, from my rather vague information." She enjoyed watching his face, attempting to identify the emotions reflected there. A hint of concern, perhaps a touch of worry, then a flash of pride. Her smile faded as she saw the beginning of a frown.

"Why wasn't I told?" he demanded. Who said he wasn't arrogant? She supposed that arrogance was part of his makeup. If he could accept her choice of profession, she would overlook his overbearing ways—within reason, of course.

"I'm telling you now, Rafe." No tone of voice could have been more reasonable. His frown remained.

"That's because I came to you. When did you intend to tell me?" His accusation hung between them. She knew she'd better plead her case better than she'd ever done in a courtroom, or his resentment of the delay would remain between them. Before she could say any more, he got up from the rug and pulled her with gentle pressure toward him. "You shouldn't be sitting on the cold floor," he scolded as he sat down on the couch and pulled her onto his lap. Since she quite enjoyed that position, she didn't complain.

"Rafe, love, I'm going to have a baby. That doesn't call for treating me like an invalid."

She watched as a tide of red moved across his cheeks. "I know, but neither one of us needs a cold. The floor's drafty."

"Of course." She hid her smile.

His face stern, his eyes serious, he repeated his question with a precision of speech that hinted at his suppressed emotions. "When did you intend to tell me?"

"I'm not sure. When I was more ready than I've felt up until now, I guess." He pulled her to him and began to kiss her along her cheekbone; then he pressed his lips to hers in a brief and wordless apology.

"Oh, Rafe." She put her arms around him. "I love you so."

"I have to expect a few unexplained quirks in your personality, I suppose. Besides, it's very comforting for me to know that." He leaned over and began to kiss her again. Between short kisses, he admitted, "Because—I don't know—what I'd do—if you didn't."

He picked her up and carried her down the hallway. The bedroom lamp was lit, casting a halo around the table on which it sat. He let her slide down his aroused body.

"Did you ask the doctor if I could make love to you?" He seemed to be having trouble with his breathing. Maybe he'd noticed the weight she had gained recently.

"No, because it didn't seem much of a possibility when I last saw him."

She watched Rafe mask his disappointment as he smiled and, in an offhand manner, suggested, "Well, I think I'll hop into the shower. I may be a while, you just go ahead and get some rest. I won't disturb you when I come to bed.'' Ashley was impressed with his ability to appear nonchalant.

''Of course, the doctor didn't have to tell me anything. He gave me some books to read.'' She indicated the two on her nightstand. ''They say that at this stage it's safe for me to enjoy my marital relationship.'' Her eyes danced with mischief as she smiled up at him.

Rafe stood drinking in the expression on her face. Never had she seemed more beautiful. He loved her so much that he didn't know how to deal with it. He was afraid he would hurt her, he'd been without her for so long. He remembered those long, restless nights when his need for a woman had kept him awake. But he had known that it wasn't a need for just any woman, and he hadn't found the courage to face Ashley.

Ashley began to disrobe, and Rafe could see the beginning of a slight curve in her stomach. His baby. They'd never even discussed having children.

''Ashley?''

She pulled a heavy flannel gown over her head and looked at him. ''Yes?'' She looked like a little girl, with ruffles around her neck and wrists and pink toes showing their tips under the ruffled hem.

''How do you feel about having a baby?''

Her radiant smile appeared once more. ''I can hardly wait. I'll admit it was a bit of a shock at first, but I was excited even then.''

''When did you find out?'' He wished he'd been with her each day, every day, to watch her body change as his child grew within her.

''A few days before Raul's hearing.'' She hopped into bed, and set the dial of the electric blanket. ''I forgot to ask you—do you sleep with an electric blanket?''

He paused, trying to adjust to the change in subject. "No, why?"

"Because I do, but there are dual controls, so you won't need to turn your side on."

"I suppose you think I'm going to sleep on one side of the bed and you'll be on the other?" He stood there with his hands on his hips, his snug pants leaving no doubt as to his condition.

"Well, maybe I won't need it tonight," she admitted a little breathlessly.

He rid himself of his clothes and crawled into bed beside her, managing to have most of her body touching him. He radiated enough heat for both of them, he knew. Returning to the previous subject, he asked, "Why didn't you tell me when I called?"

"I might have, if you hadn't told me you were coming up the next night. That's when I decided I should wait and tell you in person."

His hand slid down her leg until he found the ruffled hem, then it began the return journey against her bare skin until it came to rest at the top of her thigh.

"You didn't mention it the night I flew in," he reminded her.

Ashley's mind was not on the conversation. How could she possibly concentrate when his hand kept feathering across her abdomen and thigh. Just as she expected it to move closer to her inner thigh he would pause, then repeat his pattern.

She began to kiss him, trying to gain his entire attention. She knew she had succeeded when he took over the kiss. His tongue searched out all the hidden places within her mouth.

Ashley moaned. It had been so long. She didn't know how she'd managed to survive without his lovemaking.

When the kiss ended, Ashley was gasping for breath. Rafe continued the conversation as though nothing had interrupted them, as though his hand was not driving her crazy with its darting pattern of teasing maneuvers. "Why didn't you tell me when I flew up here?"

"Tell you what?" She'd forgotten what they had been talking about. She was too involved in relearning his body through the sensitive tips of her fingers. He'd lost weight. His body felt stripped of all surplus flesh—long, lean, and hungry. She could certainly identify with the hunger!

"That you were pregnant."

"Oh, Rafe." It took her a minute to try to think. That unbelievable feeling that Rafe managed to create in her was beginning its pulsating rhythm. His fingers had finally arrived at their destination and her hips arched with the rhythm of his touch. "I didn't tell you because we didn't do much talking that night." *And we're doing too much talking tonight!* "Love me, Rafe, please," she begged.

"I do, honey, indeed I do." She could hear the amusement in his voice. He had teased them both long enough. There would be plenty of time to catch up on the weeks they'd been apart. He recognized that there were a few things a person couldn't catch up on, but he certainly intended to do his best!

He pulled her gown up until she helped him to remove it. She no longer needed the gown to stay warm. Without the restriction of cloth between them, Rafe had unlimited freedom to love her body. He proceeded to show Ashley that she only thought she knew what lovemaking meant. He used his hands to touch her in ways she'd forgotten or never known. He used his tongue to trace the line of her breast, then to caress her until she thought she'd scream with the effort it took to hang on to her self-control. He used his mouth to chart each inch of her skin so that she was left quivering in his arms. He ran his hand reverently over the swelling that foretold the existence of their child, thankful she was the vessel he'd found to nurture his baby. Then he moved, poising himself over her, and gently eased himself to join her.

Rafe made the act of love more than bodies finding gratification. Their coming together became an act of healing. For the first time in their stormy relationship they were in complete harmony with each other. They could sense the other's need and fulfill it without verbal communication. They expressed their commitment and desire to spend the rest of their days and nights together, and as Ashley drifted into a fulfilled, satisfying sleep she remembered that they'd never discussed his career or hers, or where they might live and how.

For the first time in their relationship each acknowledged that those issues were unimportant compared with the one crucial fact—they belonged together. Everything else could be worked out.

Chapter Eleven

The smell of coffee wafted into Ashley's consciousness, and she tried to shake the sleep from her brain. She was tired, and her body felt like a football field that had been used for heavy scrimmages.

She managed to open her eyes partway and squinted to see the clock. Her bedside table was gone. In its place sat a French provincial table holding a lamp with a ruffled shade. This was not her bedroom. She shifted gingerly in the bed and spied Rafe as he stood by the window. The morning sun slanted through the blinds.

She smiled. How could she have forgotten? Rafe stood there studying the tiny face that was the only thing showing from the pink bundle he held. His awed expression held her silent and she watched him as he examined the tiny nose, which looked more like a button than a human appendage, the delicate ears tucked neatly against a well-shaped head, and the wispy hair that clung in soft curls around a beautiful face. They were in the birthing room of a San Francisco hospital where, during the early hours of the previous night, their daughter had been born.

Her mind drifted over the months that had passed and her eyelids fluttered closed once more as she remembered them.

She had never told Rafe the real reason for her leaving the law firm in Portland. Her explanation mentioned different philosophies, an inability to communicate, a mutual decision by everyone concerned. She had no idea he would be so upset until he explained his intention to relocate in Oregon. They had spent many long hours discussing their future together, and she was surprised at Rafe's insistence that she continue her career.

She knew she could never walk away from that part of her life. Too many years had been dedicated to acquiring the skills she had. But her timetable no longer seemed important or necessary.

Rafe took her with him to San Francisco, and she finally realized the wealth of the man she had married. His condominium sat on one of the famous hills overlooking the bay. Her entire house could easily have nestled in a corner of his apartment. They spent their time like tourists, or perhaps like tourists on a honeymoon.

However, Ashley knew that Rafe was right. She could no more ignore the lawyer in her than she could the wife and mother.

Her eyes fluttered open as she thought, *And I managed to have the best of both worlds.* A casual phone conversation with a friend from law school opened doors Ashley never knew existed.

"Ashley!" Susan had exclaimed. "It's great to hear from you. How long will you be in town?"

That question prompted myriad explanations about a new husband and a new residence.

"You mean you quit your job in Portland?" Susan knew how important the position had been to Ashley. Because she trusted her friend, Ashley explained exactly what had happened and almost enjoyed the explosion of her reaction.

"My God, Ashley, those people must be throwbacks to some prehistoric time. Have you checked any of their pulses lately? They must be fossilized by now."

Ashley couldn't answer for a moment because she was laughing. At last she managed to say, "Oh, Susan, you're so good for me. The reason I called was to see if you'll be free for lunch one of these days."

They had made a date, and when they met Susan had some astounding information to pass on. "I told a couple of the partners in our firm about you, including the fact you were on the *Law Review*," she added with a wink, "and a little of what happened in Portland." She stopped, her green eyes flashing with excitement. "And guess what?"

"I give up—what?"

"They want to meet you. They want to know if you intend to take the California bar exams, how much time you intend to give to work, both now and after the baby—"

"You mentioned that I was pregnant?"

"Of course. Why not? It doesn't affect how your mind works, does it? Anyway—"

"Oh, Susan, I can't believe this. Are you telling me they would consider hiring me?"

"Yes, dear friend, that's exactly what I'm telling you. They want to set up an interview with you. What do you think?"

Ashley had sat back in her chair with a sigh. "I think I'm dreaming."

As she shifted once more in the bed, she recalled that interview and the subsequent offer of employment. After she talked it over with Rafe, they had decided that she would wait until the fall to start working again, on a limited basis. Once again Rafe surprised her by his insistence on taking an active part in raising their offspring. He would plan his schedule around hers, and she would do the same with his, so that the baby would have at least one loving parent with her at all times.

Rafe had embraced the role of father-to-be with zeal. Raul pointed out that it was only because Rafe had thought he was too old to become a father and the shock had unhinged him. Only a much-loved brother could have cast such a slur against Rafe's manhood and survived.

Not only had Rafe read both books Ashley's doctor had recommended, he had also checked out other books from the library, in case he might have missed something.

As soon as they had decided to stay in California, Rafe had insisted on finding the best specialist around, made an appointment, and escorted Ashley to the doctor's office, even sitting in on part of the consultation.

It was Rafe who had insisted on attending childbirth classes. He had adopted the same attitude toward the classes and her pregnancy as he did everything else. He investigated thoroughly, read everything he could find on the subject, and could probably have conducted the class himself had the teacher suddenly fallen into a fit. Ashley thought it was no wonder he made a success of everything he tackled; he probably wore out everyone else.

"Good morning," Ashley murmured, her voice still husky from sleep. Rafe glanced up from the baby, then moved over to the chair by her bed and sat down.

"How are you feeling this morning?" His face still showed traces of the anxiety of the previous night.

"Oh, I'm just fine, love. Were you able to get some sleep?"

"A few hours," he admitted. "I managed to wake your folks with the news that after all those grandsons they now have a girl in the family." He took her hand in his and pressed it against his cheek, an endearing gesture that never failed to touch her.

"Were you sorry we had a girl?"

He looked surprised at the question. "Of course not. I placed an order for a girl just like you." He smiled. "And she is—she's beautiful."

He must be looking at her through the eyes of love. When the nurse had helped Ashley to feed the baby, she'd taken a good look at her daughter. If you could call wrinkled skin and wisps of black hair beautiful, then yes, Ashley guessed she was. She knew she'd never felt such a fierce love as she had when she held the tiny scrap in her arms. Motherhood had some definite pleasures that could be found in no other role.

"Did you call Raul and Jeanine?"

"Of course. I told them I hoped to have you home in the next day or two. They said they'd fly down over the weekend if you thought you'd be up to company by then." Rafe's eyes were still shadowed with concern. Ashley's labor had lasted several hours. Rafe hadn't realized when he attended the classes how different it would be to see Ashley hurting, and when he saw that first hard pain hit her, he wasn't sure he could handle his reaction. Their training had helped, and now, as he looked at the tiny infant, he knew he wouldn't have missed her arrival for anything.

As he watched, his tiny daughter wriggled and stretched her fingers wide, then curled them into minuscule fists once more.

Hesitantly Rafe asked, "Would you mind if we call her Teresa?"

"That's a lovely name, Rafe. If that's what you want to name her, we will."

"That was my grandmother's name. She was one of my favorite people in the whole world when I was young."

"When you were young*er*. You're still young, love."

"Not after last night. I'm not sure about having a second one."

"I am," Ashley responded in a serious tone. "I think it's important to raise children together. You know my feelings about an only child."

Rafe's smile gleamed white against his dark skin. "Yes, ma'am. I'll do my best to oblige you, ma'am. Just let me know when you're ready, ma'am."

"You can cut out the fake accent, Tex. Nobody's buying it."

The nurse came in to check on mother and child, and Rafe left Ashley to rest.

She woke up in the afternoon to find Rafe sitting by her bed, watching her with a tender expression.

"Why didn't you wake me up?"

"You're going to need all the rest you can get. I have a hunch Miss Teresa is going to keep you hopping once we get you two home." He leaned over and placed a kiss on her mouth. "By the way, Tasha and I had a nice long discussion this morning."

"Omigosh, I'd forgotten all about her."

"So she told me. As a matter of fact, she made it clear she did not approve of my arriving home at dawn this morning without you. So she tried her hand at a little re-decorating."

"Oh, no! What did she do?" Visions of some of his original oil paintings with claw marks on them danced through her head.

"She found a box of tissues, shredded them, and distributed them through several of the rooms. It was quite colorful."

"Oh, Rafe. Maybe we'd better give her away, especially now that Teresa is here."

"No way. Tasha has agreed to accept Teresa, and I intend to see that she does. You know you could never get rid of her."

If he'd spent the morning picking up tiny scraps of shredded tissues and could still sound so agreeable, Ashley knew she had no need to worry about Rafe's patience.

By the time Raul and Jeanine arrived, Ashley and Teresa were home and a routine of sorts had been established. Rafe's prediction proved right. Tasha did an admirable job of ignoring the new addition.

After examining the sleeping infant and returning to the living room, Jeanine exclaimed, "You're certainly spry this soon after giving birth!"

Raul answered for Ashley. "That's probably because she didn't gain a lot of weight during her pregnancy like some people we know."

Jeanine's nose rose in the air. "The doctor said I was just right. You were the only one complaining."

"Just right for having a baby elephant, maybe."

Ashley watched as an accent pillow sailed through the air and decided it was time to change the subject. "What's new in Oregon? The California news media seem to think the world ceases to exist at the northern state border."

"Pete Wilson was convicted on several counts." Jeanine paused, her forehead wrinkled. "I can't remember all the charges, but it was enough to keep him out of the way for a few years."

"That should have hurt Tysinger's case," Ashley responded.

Raul, stretched out in one of the lounge chairs, spoke up. "It didn't help, but he's got some wily lawyers. I have a feeling they'll keep him from being brought to trial as long as they can find one more technicality to pull out of the books."

"Have you had any more problems at the plant since the hearing last fall?" Rafe moved over and sat down next to Ashley, sliding his arm around her.

"Nothing. Jackson turned in his resignation, but I refused to take it. He's a good man and I don't expect anything similar to happen ever again." Ashley was glad to see that the subject could be discussed without creating any tension. All of that seemed to have happened in another lifetime and had little to do with the life she had established in the past few months.

Later that night Ashley finished breast-feeding Teresa and crawled into bed next to Rafe. The doctor had suggested nursing for the first few weeks, and she enjoyed the closeness with her tiny daughter.

"Rafe?"

"Hmmmm?"

"Are you asleep?"

"I was. Why?"

"Oh, nothing. I was just thinking of Tysinger."

He pulled her over so that her head rested on his chest, enjoying the feel of her curves once again. "What about him?"

"Do you really think he's guilty?"

"You bet I do, and so do most of the law-enforcement agencies. The catch is to prove it."

"I can't help but remember that if it hadn't been for Tysinger I might never have met you." She moved her hand lightly across his waist.

She could feel his chuckle deep in his chest. "That's true, my love, but somehow I don't feel like sending him a thank-you note."

She leaned on her elbow and stared down at him. "I can understand that. You would still be a happily single man if it hadn't been for him. It's a wonder you haven't insisted that he be placed behind bars for life!"

A glow of tenderness lit Rafe's eyes, and he placed his palm against her cheek, then stroked her jaw line and her neck. "Ashley, I never knew what happiness was until I married—"

Her heart melted at his admission.

"—but of course by then it was too late!"

"Rafe!"

He began to laugh at the expression on her face. Pulling her to him, he gave her a kiss that left no doubt how he felt about her. When he finally let her go, he grinned.

"Now quit fishing for compliments and get some rest. Otherwise your daughter is going to have a grumpy mama trying to feed her in a few hours." He cupped his hand around her breast. "I'm afraid I can't offer to feed her like I did Josh."

He was right. There was no need for soul-searching. Despite the odds, their marriage was working in a most satisfying manner. With a sigh of contentment, Ashley curled up beside her warm husband and fell asleep.

* * * * *

Books by Annette Broadrick

Silhouette Romance

Circumstantial Evidence #329
Provocative Peril #359
Sound of Summer #412
Unheavenly Angel #442
Strange Enchantment #501
Mystery Lover #533
That's What Friends Are For #544
Come Be My Love #609
A Love Remembered #676
Married?! #742

Silhouette Desire

Hunter's Prey #185
Bachelor Father #219
Hawk's Flight #242
Deceptions #272
Choices #283
Heat of the Night #314
Made in Heaven #336
Return to Yesterday #360
Adam's Story #367
Momentary Marriage #414
With All My Heart #433
A Touch of Spring #464
Irresistible #499
A Loving Spirit #552
Candlelight for Two #577

Silhouette Books

Silhouette Christmas Stories 1988
"Christmas Magic"

ISLAND ON THE HILL

Dixie Browning

For Liz and Randy

DIXIE BROWNING,
a native of North Carolina, has contributed greatly to Silhouette Books. Along with her many writing awards, she is an acclaimed painter and was the first president of the Watercolor Society of North Carolina. When she isn't traveling to research her books, Dixie divides her time between her home in Winston-Salem and her gallery, Browning Artworks, Ltd., on Hatteras Island. She also writes historical romances with her sister under the name Bronwyn Williams.

Her upcoming books for Silhouette include: *Twice in a Blue Moon* (August 1990's *Man of the Month*, Silhouette Desire #588) and *The Homing Instinct* (September 1990, Silhouette Romance #747).

"When Silhouette launched its first series incorporating all the best elements of romance literature, it was a turning point in my life, both as a reader and a writer. We've come a long way... together."

—Dixie Browning

Chapter One

She knew it; she just *knew* it! It had taken no more than a single look at the tall, earnest young man behind the desk, with his horn-rimmed glasses and his button-down personality... one look at the way *he* looked at *her*, and Frances knew she had been offered up on a platter to yet another of Aunt Helen's prospects. After dodging her family's efforts at matchmaking for all these years, she had developed a second sight where men were concerned, but it had been lamentably lacking today. She had marched straight into the office of Combs and Webster, her mind filled with the unbelievable prospect of actually owning her own home, and now, before she could get down to business, there'd be another one of those tedious encounters where she was forced either to make a flat, rude, negative remark or endure an evening of boring company.

Ooooh, Aunt Helen! And after that last one too...the salesman who had actually gone so far as to figure out how much they could save on rent and groceries by moving in together!

The man was on the phone and Frances was gestured into a chair where she seethed as he alternately nodded and grunted into the receiver, his thick glasses hardly obscuring the interest in his eyes as they roamed over her from the tip of her well-shod foot to the crown of her neat, straw-colored chignon. She focused her eyes on a reproduction of a third-rate painting and allowed her mind to go back to three nights ago. She had been having dinner with Aunt Helen and Uncle Jerrold in Durham and the talk had moved around to the old Cairington place on the Haw River.

"I happen to know it's going on the market," Aunt Helen had said, knowing of, though not approving Frances's determination to buy a small house of her own. "The little factor's cottage down by the water, too, I guess. Probably go together. Here, have some more turnip greens, Fancey."

Frances helped herself absently, her mind already engaged in exploring the large yellow house on the hill overlooking the best stretch of white water on the Haw. She remembered the smaller place at the foot of the hill, although it hadn't occurred to her that they were owned by the same person, but as it turned out, they were being sold either separately or together and Aunt Helen just happened to know the realtor who was listing them.

That should have tipped her off—the very fact that Aunt Helen was sending her to see the realtor, when Frances knew very well that every member of her immediate family deplored her determination to live her own life, to own her own home with no help or interference from any man.

And now, here she was, being greeted as if she were the answer to a bachelor's prayer just because she had a good job, a savings account, and was considered attractive enough to offset her uncomfortably independent personality.

Mr. Combs insisted on showing her pictures of his other listings, whether suitable or not, and because she was intent on finding a place well away from the immediate influence of well-meaning friends and relatives, she looked. She looked, that is, until she became aware of his careless brushing against her when he turned the pages. When he began answering her questions with his mouth practically buried in her hair, as if the escaping tendrils had a direct route to her brain, she stood up and planted her hands on her nicely curved hips.

"Look, Mr. Combs..."

"Call me Bobbie," he broke in smugly.

"Mr. Combs, I'm interested in the smaller house on the old Cairington property. Is it or is it not for sale separately, and if it is, is it within the limits I mentioned?"

"Well, now, I'm sure we could..."

"If it's available I'd like the key, please," she insisted adamantly.

"Oh, well I'll tell you what, Frances... I may call you that since I'm more or less a friend of the family?" he asked ingratiatingly, causing Frances to visualize several dire and painful consequences for her favorite aunt. "Since I'm all through but for one last client, why don't we pick up a picnic basket and take it out to the place? We can look over the house and I can show you all the, ah, advantages of the location, and then we'll have us a little picnic on the river. It'll be the coolest place in Chatham County, I can guarantee you," he added, practically steaming up his glasses at the prospect.

"Thanks so much, Mr. Combs, but I'd really prefer to see it alone," she said dampeningly.

"Oh, but Frances . . . your aunt calls you Fancey," he smirked, "but I don't really know you that well . . . yet." He ignored the danger flags flying in her green eyes and continued with growing enthusiasm. "I've got all the time in the world. I can tell you all about the . . . ah, the heating system! Did you know the place only has wood heat? We can discuss what it'll take to bring it up to bank standards over country ham biscuits and a bottle of Catawba wine."

She winced at the thought and stepped back, only to have him press forward, his eyes finally settling somewhere in the vicinity of her top button which, in deference to the heat, was not the *top* button but the third one down on her tailored blouse. "You can't get a bank loan on a house with only wood heat, you know," he murmured to her cleavage.

"*Mr.* Combs! Do you want to sell the house or don't you? I'm interested in the house, not in your lecherous attentions, and if you want to sell it to me, then climb back over to your side of the desk and stay there! Now, do I get that key, or don't I? There *are* other realtors in North Carolina, you know!"

She got the key. She was ramming it into her capacious white canvas and leather bag as she marched from his office, too angry to look where she was going. There was only one occupant in the small waiting room and it was just her bad luck that his long legs were stretched out, in their immaculately creased pants, across her path. She tripped over a pair of bench-made size elevens and only managed to retain her balance by dint of some fast and fancy footwork, which eroded her temper even further, as did the instinctive knowledge that he had heard every word of what passed in the office beyond.

"You careless lout! Can't you keep your clumsy feet to yourself?" she exclaimed, glaring at the amazed face of the man who had risen and extended a hand to catch her.

She shied away from him as if he were infectious and frowned at him, far too angry to be impressed by the mocking amusement in a pair of deep-set brown eyes.

"Men!" She spat out the word and whirled to go, causing her heavy purse to swing out and strike the doorjamb. Jerking it to her, she clamped it tightly to her overheated body and stomped out the door into the dusty glare of the late afternoon sun. But by the time she reached her car and unlocked it, opening the doors to allow the captured heat to escape, she had all but regained her perspective.

The two she had just left were probably saying, "Women!" in just the same disgusted tone, she acknowledged ruefully; and with just cause. There had been no excuse for her rudeness to a perfect stranger. All right, so he had stretched out his legs across a doorway. With legs that long, one had to put them somewhere, and the offices of Combs and Webster didn't supply all that much square footage.

She grinned as she cut through the campus of the university on her way to the rooming house. Besides, if *he* had been the one making the proposition, she might not have been in that much of a hurry to turn him off. It was never that sort, though, who turned up on her doorstep with some farfetched tale of being a friend of a friend of the family, or the brother of a once-removed cousin of her best friend. All such *nice* men, too, as her solicitous friends and family assured her, and everyone knew what nice men looked like.

* * *

Five weeks later the house was hers. There had been warnings and recriminations from her family, of course. They had taken her determination to own her own house as a final surrender to spinsterhood, a fate unknown among the Harris women, all good-looking and conditioned to domesticity and maternity from the time they were given their first tea set and Betsy-Wetsy doll.

It was a relief to get out of town. Chapel Hill was a captivating combination of cosmopolitan and sleepy southern town, small enough during the summer months but full to overflowing during the school year with university students. Frances's rooms had been in a large old Victorian house on a tree-shaded street, but she had felt hemmed in all the same. There was no yard she could call her own and the phone in the hall served them all, as did the noisy old furnace with its voracious appetite for oil.

It was more than that, though. Frances recognized the move as a statement to all concerned. Frances Ann Harris, maiden lady of some twenty-seven winters, is self-sufficient, self-supporting and self-satisfied, thank you, nor has she any intention of washing, cooking, and cleaning for the first man who offers her a roof over her head and a ring on her finger.

She took a week off to move. Her boss, a thoroughly married man who understood her passion for independence, offered to help her with the heavy things, but his wife, who happened to be in the shop at the time, reminded him that he was helping *her* with the freezing and canning and wouldn't have any time left over for fun.

Now, hugging herself gleefully, she stood in her freshly painted yellow living room and glowed with the enormous satisfaction of being surrounded by her very own things in her own house on her own half-acre. The mouse who shared her kitchen was *her* mouse and the clumsy woodwork in the remodeled blue bedroom was *her* clumsy woodwork. A new mother watching her only child's first steps could hardly feel more pride.

The kitchen was hopeless at the moment and Frances's newly revised budget didn't allow much leeway for improvement, not with the mortgage payments and a new floor furnace to pay for. She cooked herself a small steak and opened a bottle of Cabernet Sauvignon as a private housewarming. The public was invited to a modest affair on the weekend; friends and family, plus the inevitable young men who "just happened to be visiting and came along." Her mother still hadn't given up, worst luck!

From the tall, prim window overlooking the hill beyond her came the intrusive sound of a chainsaw and Frances lowered her feet from the coffee table and peered out at the lush woods that surrounded her on two sides; nothing but a pair of doves who were behaving in a shocking manner, and a squirrel working on a winter supply of hickory nuts.

She sauntered to the back door...*her* back door, lovely in spite of the bas-relief of countless coats of enamel. Following the sickening whine of the saw, she was just in time to see the top of one of the crepe myrtles that lined the driveway shiver, cascading a shower of rose-colored blossoms to the ground.

Feeling as if her own flesh were being assaulted, she slammed out of the door and down the steps to fly across the lawn, her shoes forgotten and the stemmed wineglass still clutched in her hand.

"You stop that! Leave that tree alone!" she commanded, coming to a breathless halt just as one of the cedars that had insinuated itself between the crepe myrtles and then grown to an enormous size began a slow, solemn descent.

Something struck her in the back, knocking the glass from her fingers, and before she could even cry out, she was sprawling flat out on the ground with a ton of something hot and hard on top of her. For several long moments she could only lie there, the breath knocked from her, as one by one her bruises and abrasions made themselves felt. The combination of rage, windedness, and the heavy weight on her back made it impossible for her to express herself until she felt the weight gingerly removed. Then slowly, cautiously, she rolled over on her back to stare up in stunned outrage at the length of blue denim and bronzed, glistening flesh that towered over her.

"Are you absolutely insane?" she demanded, her words coming softly, with an indignant terseness that tightened up her usual drawl.

A westering sun was behind the head of the individual who stood there with such arrogant unconcern after having tackled her and knocked her down, and she could see only an unlikely expanse of shoulders and a glint of silver high above where she still lay on the ground.

"No, but you must be to go barging under a falling tree like that." The words hung there, bitten off and spat out with disgust, and Frances, still snarled up in the angry brown eyes, put out a hand to ease herself into a sitting position, not caring for the disadvantage of having to look up so far.

"That tree had no business falling," she accused, wincing as her palm touched the ground. She seemed to have made contact with what little bit of gravel still remained on the driveway, which entered the Cairington property from the highway and split to serve both the houses.

"Here, get up off the ground and we'll sort it out. If I'd known any damned fool was apt to come charging out after me screaming like a banshee, I'd have yelled 'timber!'"

"'Timber!' That's another thing! You've got a fine nerve, coming onto private property and cutting your wood from my driveway! I'll have you know those cedars are privately owned and you can damned well get yourself off this place before I have you up before the law!" She ignored the outstretched hand and levered herself awkwardly off the ground, gasping as she came upright and clutching her rib cage.

"What's wrong, are you hurt? More than your sticky pride, that is?"

He reached out and she jumped back, glaring at the man who looked vaguely familiar. Lord knows there were enough of his sort around, college dropouts or even graduates who had declared themselves to be carpenters or some such, qualifications notwithstanding. Well, if this one thought he was going to do his carpentry with her wood, he was about to be disabused. Besides, he looked old enough to have learned not to go traipsing about on someone else's property with a chainsaw.

Still clutching the place where pain shafted through her with every indignant breath, she opened her mouth to speak and then closed it again on a moan.

His hands were all over her. The scent of his perspiration in her nostrils mingled with a faint masculine fragrance that was both unfamiliar and exciting, and then she brought herself up with an unladylike oath as she realized where her dazed perceptions were wandering. The fact that his firm touch was going over her with an almost professional thoroughness had nothing to do with it; but when one hand splayed out on her ribs, his fingers digging into the lift of her breast, and he ordered her to take a deep breath, she jerked herself out of his grasp and glared at him.

"Keep your hands to yourself! If I'm injured, you'll be the first to know about it...through my lawyer! Now, just pick up your saw and get yourself off this property before I...!"

"And now you listen to me for a change, you fire-breathing termagant! This just happens to be *my* property, and if I want to cut down the whole damned forest it's nobody's business but my own! Keep your outraged screechings for somebody with earplugs." So saying, he turned away and picked up the mustard-colored chainsaw, pulling the cord with immediate results. The peaceful country atmosphere was ripped wide open by the furious roar, and Frances put her hands over her ears and fled to the sanctuary of her house.

That was the first offense. The second one was maneuvering her into a position where she had no choice but to apologize.

It happened four days later, after she had driven home, slipped off her shoes, unbuttoned her blouse and dropped down into the dark green porch rocker with a sigh that blew the hair off her damp forehead. It was at least five degrees cooler here on her porch than in Chapel Hill. Part of the reason was psychological, stemming from the sound of the river which was the swiftest section of water in the area, as well as the lacy shade that danced across the cool white side of her modest frame house.

Frances lifted her collar away from her neck to allow the air to circulate while she wondered idly what she could fix for her supper without heating up the kitchen.

There was no warning of his approach until the man appeared at the side of her porch, holding, of all things, a shimmering stem of what appeared to be the finest crystal in his large, well-kept fingers. "This is yours, I believe," he said in a dark, dry voice.

"Mine?" She blinked in confusion.

"It's the same pattern of the shard I carried all over Chapel Hill and Durham trying to match; but if not, you can exchange it."

"I don't understand," she said, and then she did. When she had charged out across the yard the other evening she had been holding her wineglass and it must have landed somewhere in the driveway. "But it was broken, wasn't it?"

"Unfortunately, yes. This is a replacement," he replied urbanely.

Frances bristled, felt around with her bare feet for her shoes and fumbled at the buttons of her blouse. "That wasn't necessary," she said stiffly.

"No, I don't suppose it was, but then, I should have come to warn you before I started cutting. If you're not expecting it, it can be a pretty horrendous noise." He grinned disarmingly then and Frances steeled herself against being charmed.

"You should have come to me and asked permission before even thinking about cutting down one of my cedars," she rebuked and then she recalled his words, words that had been driven out of her head by the nasty roar of his saw. "Did you say...You mentioned that you had some connection to the property?" she said hesitantly.

The sun shone down at a low angle, turning his eyes to honey, although there was nothing sweet about his expression. "Look, Miss...I'm afraid I don't know your name, but as we're neighbors, we'd better get a few things straight. I own the house on the hill and I'm moving in over the next few days. Cabel McCloud, by the way." His jaw, if anything, grew even more implacable and he set the glass on the floor with a fine disregard for its fragility.

"Frances Harris," she returned, noting almost absently that in spite of a fine dusting of silver in his thick, close-cropped hair (hair that fit his well-shaped head like the fur of a jungle animal), Cabel McCloud was probably a few years under forty. He was probably used to having every female within range panting after that fine physique of his, too, she added witheringly to herself.

"Miss Harris," his nod was all but imperceptible, "for the record, I'm not a sociable neighbor. I'd have snapped up this place of yours just to keep it empty if you hadn't beat me to it, but..."

"That was you! In Combs's office that day...you tripped me up!" she exclaimed, planting her nylon-clad feet firmly on the floor as she rose in one swift, indignant motion.

"I did not trip you up!" he roared. "Dammit, woman, don't go making me the scapegoat for your own clumsiness! Now, as I was saying, I'm moving in, and before the rainy season starts I plan to open up that driveway so a little air can circulate. Otherwise, it'll stay wet and freeze come winter, and while that might not bother you here on the low road, I don't plan to have to toboggan down the hill. I'll leave your flowering thingamabobs alone, but those cedars will have to go."

Frances was stricken, though determined not to reveal it. "Oh, and I suppose you just happen to have a use for the wood," she said with calculated sweetness.

He looked nonplussed for a moment and it occurred to her that a carpenter, unless he was an awfully successful one, wouldn't be able to buy a two-story, hundred-year-old house in prime condition, plus several acres of riverfront property.

"As a matter of fact, I intended to split it with you, although legally I'm entitled to keep the whole works. In fact, legally, I could bulldoze every tree standing and you wouldn't be able to open your mouth about it... legally, that is," he added with deliberate sarcasm. "You bought the half-acre plot this shack sits on and you have right-of-way in from the highway, but just keep in mind that every time you drive in or out, you're doing so only with my permission."

She caught her breath as the impact of his words hit her, taking away that fine freedom, the feeling of being queen of all she surveyed, but as she stared helplessly into his mocking eyes, all she could think to say was, "It's not a shack!"

"Mill house, farm manager's house, whatever," he said disparagingly, "just keep in mind what I said. And Miss Harris, while we're at it, we may as well lay the cards on the table. Just so you don't get any ideas about being too neighborly, I'm a bachelor, Miss Harris...by choice, I am *not* fond of women who offer to cook meals for me, nor do I need any buttons sewn on. And if my house needs cleaning, then I'll have a housekeeper in. I am not lonely, nor am I pining away from a broken heart. As far as I'm concerned, women are welcome in my bed, but not in my life. Is that clear enough for you?"

Under the apricot tan she had acquired so easily, Frances could almost feel the color drain from her face as the impact of his words struck her. That *he* should think *she* was interested in trapping *him*! "Mr. McCloud, allow me to lay my own cards on the table. I happen to be twenty-seven years old and single . . . by choice," she stressed. "I am perfectly able to change a tire and replace a fuse. I can chop my own wood and shovel snow, and if you happen to hear hysterical laughter floating up the hill on a summer breeze, don't be alarmed; it will only be me, expressing my heartfelt thanks for having escaped from all the overbearing, egotistical, self-important males who think every female they meet is after their scalp. And as far as you, personally, are concerned, why I'd rather send for a man from a mail-order catalog!"

There was more jammed up in her seething brain but her tongue proved to be the bottleneck. She fumed importently and settled for blowing an irritating tendril of hair off her forehead as her breasts heaved in exasperation.

Then, with a sigh that (had she been in any frame of mind to notice) drew Cabel McCloud's eyes from her flushed cheeks to her agitated breasts, she forced herself to continue on another tack. "I owe you an apology for the other day. You were right about the driveway and even if you weren't, the land, as you so kindly informed me, belongs to you and I only use it on sufferance. As for this," she leaned over and lifted the delicate stemware from the porch floor, tilting it to catch the coppery rays of the sun, "it wasn't necessary for you to replace it since we've both agreed that I was at fault . . . well, if not actually at fault, then . . . ah . . . wrong in my . . . my accusations." She was growing uncomfortable under the level gaze; something about the man got under her skin the first time she had ever seen him and he didn't improve on further acquaintance. "At any rate," she finished in a rush, "it would make me feel better if you'd return it and get your money back." She held it out to him and he glanced at it, not bothering to relieve her of it—to her acute embarrassment. Finally she let her arm fall again.

"But then, I've no particular wish to make you feel better, Miss Harris. You can repay me for the privilege of sharpening your tongue on my hide by taking the blasted thing, since I spent the best part of a morning locating it." His eyes dropped momentarily to an all but invisible line between his thumb and forefinger. "Not to mention cutting myself on the piece I took along to match."

"Oh, that's just too bad, Mr. McCloud," she cooed, shamelessly enjoying the chance to rile him. "If you'll come in I'll bandage it up for you and make it all better."

"Don't try playing the flirt with me, Miss Harris," he retorted with blistering mockery. "It's an art that has to be learned young to be effective and it's a little late for you to be trying it out." He turned and strode off up the hill. Frances's fingers tightened around the stem as if she'd like to throw it after him, but instead, her lips curved into a reluctant grin and she found herself laughing aloud for no good reason at all.

Chapter Two

After living and working in the area for five years, ever since graduating from the university, Frances had settled into a full and satisfying routine. Her social life was well under control and she meant to keep it that way in spite of all the machinations of those who thought a woman incomplete without a man permanently attached. She had almost been caught in that trap once, during her senior year, and she considered the end of that relationship a deliverance, an escape.

Now she did. At the time, she hadn't felt quite so fortunate, but it had been a long time since she had even thought of the man who had come on so strongly, almost convincing her that unless she moved into the house he owned just west of Carrboro, his life would be severely blighted. He had hinted at marriage, but before he could do more than hint, Frances had discovered that since his mother, with whom he had lived, had died two and a half years before, he had lived with three different girls, and the last one had got tired of being an unpaid and unwed housekeeper and moved out. That had been just about two weeks before Mike had widened his eyes over a stein of beer and crossed the floor to drop into the seat opposite Frances with an implausible tale about recognizing her from some previous life.

Chapel Hill was like that. In spite of the seasonal influx of students, a good number of whom stayed on long after graduation, it was essentially a small town where all circles overlapped and sooner or later, everyone knew everyone else's business.

Which was why it was so infernally easy for her mother and her two married sisters to shuffle their acquaintances and come up with a perfectly reasonable excuse to direct one man after another into her pathway.

Probably she should have moved clean out of the state. Bynum wasn't all that far from where her widowed mother lived in Saxapahaw, and with a sister living on a tobacco farm in Moore County and another at Eli Whitney, plus Aunt Helen in Durham, she was still their favorite charity. Send poor Frances a man; she's still wary after that Mike fellow, but she's bound to settle for someone else sooner or later.

If she had feared for her privacy as far as her neighbor was concerned, however, she needn't have worried. She was left strictly alone to potter about her four rooms, two porches, a bath, and a half-acre of weeds which, when properly mowed, resembled a lawn nearly enough to satisfy all but the most fastidious. She took great pleasure in rearranging her few pieces of furniture so that the thrift shop and yard sale items weren't too obvious. She turned down several dates, using the excuse of getting settled and then turned down a few offers to help with that chore.

About the only one of her circle who didn't keep trying to mate her up with all the leftover males of his acquaintance was her boss, Howard Stinson, who only cast her a resigned sort of look when she harped overly long on the subject of blessed singleness. He understood and sympathized; you're a short time single and a long time married, she had heard him say once over the phone. To one of his single friends, she presumed. He was either warning or commiserating.

She didn't see very much of her neighbor but that wasn't to say she wasn't aware of his presence. There evolved a more or less regular schedule of visitations and Frances happened to be on her front porch or at a window as often as not when McCloud's girl friends came to see him. The redhead, a real knockout who flashed up the drive in a yellow Spitfire about six o'clock at least three evenings a week, usually brought a picnic basket with her, and the two of them had to pass right by Frances's house to reach the clearing on the riverbank, where they proceeded to enjoy the fried chicken and wine as well as a little necking. If they insisted on settling down right in front of her porch, she didn't see why she should be forced to stay inside, and so she turned her back to the river, propped her feet up on the window sill, and rocked while she cooled off and read the *Advocate*. Her gaze *might* have strayed occasionally to the couple on the blanket and Cabel McCloud *might* have caught her eye once or twice, but there was certainly nothing deliberate about it. Even if it appeared to her that he actually winked at her now and then, it was too far to be sure.

Her own dates usually came to pick her up at her house, although sometimes she met them in town for a drink at Crook's Corner and a film, or some live music at one or another of the bars. One or two of them hinted rather strongly that they would have preferred an evening at home, but Frances wasn't falling for that one; a home cooked meal and then all the reasons why it would be better to stay over than drive back to town so late.

Her own social life was every bit as satisfying as Cabel McCloud's seemed to be, even though he seemed satisfied with one or two partners instead of the half a dozen or so that Frances juggled. There was the pharmacist who was divorced and made no bones about the fact that he was looking for a stepmother for his six-year-old daughter. Frances enjoyed seeing him once every week or so because they both had a passion for Greek food and wine. Then there was the grad student who was a cousin of one of her brothers-in-law. He was a wonderful dancer and an entertaining companion at parties. There were others, and if they still stuck after finding out that she didn't lend money or records, that she didn't patch jeans or darn socks, and she didn't sleep around, then she was perfectly willing to see them on a regular basis, paying her own way and understanding when another female came along who promised more than Frances was willing to deliver.

It was the paying of her own way that cut into her social life more than the lack of suitable partners, for with a mortgage to consider and a newly installed floor furnace—neccessary before any bank would lend her money to buy her house—there didn't seem to be much left over for fun these days. And then there were the little extras she couldn't resist, such as the swing for her front porch and the bentwood rocker for the living room. And the habit of regular meals.

Tossing herself a chef's salad one Friday afternoon after work, she could hear the sound of Cabel's redhead coming from the riverside picnic site. His soft baritone didn't carry, but the girl's shrill laughter rang out so often that Frances wondered wryly if he were telling jokes or tickling her. From the looks of the clouds rolling up over the treetops, he'd better be paying less attention to his little playmate and more to the weather, she decided. While Mr. McCloud might be able to take a sudden squall in stride, his girl friend looked the sort to come apart at the seams with the first drop of rain.

Not that Frances had been spying on them, but those eyelashes looked far too thick, long, and black to go with the bouffant copper hair, and if that knit top shrunk half an inch, she could be held for indecent exposure. Even from here, it was impossible to miss all that overstated sex appeal, and when little Red flapped those lashes up at Cabel, Frances could almost feel the breeze from where she sat munching her raw broccoli.

And of course, manlike, he lapped it up! For a misogynist, Cabel McCloud had a way of rationalizing his lapses. But then he hadn't exactly said he hated women, had he? It was marriage he distrusted. She wondered disparagingly what the two of them shared besides the picnic basket.

When the first big drops struck the side windows, Frances put down her salad and dashed out to gather up her laundry from the line. She had fallen into the habit of doing her washing Thursday nights and hanging it out Friday morning before work, and she was lucky this time that the rain had held off. If it had come any earlier, she'd have had it all to do over. The rain was upon her as she crammed the last pair of nylon bikini briefs into her basket, and she ran for the back door, shouldering it open just as she heard Cabel call out from the front. The scent of rain on parched earth was strong in her nostrils as she called out for him to come in.

"Through here," she panted breathlessly, planking her basket down on the table that served as work surface and dining table until she could afford to have more cabinets built in her kitchen.

It was the first time he had been in her house, and she couldn't help but think how his shoulders dwarfed the dimensions of the room. Not only did his physique fill the doorway, but his personality seemed to overflow, crowding her against the table as he entered with his red-headed friend hovering behind him.

As Frances looked beyond him, she felt a peculiar shaft of sympathy. As she had half expected, the poor girl hadn't fared very well in the weather. Not only had her mascara run and given her the look of a sad raccoon, but her hair was coming unglued and now looked more like a brillo pad than anything else.

"Why don't I show you where you can dry off," Frances suggested, sidling past the bulk of Cabel McCloud. "I'm Frances Harris."

"Sorry, Frances. This is Terri Bollich. Terri works with the firm," Cabel said, making himself at home by hooking a chair over and straddling it.

Not bothering to reply, Frances ushered the girl into the spare bedroom, showing her the bath and handing her a towel. What firm? she wondered. The few times they had come into contact with each other she and her neighbor had cautiously avoided anything that could be construed as personal, and so she had no idea what he did for a living. All she knew was that he left the house about half an hour before she did in the morning driving a maroon 450 SL, and he wore suits that discreetly shouted their exclusive origins.

"You're welcome to anything you need," she told Terri Bollich. "I can lend you something dry to wear if you'd like, although..." she broke off, looking doubtfully at the girl who couldn't be more than five-feet-three or four and who was built like a roller coaster. Frances herself stood five-feet-seven in her stocking feet, and while she wasn't exactly unendowed, her figure was a little more restrained.

"Thanks, but Cabel will lend me his shirt," Terri said, speaking for the first time in her little-girl whisper.

Frances left her to it and returned to the kitchen to collect the basket of rain-dampened clothes. Through the windows she could see the fronds of ailanthus tossing in the gray sheets of rain like palm trees in a hurricane as the fury on her tin roof almost deafened her.

"Thanks for the shelter," Cabel remarked laconically, leaning over to sweep up a pair of wispy ivory panties from the floor and drop them on her basket.

Tight-lipped, she stuffed the intimate garment under her more prosaic jeans. "You're perfectly welcome to stay as long as you need to. I have things to do in the bedroom and you can finish your picnic here if you want to."

"You'll have to share it with us," Cabel invited politely. "I insist, Frances. After all, it's the least we can do after we barged in on you uninvited."

"No thank you, Mr. McCloud," she answered stiffly. She could smell the scent of sun-dried laundry mingling with some masculine fragrance that seemed to invade the sanctuary of her small kitchen, turning it into something unfamiliar, and she needed to escape. "If you..."

She was interrupted by a click-click sound, and almost immediately a blast of thunder seemed to lift the house off its foundation. Thunder storms were her own particular *bête noire*, although she had successfully hidden the fact for years, and now Frances stood paralyzed as the color drained from her face and she struggled to get her breath again. Her fingers clutched the laundry basket as if it were a life preserver and when Cabel's voice filtered through her consciousness, it was several long moments before she could take in his words.

"Frances! Are you all right? What is it, girl?" He had moved swiftly to her side, coming up from the chair in a single lithe movement, and she blinked and forced a smile to her stiff lips, one that didn't convince anyone of anything.

"Just...just startled, that's all," she assured him shakily. "That one was close."

His arms came around her, and for just a fraction of an instant, she allowed herself the inestimable comfort of burrowing into his chest, drawing from the tough strength of him, and then she stiffened away and picked up her basket from where she had dumped it on the table. She turned away and bumped the basket on the door frame, muttering some excuse or another under her breath in her haste to get away before the next blast. With Cabel's terse voice in her ears above the steady rumble of thunder, she slammed her bedroom door closed as if the hounds of hell were on her heels and leaned against it.

"Frances! Open this door!" He was just on the other side and Frances struggled to overcome a hysterical giggle that rose in her throat. Fat chance she'd have of maintaining her pose of independence if he discovered she fell apart at a silly summer storm. She could take spiders and snakes and things that go bump in the night, but a close encounter with thunder and lightning was her undoing. Aware of his nearness just on the other side of her door, she crossed silently and scuttled to the center of her bed, carefully avoiding the thought of all the metal bedsprings beneath her. One of these days I'm going to read a really good scientific book about lightning, she promised herself, and then I won't be worrying about bedsprings and running water and tall trees.

The bubble of mirth erupted when she heard Terri's husky little cry outside her room. "Oh, Cabel, I'm just scared to death of all this lightning. Come sit on the couch with me till it's over, will you?"

If anything could cure her terror, that came close, and she relaxed somewhat and stretched out on her bed while the celestial bowling match passed over her head and continued on downriver, telling herself that if anything got hit, it would be the house on the hill, not the one in the hollow.

It there had been a way to get to the kitchen without having to go through the living room, she'd have done it. As it was, she settled for making as much noise as she could, and she avoided looking at where the two of them still sat on her sofa, with Cabel's arm across Terri's shoulder. It was none of her business if they wanted a cuddling session...within the bounds of decency, she amended, as she averted her face and hurried through to the kitchen. In spite of her precautions to avoid embarrassing the couple, she couldn't help see the look of concern Cabel sent her way.

Did he think she was offended, for goodness sake? She was no prude! She scraped the remains of a perfectly good salad in the garbage and rinsed the bowl under the faucet, managing to splash her denim skirt in the process. It was certainly no business of hers if they wanted to...

She whirled around on hearing someone enter the kitchen and dropped the paring knife she was washing.

"Why don't you watch where you're going?" she demanded illogically. She bent over to retrieve the knife at the same time he did, and their heads met forcefully.

"Oh, good Lord, why can't you leave me alone," she groaned, backing up while she felt her forehead for damage.

"You're falling to pieces," Cabel accused, clamping a steadying hand on her upper arm to swing her around the light of the window. He examined her face minutely. "Head still intact but nerves gone to pot," he diagnosed, and she couldn't keep a grin from trembling on her lips.

He answered it with one of his own and Frances thought it unfair for a man to have a dimple in one cheek while she had no such adornment. Far more effective than a matching pair, too, for it gave him a rakish sort of air that counteracted the sobering effect of his lightly silvered hair.

"Cab-el-l-l," Terri wailed from the living room. "I'm cold. Can't we go now?"

"Terri's cold, Cabel," Frances repeated with mock concern. "Surely you didn't refuse to give the poor girl the shirt off your back?"

She had forgotten the hand on her arm and now it tightened unmercifully as its owner shook her wrathfully. "Don't get smart with me, Miss Harris, or I might think you're jealous," he said with an outrageous gleam in his wicked eyes. "I've always heard frustration was a problem with women who were left too long to wither on the vine."

If it hadn't been for that gleam, Frances would have brained him, but something about the man, some imp of mischief that belied the aggressive thrust of his jaw, touched an answering chord in her, and she bit her bottom lip to keep it from giving her away.

"Cabel!" came the petulant cry from behind them. "I want to go now. Your house is ever so much more comfy."

"Say 'Thank you' to Miss Harris for her hospitality, Terri," Cabel prompted, and Frances thought that if he were hers, she'd tell him a thing or so. The insufferable male animal!

She smiled at the poor washed-out-looking girl with a mixture of sympathy and amusement, neither of which was reciprocated.

For the next few days her employer, Howard Stinson, seemed preoccupied and was out of the shop as often as he was in. That left Frances in charge of handling the incoming stock as well as serving the few customers who found their way to the small import shop, for the girl who worked there during the school year, when they did most of their business, wouldn't be starting for several weeks yet. Margaret Shober, the bookkeeper, a housewife whose husband had left her for greener and younger pastures, came in from nine to one, and Frances listened to her complaining that unless they did some reordering soon, by the time their peak season rolled around, there'd be nothing left to sell. That wasn't Frances's responsibility, though. Mr. Stinson did the ordering, although he had promised Frances when she had first come to work there that once she got the hang of things, she might occasionally go on a buying trip.

During the middle of the week they were adopted by a ridiculous stray cat who wouldn't take no for an answer, and Frances fell in love with the waif. She—they were always females, needing an expensive trip to a vet to make them sociably acceptable—was three-legged and extremely pregnant. When Margaret declared she couldn't take care of so much as another houseplant, Frances took the poor thing home with her, fleas, incipient kittens and all. Tripod rewarded her by following her around to stroke her leg at every step while quivering her bushy tail in ecstasy.

Tripod had been in residence about a week when Cabel brought home his dog. Frances first knew of the addition to the hill when Tripod came flying across the porch, her black and orange fur on end and a wild light in her yellow eyes. Close on her heels came an even more pregnant tricolored English setter, ears flapping in anticipation as she took off into the woods after the cat.

"Cabel!" Frances yelled around the corner of her house to the tall, jeans-clad man who came swinging lithely down the hill with a leash and collar in his hand. "Is that creature yours?"

"If you mean Mollie, then yes. What's all the ruckus? She took off as if you were handing out spare ribs at your kitchen door." He grinned easily and leaped up onto the porch to tower over her.

Frances glared at him, her hands planted firmly on her hips. "Your dog is chasing my cat," she accused. "What are you going to do about it?"

Dark, bushy brows lifted over innocent brown eyes. "I didn't even know you had a cat."

"Well, I do, and what's more she's pregnant and it doesn't do her a bit of good to be..."

The thought struck them both at the same instant, and they stared at each other and then crumpled into laughter. Frances howled until tears streaked her cheeks and Cabel leaned helplessly against the side of the house, wiping his eyes as he subsided into a few helpless gasps.

"Good Lord, can you picture it? The two of them are probably out there in the woods right now comparing notes on..."

"On pickles and ice cream and the horrible habits of footloose males," Frances filled in for him, breathing deeply in an effort to steady herself. She dropped down into the rocker and Cabel took the swing, and they smiled at each other for several moments before Frances caught herself up and started to babble to cover an unexpected feeling of awkwardness. "Mine was a stray. She showed up at the shop last week, and we were afraid of getting fleas in the stock and so I brought her home with me."

"So was mine...a stray, that is. Friend of mine's a vet and someone dropped the poor wretch off with a note to find her a home, so I got stuck."

They discussed the fruits of their respective pets' labors and Cabel suggested some of Frances's boyfriends might be interested in a pup who was at least half bird-dog.

"Some of your girl friends might want a kitten. There's bound to be at least one orange one in the litter that would match Terri's hair. Maybe she could train it to ride with her in the Spitfire."

"You're a wicked woman, Frances Harris," Cabel chided softly.

"Indeed I am, Cabel McCloud, and you'd better not forget it."

"I'm not likely to," he promised. "I wonder...just how far does your wickedness extend?" he mused, slanting her a provocative glance from beneath lazy lids.

"You aren't likely to find out," she answered shortly, irritated to discover herself coloring. To hide her embarrassment, she turned to the edge of the porch and called her cat, adding a whistle for the dog, as well. Funny how she couldn't be around the man for more than five minutes without getting flustered. If he didn't say something outrageous, why then did he look at her in such a way that she bridled like a fifteen-year-old, which was ridiculous, considering her age and experience.

The kittens arrived a week after Cabel's pups and Frances wondered how she could bear to give the darlings away. There were two grays and an orange, which she promptly named Terri. She had counted on giving at least one cat to Mr. Stinson, who had four children under high-school age, but he seemed so morose lately she didn't know how to bring up the subject.

Her oldest sister, Kay, who had married a veterinarian and lived at Eli Whitney, called to say that she had a friend she'd like Frances to meet, and wouldn't she like to come to dinner one night next week.

Frances made an excuse, as she did when Aunt Helen called from Durham about a nephew of Uncle Jerrold's, who, of course, wasn't a blood relative and was an awfully lonely young man who had come to Duke to do something concerning computers.

"Aunt Helen, I'm really not in the mood at the moment. Work's getting into the busy season, and there's the house, and I've a litter of kittens to get rid of." As if any of those things would keep her from finding time to spend with a man who really interested her. Just lately, she seemed to have lost interest in all the men she had dated, although she noticed that Cabel's social life was in full bloom. Terri had some formidable competition these days in the form of a tall, svelte brunette who arrived one Friday with a suitcase and didn't leave until Monday morning. She had followed Cabel's Mercedes down the driveway in her light blue Impala and Frances, in turn, had trailed along after them in her four-year-old Aspen.

"What?" She brought her attention back to her aunt's conversation with a start. "Sean? Oh, well, I'll meet him sooner or later. Yes, you too, Aunt Helen. 'Bye now."

Gathering up the orange kitten in her lap, she settled down in the bentwood rocker and stared unseeingly at the watercolor that had been one of her first purchases of original art. Another man in the offing, and this one sounded no more fascinating than any of the others. Computers! What on earth had made Aunt Helen think they'd have anything in common?

Well, he'd turn up sooner or later, probably with a jar of homemade preserves. Her aunt usually sent preserves or pickles, while her mother always sent along something from the garden with any man between the ages of eighteen and forty who happened to be coming this way. Her sisters weren't so subtle. They simply handed out her phone number to the prospective victim and informed him that they had a sister who lived near Chapel Hill and would be delighted to show them around and give them a home cooked meal.

"Oh, horse feathers!" she sniffed, plunking the kitten back in the secretary drawer with the others. She had yet to determine the sex of her babies. Her own system had always depended solely on color; orange ones were male, gray ones female, and all others whatever the prospective taker wanted them to be. Meanwhile, judging from the sounds outside, Tripod had got herself stranded up a tree again. She went up like a shot but coming down with three legs was another matter.

Not bothering to drag the ladder from under the house, Frances located the frightened cat, treed by Cabel's

Mollie, no doubt, and surveyed the layout of the branches. She grasped the lowest one tentatively and swung herself up, feeling above her for the next rung up among the lush cover of leaves.

Chapter Three

Quit backing away, you silly cat," Frances grumbled. Her toe was on a branch that was none too steady as she stretched for the next handhold, and her fingers were actually touching the next branch when an angry voice below her erupted: "What the heck's going on up there?"

The words startled her and she felt her foot slip; then everything seemed to happen at once, Mollie yapped, Tripod leaped to the next tree, and Frances landed on the ground with a solid thud.

It seemed ages before the air began to fill her tortured lungs again and she blinked rapidly, trying to keep the black spots that danced before her eyes from merging into an enveloping darkness. She felt hands on her body and was too far out of things to do anything about it, even when they went over her with a thoroughness that would ordinarily have brought a sharp retort to her lips.

"Can you breathe all right?" Cabel growled at her. "Does it hurt anywhere in particular?" One of his hands was sliding down her leg and the other one was pressed against her rib cage just under her breast. She managed to gasp out that she'd feel a darned sight better if he'd get his damned paws off her!

"Temper still intact, I see," he came back, ignoring her suggestion. "Now, let's see if you can sit up."

"You sit up if you want to! I'm staying right here where I am!"

He lifted her carefully, feeling her back and the back of her head. "This hurt?" He pressed a lump on one side of her head and she caught her breath.

"Of course it hurts, you stupid idiot! What did you expect? Every single time I see you I end up getting battered and broken!"

He ignored her, his voice a deep, soothing rumble as he parted her hair gently over the rapidly swelling lump. "Skin's not broken, at least, but we'll watch it, anyway. Try standing up now and we'll check out your legs."

She pushed him away, frowning, as a solid weight of pain raced through her shoulder.

"You seem to have landed on your head and shoulder, but there's no telling what you struck on the way down. Anybody as clumsy as you are ought to have sense enough to stay on the ground. Even if you felt you had to go chasing that lopsided animal of yours, you should have used a ladder. An idiot would have known better than to go climbing up the way you did."

"An idiot would also know when he wasn't wanted! Why don't you leave me alone, Cabel McCloud? Haven't you done enough harm already?"

She thought she saw his eyebrows shoot up but she couldn't be sure because his whole face was shimmering like a rainbow. Then he extended a finger and wiped a tear away from her cheek, studying it, and then looking at her as if he'd never seen her before.

"I'm not crying!" she declared tearfully.

"No, of course you aren't. Come on, now, up we go." He lifted her carefully, checking the position of her feet and running a hand down her thigh. "Anything hurt?" he asked mildly.

"Of course not! What could possibly hurt?"

"Good thing you had jeans on or you'd have scratched your hide on those branches. Although," he added judiciously, "you really shouldn't wear jeans in public. Not built for them. Some women are, but you're not."

She stopped in her tracks and glared up at him, too outraged to come up with words lethal enough to do justice to the occasion, but when he urged her along, she went helplessly because she suddenly didn't feel up to resisting any more. "I don't care what I look like," she lied under her breath. "I dress for convenience, not looks."

"Mmmm hmmm," was all he said as he lifted her in his arms and mounted the steps as if she weighed no more than one of her kittens. He went straight into her bedroom where he laid her carefully on the bed. By the time he straightened up and reached for her waistband, she had recovered her wits again.

"What do you think you're doing?" she demanded, pushing his hand away.

"Thought I'd check you out for any superficial ailments now that we've pretty well ruled out structural damage," he replied calmly.

"Check me out, the devil! If I need checking, I'll do it myself! Why don't you go on home? Isn't Terri waiting for you? Or maybe it's the brunette's turn today. She's got a lot more class, you know. I'd go with her, if I were you...quality's worth the extra cost in the end."

He grinned wickedly. "I'll have to bring her over for a closer inspection. One of her eyes might have just the slightest cast, I can't be sure. Maybe because whenever I get close enough to check it out, it's never her eyes I'm thinking about."

"God, you're dreadful! I only hope the poor creature doesn't wake up one of these days and find herself hog-tied to you."

"No chance of that. My policy of noninvolvement, remember? So far I've managed to enjoy the frosting without having to eat the cake and I see no reason to change," he replied with insufferable smugness.

"A steady diet of frosting can make you sick as a dog—I hope. Now, will you just clear out of my bedroom and leave me in peace?" Her head was beginning to throb by now and assorted aches and pains were making themselves felt, primarily in the area of her shoulder. She wriggled an arm experimentally, deciding maybe she'd better find out if she was going to need any help before he left.

"Trouble?" he asked quickly, his eyes narrowing as he caught her subtle movements.

"That's what I'm trying to find out," she grumbled, sitting up and lifting her arm cautiously. No bones broken, but all the same...

"Turn around," Cabel ordered, turning her before she could comply. His hand brushed her shirt lightly, then went to the buttons and began unfastening them very efficiently.

"Stop that!"

"Don't be any more of an idiot than nature made you. I'm not interested in your hidden charms...if any. I only want to see the extent of the damage back here. Your shoulder's bleeding all over your shirt." He completed his work and slipped the garment from her, taking special care with her injured shoulder.

Frances peered around, trying to see what had happened, but in spite of having an unusually swanlike neck, which her mother had always insisted was her best feature, she couldn't see over her shoulder.

"Hmmm, scraped rather badly, but I don't think it's anything I can't patch up. Where's your first-aid cabinet?"

Swallowing a feeling of queaziness as she saw her ruined shirt, Frances nodded to the bathroom and sat there looking helpless, ill at ease, and probably utterly ridiculous in her jeans and her lacy bra. But for all the attention he paid her figure, she might have been made of biscuit dough. Drat the man, anyway! She had seldom, if ever, met anyone who irritated her quite so thoroughly!

Returning a few minutes later, Cabel dropped the strap of her bra and then deftly unfastened it while Frances grabbed up her shirt and clutched it in front of her. She leaned forward, drawing up her knees and crossing her ankles for balance as he ministered to her with surprising gentleness. Fighting the urge to let herself go with the soothing spell of his hands, she said crossly, "I could have done it. You didn't need to bother."

"Show me just how you would have managed, then."

She slumped. Without even trying she realized that one of the few inaccessible places on her own body was her shoulder blade. "I could have got someone else to help me," she muttered ungraciously.

Cabel stepped back to survey his handiwork and Frances flexed her shoulder under its covering of gauze and adhesive tape. "It's a good thing you're such a liberated lady," he declared, "because you're going to have to do without this for several days."

Frances peered around to see him swinging her bra from one forefinger. She grabbed at it, almost losing the shirt that was the only thing that stood between her and toplessness in the process. "All right, *now* if you're quite finished, would you please get out of here and stop meddling in my affairs?"

Before he could reply one way or another to her rudeness, someone carolled from the front door, and Frances looked up with a stricken expression on her face to see her mother stroll into the bedroom.

For just a moment no one spoke. Then all three of them spoke at once. They backed off and tried again and this time her mother's shocked tones won out. "Fancey Ann! Why didn't you tell me?"

"Why didn't I tell you what? That I fell out of a tree and had to have my back plastered up?" Frances snapped, not caring for the gleam in her mother's eye at all.

"And your doctor...?" Patsy Harris turned to Cabel, extending an eager hand, and both Frances and Cabel hurried to set her straight.

"I'm Frances's neighbor, Cabel McCloud. I just happened along about the time the accident took place, so of course I did what I could. No permanent damage, I assure you."

Meanwhile, at the sound of Cabel's urbane disclaimer of any responsibility, Frances almost choked as she made the introductions.

"Fancey's neighbor? Would that be the old Cairington place? My, it's a wonderful old house, isn't it? I know you and your wife..." She paused, looking hopefully at Cabel with her sandy-colored brows lifted questioningly above faded blue eyes, and Frances groaned, causing both of them to look at her curiously.

"No wife, Mrs. Harris. I bought it because I couldn't resist the view, but except for a housekeeper who comes to rake out the place three days a week, I'm alone."

Alone, my foot, Frances thought uncharitably. The bed doesn't even have time to cool off the way he shuffles them in and out of there!

"Oh, what a shame," Patsy Harris gushed in her best poor-little-me-great-big-you manner. "I mean, to rattle all alone in that huge old place. You must be terribly lonesome."

"Mama," Frances intoned warningly.

Patsy turned an innocent look on her second daughter and then, with a sudden switch of topic that was typical of her, added, "Fancey, I do wish you wouldn't wear those dreadful trousers. You just don't have the figure for them. All the Harris women are built on more womanly lines than these liberated bean poles you see running around town looking like ragamuffins."

Frances stifled a desire to giggle. Here she sat, mortally wounded for all her mother knew, without a stitch on above the waist, and her mother was concerned about the impression she was making on her neighbor in her blue jeans!

"There now, Mr. McCloud, don't you think Fancey has the loveliest throat you ever saw? So graceful...takes after my own mother, you know. She was a Sanford on her mother's side and they did say..."

"Mama!" Frances cried. Then, turning in dismay to see the carefully concealed amusement in Cabel's eyes, she grimaced at him. "There, you see? All my own teeth, too," she pointed out with an edge of rashness coloring her voice. Then, to her everlasting shame, she burst into tears. And while Cabel held her tenderly and eased her arms into her stiff, ruined shirt, Patsy Harris stood by wringing her hands and wondering aloud if she should summon a doctor.

"She'll be all right, Mrs. Harris." Cabel's authoritative voice cut through Patsy's soft ditherings like a hot knife through butter. "I was getting ready to take her up to my house for supper and you're welcome to join us if you'd care to."

For some obscure reason she was too spent to determine, Frances chose not to argue. She sniffed and brushed his hand away when he would have done her buttoning up for her. She heard her mother saying something about her television set being on the blink. "I'm going by Eli Whitney to see Milo and Kay... that's my youngest daughter, you know. I said I'd be in time for supper, so..."

Cabel saw her out and Frances tried not to listen as Patsy pumped him for additional information. There was nothing at all subtle about her methods, but Cabel chose to find her outrageous questions amusing. He also chose not to answer them, but he did it in such a charming way that no one could take offense. Well, it wasn't as if there were any big secret about her family's matchmaking propensities. Frances had probably mentioned it to Cabel before and if not, then he might have a clue now as to why she preferred to be independent.

He returned from seeing Patsy to her car and Frances hurried from the bedroom to keep him from joining her there. "Thanks for everything, Cabel, and I apologize for the... oh, you know."

"Any services rendered were probably owed. This time I'll have to accept responsibility for startling you out of the tree."

"How about sharing it equally with me, then? I seem to have a terminal case of klutziness," she admitted wryly, adding to herself, at least where you're concerned. "Oh, and about the interrogation Mama put you through...don't feel singled out. It happens to all males who run across the female members of my family, I'm afraid. You handled it like a pro."

"Patsy's just a little more open about it than most women," he grinned. "I like her. Now, how about getting out of that gory shirt and then I'll feed you." He leaned against the secretary, now bare of kittens, and crossed his arms over the broad expanse of his chest, eyeing her analytically. "Wear a dress. Your hips are too broad for pants, especially as your waist is practically nonexistent," he said solemnly. "Fancey Ann, you'll never get yourself a man parading around here in those dreadful pants."

She bridled, then her mobile mouth twisted into a grin as she pretended to swing at him. But she drew back just short of connecting with that all too solid flesh. It wasn't fear of retribution, either, she decided as she slipped on a loose-fitting gauzy peasant gown of blacks, reds and golds. In spite of the momentary peace that existed between them, there was an underlying thread of something that didn't bear analysis. At least on her side there was, and she had an idea that any physical contact between them might just stretch that peace to the breaking point.

Back in the living room, she suffered his appraisal with ill-concealed impatience. "Anything else you'd like disguised? Should I pull a sack over my head, maybe?" After all, plenty of other men had seen her in pants and managed to keep their opinions to themselves; in fact a few even came up with a compliment. "Not all men are so narrow-minded as to think only women built like greyhounds should be allowed to wear jeans!"

"That rankled, didn't it?" he grinned. "I don't suppose anything I could say now would help, so I'll keep my opinions to myself, but allow me to tell you how nice your hair looks."

She shot him a suspicious glance. Considering that all women who could no longer call themselves girls should wear a hairstyle suitable to their maturity, Frances had worn hers up in several different styles for the past few years. Today, only because she was in a hurry, she had brushed the pinestraw out and removed the remaining hairpins and let it hang. Like a pale gold, silken cloud, she had hoped, although Cabel probably thought it looked more like a haystack.

They crossed the several hundred feet of sloping lawn that separated the two houses, and Frances was unable to keep herself from glancing at him as he swung along lithely beside her. No more tender solicitation now. She might have been a fishing buddy coming up from the river beside him for all the attention he paid her over the sometimes quite steep hillside. Unless she was torn and bleeding, he couldn't bother to extend a hand, she thought scornfully, angry with Cabel for ignoring her and with herself for caring. She supposed she was fortunate he was even thinking of feeding her.

"To what do I owe the honor?" she inquired disdainfully, mounting the broad, gracious steps to the verandah.

He treated her to a lift of one sardonic brow as he held open the huge, beveled glass door. "Mmmmm? You sound as if you'd rather not accept my hospitality. Don't feel obligated, Fancey. I don't mind eating alone in the least. Do it . . . oh, one or two nights a week,'' he admitted with suspect candor.

Nevertheless, he took her arm and ushered her into the spacious entrance hall. Frances swallowed her ragged pride rather than turn away. She wanted to eat with him. She wanted to see his home, and what's more, as much as she hated to admit it, she wanted to be with him, to spar with him in that particular way that seemed to make the nerves lift along her spine. But then, she had always enjoyed a good argument; her father had told her she should have gone in for a law career instead of majoring in art history.

The house was surprisingly attractive, although later she wondered why she should have been surprised. Filled with a compatible selection of modern and period furniture, with pleasing, unobtrusive colors, it hardly seemed the place for a single man living alone, especially not a man who had professed himself a confirmed bachelor. But then she too was enjoying her home and she certainly had no intention of marrying.

In the kitchen they ate country ham, potato salad, and homemade watermelon pickles that were blue-ribbon quality. ''My housekeeper's a terrible woman but a wonderful cook,'' Cabel confided, tipping back his chair with a sigh of repletion.

''You don't exactly rough it here, do you?'' she asked wryly.

His grin quickened. ''Disappointed? Were you looking forward to a chance to show me your proper appreciation for all the help I've been to you, Fancey?''

''Don't call me that,'' she snapped irritably. ''No, I'm not disappointed, and I certainly don't owe you any appreciation. After all, if you hadn't sneaked up and scared the daylights out of me, I wouldn't have fallen in the first place!"

"You, with what you yourself called a terminal case of klutziness? You'd have simply climbed higher and fallen even further if I hadn't showed up and saved you from your own foolishness," he jeered.

"I've had enough!" she cried, getting to her feet so suddenly that the table jarred.

"But Fancey, we haven't even had dessert yet," he taunted.

"You eat it! You could do with the sugar!"

"Worried about your hips?" he chided softly, provocatively.

"No, damn you, I like my hips just the way they are!"

Leaning over to make a slow, deliberate study, he nodded. "On second thought, I'm inclined to agree with you," he murmured judiciously.

Choking on her indignation, Frances stalked across the big, old-fashioned kitchen, and without seeming to have moved, Cabel was there before her, leaning indolently in the doorway so as to block her exit. "Oh, but you haven't had the grand tour yet."

"I'll buy the book!"

Her anger only seemed to amuse him, and that made her even angrier. She tucked her chin under as if considering a charge.

"Fancey, why do you suppose we can't be together five minutes without sparks flying. Have you given it any thought?" he asked as if he were seeking information about the best lawn food to try.

Nonplussed, she blinked at him. "Well, I suppose it's because we...we just don't like each other," she offered slowly, wondering as she said it if it were true.

Shifting away from the doorway, he studied her quizzically. "I wonder," he mused, running a well-kept hand through the thatch of his close-cropped hair. "Purely academic question, Fancey, but have you ever been in love?"

"Have I ever...well, not that it's any business of yours, but no, I haven't! At least," she tacked on hesitantly, "I thought I was once, but I've concluded that I'm not the type."

"Not the type?" His thick eyebrows climbed astonishingly.

She turned away, flustered, wondering how she had ever gotten herself into such a discussion. "Not the romantic type...the sort to believe in hearts and flowers forevermore. You ought to understand, for goodness sake, you said you felt the same way," she finished with an unaccountable breathlessness. The proportions of the large kitchen seemed to have shrunk, bringing Cabel uncomfortably close to her.

"But what if in spite of all your good intentions you found yourself interested in a man...that way," he persisted smoothly.

"I'd put it down to pure biology and forget it," she retorted.

Cabel threw back his head and laughed unrestrainedly. Feeling at a disadvantage for some unfathomable reason, Frances tried to slip past him, but he was too quick for her. His hands came down on her shoulders quite suddenly, and only when she gasped and flinched away did he remove them, a stricken look on his face. "God, Frances, I forgot."

"I want to go home, Cabel," she managed weakly. It wasn't the pain in her shoulder that was making her want to run and hide, but the shattering feeling that she was dangling on strings and she couldn't even see the puppeteer.

"Frances..."

"*If* you please!"

"But I don't please, Fancey Ann." The mockery was back full force, wiping out any momentary softening. "Besides, your manners are lamentable. Didn't your mother ever tell you it was rude to eat and run? A woman your age...what is it, thirty? Thirty-five?"

"It's twenty-seven," she gasped, and he caught her mid-gasp. He caught her before she could do more than lift a hand in feeble protest, her hand trapped between the hardness of his chest and the softness of hers.

Cabel took full advantage of her awkward position to kiss her thoroughly, with a practiced sureness that left her other hand fluttering helplessly in the air. Her muffled protests grew weaker and weaker as his mastery took effect. And when the hand that was trapped found its way up to clutch his collar, he eased his hold enough for her to slide her other arm around his waist.

Even as he explored her mouth boldly, taking his time with evident pleasure, he was careful not to touch her wounded shoulder. Instead, with one arm holding her about the small of her back, he allowed his other hand to trail slowly up her side, giving her all the time in the world to lodge a complaint. Then he pulled his hand deliberately around so that it was lifting the small fullness of her breast, weighing the value of it in the palm of his hand.

She stiffened, sensing a mockery in the very playfulness of the gesture. He lifted his head to gaze down at her quizzically.

"Let me go," she whispered hoarsely, struggling to pull her scattered defenses together.

"I don't think I want to let you go," he murmured, nuzzling the sensitive nerve at the side of her neck.

She writhed against the sensations that the touch of his tongue sent coursing through her body. And his hand, the one that had held her waist against escape, dropped to her hips and splayed out to caress their roundness, pressing her hard against him with devastating frankness. "Stop that! You have your nerve!"

"I do, don't I?" he agreed easily as he caught the peak of her breast between thumb and forefinger.

Frances was stunningly aware of the effect he was having on her traitorous body and, what was worse, she knew he was just as aware. Her own body could no more disguise her reactions to him than his could to her.

"Once more, Fancey Ann," he whispered, his mouth hovering just above her swollen, throbbing lips to taunt her. But before he could taste their promise, they were interrupted by the sound of a car crunching up on the gravel driveway.

Frances's back was to the door, which put her at a disadvantage, especially as Cabel, instead of releasing her and going to greet his visitor, lowered his head to hers and proceeded to carry on with his ruthlessly masculine assault on her senses. The slam of the car door coincided with the entrance of his pointed tongue in her mouth. As footsteps mounted the steps and crossed the verandah, he slid his hands up her back slowly, deliberately caressing her until he inadvertently touched the bandage he had placed on her shoulder.

She winced and ducked under the pain even as he lifted his head to stare down at her. "Oh, Lord, Frances, I'm sorry. I forgot about your battle scars."

"You didn't forget a damned thing," she accused stiffly, her voice low in his ear as she sensed the presence of someone just on the other side of the open door. "Let me go!"

"Well! Maybe I'd better go out and come in again," said a low, melodious drawl from behind her. "We did have a dinner date, didn't we, darling? I haven't mistaken the night?"

His hands slipped slowly, almost reluctantly, from Frances's arms and he said, "No, you didn't make a mistake, Olivia. Come on in, Frances was just leaving. Frances, this is Olivia Dawson. Olivia, Frances Harris, a neighbor of mine."

"A close neighbor, I see," insinuated the elegant brunette. It was the same one Frances had seen driving past several times and now, at close range she was even more beautiful, the magnolialike perfection of her skin making Frances uncomfortably aware of the flushed sheen of her own face, just as the woman's small, coral-tinted lips mocked the nakedness of Frances's own more generous mouth. There was certainly nothing neighborly-looking in the crystal clear blue eyes that swept her with chilling dislike. Frances mumbled something and brushed past the two of them, not sparing a glance for Cabel. As her steps gathered an unladylike haste, she prayed she wouldn't trip over her own hurrying feet, for Lord knows, she couldn't see where she was going for the silly, stupid tears in her eyes!

Chapter Four

While the generous display of the crepe myrtles reached its peak and waned and the sourwoods rushed the season with a tinge of russet, Frances avoided any contact with Cabel. Her free half-days and her Sundays she spent visiting friends and family or canoeing downriver from Chicken Bridge, to stop off at her own house and provide dinner for the owner of the canoe.

The heating contractor sent a reminder that another payment for her expensive floor furnace was due, and after writing the hefty check she wondered how she was going to afford to operate the thing. Efficient it might be; free it was not!

But the wood stove that had come with the house still sat there, a constant reminder that previous residents had not had to range far to come up with a supply of heating material. And so the first free afternoon she had, Frances set forth, accompanied by both Tripod and Mollie, who seemed to have been drawn closer to some sort of an understanding by their mutual maternity.

Would that their owners could resolve their differences so easily, Frances thought, casting an unwilling glance at the pale yellow house she had fled a few weeks ago. Since then, they had greeted each other in passing and that was the extent of it. Which was not to say Frances hadn't watched that tall, lean figure emerge tiredly from the maroon sedan and climb the steps with a briefcase that seemed to grow thicker and heavier every day.

Armed now with a brand new handsaw, Frances located two likely prospects for her wood stove. One, a standing pine, was already dead, and the other was a hardwood tree of some sort that must have blown over during one of the summer storms. She surveyed the fallen tree doubtfully, wondering where to start. Somehow, back in the living room, thinking of a big pot of Brunswick stew simmering away on the cast-iron stove while the fall rains beat down on her tin roof, it had all seemed so plausible; but faced with the actual prospect—whacking up a full grown tree into serving-size pieces—was quite another matter.

It took her no more than thirty minutes to discover that a handsaw, and a cheap one, at that, wasn't equal to the job. She had tried her father's hatchet on some of the hardwood branches and watched it bounce back as if she were trying to cut marble. The standing pine was still standing, only now it had a blue-handled saw jammed in its resinous flesh. Frances plunked herself down on the hardwood and unbuttoned her shirt. The cool early autumn day had heated up rapidly once she began exerting herself. She had dressed for the task in a flannel shirt and her jeans, remembering with a sting of anger Cabel's acidulous remarks about her hips.

Of course her mother had said the same thing, but that hadn't bothered her nearly as much.

"Hell's bells, Mollie, what am I going to do, rent a beaver?" she demanded of the patient setter.

Mollie's attention, however, had switched to another direction, and following it, Frances was chagrined to see Cabel come striding through the woods like some silver-thatched Paul Bunyan.

Fine! Just what she needed—a witness to her failure!

"Mind telling me what's going on?" he asked mildly, surveying the scene with an expression in which Frances managed to read condescension, amusement, and mockery.

She cast him a sullen look from under her brows, taking in the worn white dress shirt and the equally worn jeans that clung to his muscular thighs with disconcerting faithfulness. The shirt, she noticed disdainfully, was open to reveal a thick pelt of chest hair that he must be trying to show off. Big macho deal!

"I'm cutting wood," she answered grudgingly.

He knelt and levered the saw from the pine with an easy, one-handed effort and then dropped down beside her. "Where'd you get it, a toy store?"

"A hardware store!"

"In the toy department. Was it deliberate? Is it part of the ploy to bungle the job so that some naïve male will come along and say, move over, little girl, and let a man take a whack at it?" He tilted his head to cast her a skeptical look. Frances could have strangled him! The fact that she couldn't absolutely swear to the purity of her motives, knowing full well he had a chain saw and was adept at using it, had been pushed to the outer fringes of her consciousness; but she couldn't in all honesty tell him it hadn't occurred to her... which made her present position unbearable!

"If you'll give me my toy saw, Mr. McCloud, I'll finish the job later. If there's one thing I don't need, it's a know-it-all sidewalk superintendent who sits around flexing his muscles and making snide remarks while..."

"While you sit on a log and try to figure out how the hell to get the wood chopped."

She jumped to her feet and reached for the saw, but unless she cared to risk slicing a few fingers by grabbing the blade, she was helpless, for Cabel's strong, well-cared-for hand was wrapped firmly around the shiny blue handle.

"Just as a matter of interest, Fancey Ann..."

"Don't call me that!" she broke in.

"Just as a matter of interest, which was it you objected to most, the flexing of my muscles or the snide remarks? Or maybe it was the know-it-all bit. The male superiority thing that has your girlish nerves all atingle, hmmm?"

Mollie distracted their attention for a moment as she charged furiously at a pine cone, and when she gave it up and trotted off into the woods after livelier quarry, Frances turned to stare in front of her, a helplessness seeping into her bones that made her no match for Cable's sarcasm.

"If you'll give me my saw, I'll see about having it sharpened," she said indifferently. She held out her hand and they both looked at it, seeing the contrast between the long, slender fingers and soft white palm with its angry red blisters, against his own hand, with its light covering of dark hair on the back and the strong, square-tipped fingers.

"You do that, Frances. Meanwhile, I'll bring my chain saw out and cut it into manageable sections for you. Do you want the dead pine, too? Some people don't like to burn pine on account of the resin."

"So what are you now, an expert on home heating?" she asked with a defensive sarcasm of her own.

"I'm an investment broker," he replied matter-of-factly, "but I have fireplaces, including those in the bedrooms, and I've picked up a few tips in anticipation...of the winter, that is," he added with an enigmatic glance at her flushed face.

"An investment broker!" But then, why not? She shouldn't be surprised that a man who wore custom-tailored suits as if he'd been born to them, and who drove a car that cost more than she made in a year...in *two* years!...should do more than dabble in this and that. For all the care and attention he had given her shoulder after the last time they had met in these woods, he might have been a doctor.

"How's the shoulder?" he asked with another of those disconcerting feats of mind reading he practiced too often for her comfort.

"Fine."

"You haven't fallen for anyone lately, then?" he cracked, and she glared up at him.

"Is that supposed to be humorous?" she demanded sweetly.

He lifted his lumberjack shoulders...developed, no doubt, from lugging a briefcase around...and she couldn't help but be aware of the scent of his clean sweat. "You fell for me the first few times we met. In the realtor's office, remember? Don't know which I found harder to forget, your natural grace or your ladylike vocabulary."

"Oh, thanks a heap! It took me all of two minutes to forget the clumsy dolt who deliberately tried to trip me up!"

"If you'd given it another two minutes you might have remembered that I wasn't the one who lost my balance, or my temper, either," he said with maddening aplomb.

"Oh, shut up and give me my saw!"

As if she hadn't spoken, Cabel went on musingly. "You know, it's always been my experience that anyone who resorts to telling someone to shut up is admitting defeat, confessing that he...or she hasn't a single fact on his...or her side of the argument."

"I'm glad to see you realize we're arguing," she rejoined bitterly.

"When do we do anything else?"

"My saw...please?" she begged through clenched teeth. There was just no winning with this insufferable creature! He managed to twist her words so that she came out looking silly and childish, a hopeless case!

She extended her hand and he dropped the saw and caught her, pulling her to him so that she lost her balance and fell heavily against his side. Before she could right herself again, he was holding her with one arm, while with his other he stroked the tendrils of untidy hair from her overheated face.

"Calm down, girl, calm down," he soothed, as one might gentle a high-strung colt. "It's only words. You rise so beautifully, I can't help playing with you."

One strain of thought ran like a clear stream through her rocky emotions: she wasn't about to lose the last threads of her dignity by wrestling with him. If it pleased him to treat her like a child with a temper tantrum, why then she'd just humor him until he got tired of playacting and then she'd get up and walk away...without a word. Without a backward glance. She'd heat with gas instead of wood, if it bankrupted her, before she'd accept any help from him.

One stroking finger twisted a corkscrew curl. The warmth and humidity always made her hair react that way, and she was both warm and humid at the moment. He tucked it gently behind her ear and then began tracing the recesses of her ear, fingering the soft lobe caressingly. "Did anyone ever tell you you have lovely ears, Fancey Ann?" he mused. "You do; pink and white, small and flat, my kind of ear altogether."

"And you're a connoisseur, of course," she tried to sound sarcastic but it came out as breathless.

"Naturally. I'm an ear-eye-nose-and-throat specialist, actually, and I've already seen the quality of your eyes. They're unusually large, clear, direct, and in spite of all indications to the contrary, rather vulnerable sometimes."

She opened her mouth to argue and he closed it by the simple expedient of lifting her chin and holding it. "Now, your nose," he began, and she raised a defensive hand to that part of her anatomy. It wasn't a particularly delicate nose, neither classically refined nor pertly retroussé.

"Your nose is what I'd call proud," he declared sagely. "Not so small as to be insignificant. No woman worth looking at twice gets by with an insignificant nose; on the other hand, it can't be so large that it interferes with your kissing. Yours is just about right, I'd say, but then, only time will tell. Noses are cartilage, you know, and so every time you tell a lie, it goes on growing."

A burst of stifled mirth erupted, and Cabel gave her a look of hurt indignation before going on to her next feature. "Your mother alerted me to the loveliness of your swanlike neck...although I'd already noticed. It was the third thing I noticed about you... maybe the fourth, but then, you have to remember, you were standing at the time and I was sitting down."

"Cabel, for Lord's sake, stop it!" Frances exploded weakly, surrendering to the helpless laughter that had replaced all her frustrated anger. How did he do it? How could the outrageous creature manage to disarm her every single time? "You make me feel like a heifer at a fatstock sale!"

"Hmm, well, if that were the case, I'd say timing was just as important as overall presentation."

She had to hear him out. With a dreadful sort of fascination, she heard him explain that if she went on the block right after a plumper offering, she might appear too weak, and if she went on immediately following an adolescent type, then of course, she'd lose in value because any prospective buyer would be forced to consider the number of years' service she was still good for. "All in all, I'd say that given proper presentation and an appreciative, carefully selected clientele, you'd go for close to top money. As an investment broker, I know what I'm talking about, so..."

Frances twisted out from under his arm, laughing as she stood and backed away from him. "You're impossible, do you know that?"

He nodded judiciously. "I've been called that...among other things."

"I can well imagine some of the other things," she came back witheringly.

"You did...at least I hope they were only imagination," he grinned, levering himself off the log in one easy motion. Frances wondered fleetingly what an investment broker did to keep himself in the peak of condition. Cabel was like a sleek jungle cat in his prime; capable of coming from a state of utter relaxation to full alert with nothing lost in the transition. She sighed unconsciously as she turned away to where the tin roof of her house showed through the branches of pine and poplar. The sun had already dropped out of sight and in spite of the echoing colors of its warmth, the air had taken on a briskness that presaged autumn.

"Come on, I'll make a deal with you," Cabel announced easily, a hand on the small of her back as he steered her through the clearing. Their footsteps were silent on the damp, pungent humus. "I'll saw wood while you cook us something hot and satisfying for dinner, all right? I'm in the mood for something besides Hazel's cold offering."

She slanted him a mocking look. "Aren't you afraid of being compromised?"

"We both know where we stand," he pointed out reasonably, "so I wouldn't expect you to trade on a momentary lapse. If we swap services, then we're even. The trees need cutting . . . beetles long gone from the pine, of course, but we need to keep an eye open for any more infestation, and the hardwood...it's elm, I'm sorry to say."

"So? That's not good?"

"Oh, it'll burn all right, at least it will after it dries out, but it won't split. Crazy grain. I'll have to saw it up into small chunks and then we'll stack it and let it dry."

There were three quarts of Brunswick stew left that her mother had put up last season and Frances tipped one of them into a copper-bottomed pot. Brunswick stew went with wood chopping and, besides, she hadn't all that much to choose from. By the time Cabel came into the back door, wiping his hands on the seat of his jeans, the aroma of well-seasoned meats and vegetables filled the air.

Lest he think she was parading her domesticity out for him to admire, Frances told him quickly that her mother had canned the stew. The biscuits were her own, though, and Cabel accounted for seven of those before sitting back to enjoy one more cup of coffee.

"If the weather holds, we'll haul the wood to that flat spot beside your chimney next week, all right? Don't worry, you can do your share. I believe in full equality of the sexes, given equal tools." His grin mocked the quick lift of her chin and Frances relaxed again. "You're too quick off the mark, girl, much too quick," he teased.

She subsided. There was no denying that almost everything this man did or said abraded her nerves, but there was no point in carrying things to ridiculous extremes; and so, being of a basically open nature, she simply nodded. "I think it must be my conditioning. You know, the dolls and tea sets for girls, guns and cars for boys. Saxapahaw wasn't exactly the most progressive place to grow up in. Not that I'd trade it for anywhere else," she added hastily, "but all the same..." Her words trailed off as she lifted her shoulders expressively. "I just felt pushed into rebelling, somehow."

Surprisingly, Cabel volunteered the information that he had grown up in a town house in Chicago. "Went from town house to condominium to apartment, with damned little grass growing under my feet except for the few weeks I took off every year. Friend of mine had a place in upper Maine where the only females were moose and there wasn't a damned thing to hear or see except mosquitoes buzzing and fish jumping." He smiled an inward sort of smile that did strange things in the region of Frances's heart and she told herself it was the stew. "Did you ever see a grown man play at cowboys and Indians?"

"Is that anything like playing Paul Bunyan?" she asked innocently.

"Touché. Now you know I'd have chopped that wood if you and an army of liberated females tried to keep me from it." His smile broadened and he stood up, leading the way into her living room as if he were the host, she the guest. "Wouldn't we be more comfortable in here?"

"Unless you have a date," she said. "It's after nine, you know."

"Hmmm. Well, if I did, it's too late now," he answered, frustrating her curiosity. She snapped on the overhead light and Cabel immediately switched it off, turning on a smaller lamp instead as he murmured something about eyestrain. "This is nice," he gestured toward a small watercolor.

"I like it, too. I have another one by that artist in..." She broke off, her lips tightening as she thought of the connotation he'd put on the information that the other painting was in her bedroom. Come up and see my etchings! "And then there's the woodcut," she supplied hastily, pointing at a work that wasn't particularly outstanding but that had been given her by a bachelor friend of her youngest sister when he discovered she was interested in art. It filled a space and wasn't all that bad, really, but she preferred the immediacy of watercolor.

Cabel took the couch and Frances settled for the bentwood rocker, which had proved more decorative than comfortable in the long run. To her acute discomfort, now that they were seated in her small, but attractively decorated living room, conversation languished. Cabel smiled at her expectantly and she shifted on the caned bottom and racked her brain for a noncontroversial topic.

"D...do you think we'll have any more warm weather?" she assayed brightly when the silence became more than she could bear.

Cabel leaned back, stretched an arm out across the back of the chesterfield and laughed that deep, magnificent, unrestrained laughter that brought her to her feet angrily.

"Damn it, Cabel McCloud, you do it on purpose, don't you?" she charged. Untended since her foray into the woods, her once-neat hair had slipped its moorings, and now she blew upward at an irritating tendril.

His laughter dwindled into a few rich chuckles and he shook his head, his eyes sparkling wickedly up at her. "Oh, Lord, Fancey, if I do," he assured her, "it's because I can't help myself. You're so absolutely irresistible as a crusty little spinster, all full of bristly defenses, that I just can't help trying to poke a few holes in your armor."

"Damn you to hell and back, Cabel McCloud, you're the rudest creature I've ever met!" She pointed one trembling finger in the direction of her front door. "You're perfectly entitled to your own opinion of me, but you might have the...the kindness to keep it to yourself! Get out of my house!"

He rose from his seated position and she found herself all too close for comfort, but before she could back away he slid both his hands up her arms from elbow to shoulder and shook her gently. "Easy does it, girl. You'll blow a gasket."

"Out!" His nearness was having an unfortunate effect on her knees, and her mouth was suddenly dry. She moistened it with the tip of her tongue and prepared to level him with her second barrage when he swooped and caught her unprepared, covering her surprised mouth with his own. As a moan of pure hopeless rage escaped her, she felt herself begin to fall apart, the strength seeped from her feeble brain as Cabel tangled an ungentle hand in her hair and held her captive to the depredations of his searching mouth. The heat of his hard body quickly permeated the thin fabric that separated them, forcing her dazed awareness of every muscle in the long length of him, and she moved imperceptibly closer, nearer to the flame that drew her to destruction. It was as if every atom of his masculinity were impressed on the soft vulnerability of her body and she wanted more, far more than she had ever wanted from any man before.

"God, you go to a man's head," Cabel murmured against the exquisite sensitivity of her throat. His tongue touched the pulse that fluttered there like an imprisoned bird, and she became aware that her hands were inside his shirt, her fingers digging into the taut flesh of his back.

"I think the rest of this evening's a foregone conclusion, hmm?" He began moving her into the bedroom, his arms holding her body so close that she could feel the play of muscles in his hard thighs as he walked her backward.

She grasped at a fragment of self-preservation. "What do you mean?" She knew what he meant! Her body knew, even while her mind was rejecting the casual thing Cabel had in mind. From making fun of her he thought he could go immediately to making love to her and it just wasn't on! Not by a long shot!

With some last resource of strength, she pulled herself away from him and clasped her arms across her chest, not flinching away from the question she saw in those passion-darkened eyes. "It won't wash, Cabel. I'm not another of your panting little playmates, who's willing to take any scrap of attention and be grateful for it."

Before she could look away from the hurtful intensity of those golden brown eyes, she saw the shutters come down. Oh, yes, he'd be backing off now, knowing he'd had a lucky escape! "Unless you've had a pretty drastic change of mind lately," she dared.

"Have you? Are you willing to admit you're not as independent as you thought?"

Armor securely in place now, Frances shook her head emphatically. "The day I need a man in my life will be a long time coming, Cabel McCloud, so you can just keep your fun and games for a more willing player! Now, will you please leave?"

"Oh, come on, Fancey Ann, where's your sense of humor? That happens to be one of the most delightful things about you, you know, the fact that we can swap a few bullets and a few kisses with no danger of entanglement to either one of us. Good Lord, if I wasn't convinced that you're a dyed-in-the-wool spinster with no hopes...I mean, no desire to find a man, that I wouldn't touch you with a barge pole." He was leaning back against the wall now, arms crossed, as were hers, and they eyed each other warily...at least it was wariness on her part. But for the life of her, she couldn't decipher the strange glitter in Cabel's eyes, and for some reason it made her nervous. She backed away another step.

"Why do you think I'd have dared to offer to cut your wood, or asked you to fix me a hot meal? Would I have allowed myself in your bedroom, even to patch up your shoulder, if I didn't know you were above any tricks? Come on, Fancey, we both need a cool, impersonal friend, someone we can relax around."

"I wouldn't call what you had in mind exactly impersonal," she reproached, trying for a slightly bored sophistication only to have the effect spoiled by a stupid blush.

"No problem. These things happen, honey, you're old enough to know that. Doesn't mean a thing, just old Mother Nature reminding us we're still alive and kicking," he replied easily, measuring her with a look she couldn't begin to understand.

Her head tilted doubtfully. She was vaguely relieved. Well, of *course* she was relieved, she snapped to herself, but then, why did it feel so much like disappointment? Why was it that all she could think of was what it might have been like to lie in those hard, muscular arms all night, giving herself up to the pure pleasure of the moment without a thought of tomorrow?

"Pax?" Cabel asked softly, interrupting her troublesome thoughts.

"Pax," she agreed reluctantly, watching him go with a swiftly fading smile.

Chapter Five

For the next week or so Frances and Cabel circled about each other warily, like two boxers sizing up the opponent's weaknesses. If there was an element of amusement in Cabel's attitude, France chose not to recognize it. For herself, she discovered she was spending far too much time thinking about her irritating, puzzling neighbor and she resolved to put her mind to other things. To other men, at least.

Doyle O'Hanlon, a man she had dated infrequently for a couple of years, moved from the periphery of her social life to front and center. She went dancing with him twice in one week and sat and listened to the Cowboy Band and drank beer, which she abhorred, at Cat's Cradle one rainy Saturday night.

On the next weekend he ordered her to wear her best bib and tucker for he was taking her to a new supper club that had opened up near Durham.

It would be a relief to go somewhere where she wouldn't be rubbing elbows with the college crowd, which got younger every year, and she decided on her coolest gown—a short, layered chiffon in shades of bronze, gold, and black—that hung from spaghetti straps to swirl loosely about her knees in handkerchief points. Her bronze slides had three-inch heels, which put her on an eye level with her date and she decided that that might not be a bad thing either. Doyle had been hinting rather strongly that it was about time for a few quiet evenings *à deux* in Frances's riverside cottage; and by the time the evening was less than an hour old, she was fairly certain she was reading the message in those light gray eyes accurately. Her spine stiffened accordingly.

The club was a converted old plantation-type house of doubtful vintage, but charming nevertheless. A surprisingly good dance band was on hand and music of the forties flowed nostalgically through the open French windows as they walked from the parking lot to the paved terrace where several couples were already dancing.

Opening into a large central ballroom were small secluded alcoves, with two or three tables in each, and the light was dimly romantic as Doyle ushered her after the maître d'hotel to their reserved table. The scent of roses and magnolias mingled freely with the fragrance of expensive perfume, fine tobacco, and freshly risen yeast rolls. Frances leaned back expansively and thought, this is more like it! This is the sort of place a man brings a girl friend, but how many men would bring a wife here once the honeymoon was over?

"Dance?" Doyle invited after they had ordered from the over-sized menu. The selection was impressively small, there were no prices visible, and Frances felt the first tinge of dismay mar her pleasure. Oh, Lord, she hoped Doyle wasn't beginning on a last-ditch effort to lure her into his bed . . . or himself into hers. She was no stranger to the look-how-much-I-spent-on-you approach, which was one of the reasons she liked to pay her own way whenever she went out with a man, if she could do it without giving offense. On a date like this one, though, she had an idea that it wouldn't work.

They moved into the main room, with Frances following Doyle's intricate steps easily. She was a good dancer; she enjoyed it, but she wasn't really comfortable when her partner insisted on holding her as closely as Doyle was doing now, with his hand dropping below her waist in a suggestive manner that brought warmth to her face and a sparkle of irritation to her eyes.

"Mmm, that looks good," she murmured in an effort to distract him. He followed her glance to where a red-coated waiter carried a tray of baked country ham, candied yams and decorative curls of something green.

"I still haven't lived in the South long enough to take grits and greens with my candlelit dinners," he dismissed, nuzzling her neck.

"It's too warm for that, Doyle. Besides, I'm hungry," she insisted, backing away.

"Mmmm, so'm I."

Before she was called on to parry that remark the music ended and she led the way thankfully back to their table. Romantic candlelight was a lot safer when they had the distance of the table between them.

While they were dancing, one of the tables in their alcove had been occupied and now the waiter was leading another couple to the third table. Frances looked around casually as she was being seated.

It was Cabel, and with him was Olivia, her black and white beauty set off almost too perfectly by a black lace dress that must have been crocheted onto her body, so well did it fit. Cabel smiled in a manner she preferred to call facetious and offered her the slightest bow, while his date lifted her nose another degree and turned her back.

During the next hour Frances was miserably aware of the pair behind her. They were seated so that her back was to Olivia's, which meant that Cabel could stare at the back of her head...as well as anything else he wanted to, and she couldn't do a thing about it.

Don't be an utter fool, Frances Ann Harris! Why on earth should the man stare at your scrawny neck when he has someone as lovely as Olivia Dawson seated across the table from him?

Olivia's seductive voice could be heard under the band, a continuous background, like the music of the Haw as it rushed over the rocks on its eager way to the sea. Only Olivia's voice wasn't all that welcome a sound. Frances found herself listening unconsciously for Cabel's deep, infrequent replies, and Doyle had to speak to her twice to gain her attention.

"What's wrong, sweetheart? I thought you'd love this place. I had to pawn the family jewels to book a reservation."

She groaned inwardly. The opening shot of the battle had just been fired, she was afraid. "I know, Doyle, and I adore it, I really do. The food..." She had scarcely tasted the crisp-edged pink beef and the fresh spinach and the wild rice. "The food's superb and the band...I haven't heard a band like that since..."

"Since you were a girl back in the forties," he finished for her.

"Well, let's just say my parents collected records then and I wore them out when I was growing up, dancing sock-footed with Kay and Jean."

"Let's dance," Doyle said now restlessly. "Keep in mind, I'm not one of your sisters," he added meaningfully as he drew her to his side to pass between the tables. Cabel and Olivia stood just as they neared, and the four of them were forced to wait until the passing waiter had ducked agilely into their alcove to avoid a pair of dreamy dancers.

There was no help for it. Cabel was looking down at her expectantly, and she made the introductions while he beamingly extended a hand, as if Doyle were the very person he had been wanting to meet.

"Doyle O'Hanlon," Cabel repeated. "Would that have anything to do with O'Hanlon Electronics at Research Triangle Park?"

"Sorry. I'm with a small publishing firm. Sales end of it." He held onto Frances's elbow limply as he allowed his eyes the pleasure of Olivia's extremely low-cut dress.

"Interesting coincidence. Olivia's in sales, too," Cable informed them. "You two would probably have a lot in common, O'Hanlon. I'll take Frances off your hands for a few minutes if you'd like to explore the area. No point in her having to stand here alone."

He practically railroaded the two of them onto the floor and Frances was livid! Really, of all the high-handed...! She told him in an angry whisper just what she thought of his removing her date so peremptorily. He just grinned down at her.

"Come along then, if you had your heart set on dancing. I don't mind filling in for your lecherous Irishman."

"Doyle is not a lecherous Irishman and I don't care to dance with you, Cabel," Frances repeated repressively, holding back when he would have led her out into the swirl of dancers.

He gave her arm a jerk that caused her almost to fall against him, and then he wrapped her securely in both arms, disdaining the traditional manner of holding her waist and hand. After the first few seconds of allowing her arms to hang limply at her sides, Frances did the only possible thing and raised them to his shoulders. From there one of them, of its own volition, made its way to the back of his neck, and as the strains of "Moonlight Becomes You" drifted over the dimly lighted room, she closed her eyes and gave herself up to the pure pleasure of dancing with the man.

The hand on her waist dropped to her hip and she didn't protest. Through the sheer fabric of her gown, she was startlingly aware of Cable's muscular thighs as they stroked against her softer ones to follow the dreamy strains of music. She inhaled in light, shallow little breaths, terribly conscious of the scent of him, the fragrance of clean linen, of tobacco and some elusive, exotic cologne, as well as a hint of male muskiness that seemed to grow more arresting as they danced.

Time hung suspended in the heat of the early autumn night and she was only aware that the music had ended when she felt the coolness of the night air strike her bare arms. "Cabel?" she questioned, looking doubtfully up into the shadowy face above hers. They were on one of the terraces, with potted palms and oleanders rustling in the light breeze, the same breeze that slithered her gown against her nylon panty hose, making her shiveringly aware of the raw state of her nerves.

"Our friends seemed so preoccupied I thought it only fair to give them more time to get acquainted. Who knows, I may have lighted a flame in two hearts tonight. How do you like me in the role of cupid?" he teased with a lazy, provocative grin.

"Olivia must be getting too close for comfort," Frances retorted witheringly, glad of an opportunity to put a little space between them. She needed to catch her breath after the exertion of dancing.

"Snap! From the looks of things, O'Hanlon thought he had a one-way ticket to heaven. Unless you mean business, Fancey, you ought to have better sense than to put yourself in such a position."

"I don't know what you mean," she prevaricated.

"You know exactly what I mean," he mocked lightly. "Three times last week and now the final knockout punch, the wining and dining and romantic music and a slow, leisurely drive home in the moonlight. Do you honestly expect to be able to palm him off at the front door with a quick good-night kiss?"

"Is that what you had in mind when you brought Olivia here?" she sniffed, moving away to lean against the stone baluster that overlooked a boxwood maze.

He followed her and dropped an arm across her shoulders, drawing her almost casually to his side. "I'm only a man, Fancey, and you'll have to admit, Olivia's a pretty fetching female. What do you think of her now? You only got a quick glimpse when the pair of you met." He looked down at her with an outrageous expression of innocent inquiry and Frances took a deep breath, determined not to be taunted into anything this time.

"She's beautiful. Certainly a darn sight better than the redhead," she added acerbically.

"Oh, that was... Gerri? Sherri?"

"Terri!"

"Right! Terri... uh... whatchamacallit! Well, I must admit, the wrappings were intriguing but the package was empty. Not so much as a tantalizing little rattle... just plain empty," he said dolefully.

"God, you're awful! No woman deserves such treatment!"

"They love it, Fancey. They eat it up and come back for more. Come on now, admit it, Fancey, don't you enjoy being pursued and then treated to a taste of caveman tactics? Doesn't it make you quiver inside with righteous indignation when the dastardly male animal proves all your pet theories for you?"

"Oh, shut up!"

"We covered that subject before. Do I take it you're surrendering? Crying Uncle?" He turned her deftly and she found herself once more gathered to that snowy front, her cheek against the sensuous midnight velvet of his lapel.

"I think I hate you, Cabel McCloud," she muttered, trying desperately not to let herself be stirred by all that blatant masculinity.

"Sure you do, Fancey Ann, sure you do. But then, we both know that a thoroughgoing liberated lady like you can take her pleasure where she finds it, just like we happy bachelors, without worrying about any deeper commitment, and it's just occurred to me that since we share that attitude, we may as well share the pleasure. Convenient, if nothing else, and if we find we're still indifferent to each other then there's nothing lost, hmmm?"

She opened her mouth to rage at him; the words were already on her tongue, but he captured her mouth, shattering her senses with an assault that left her clinging to him helplessly.

Oh, when would she learn? When would she know enough to turn and walk away instead of rising to his bait and leaving herself wide open for the hook?

Fragile chiffon proved no barrier at all to searching hands, and Cabel sought out the soft tenderness of her breasts, bringing them to a state of aching arousal.

"Cabel, stop it!" she gasped once when his mouth left hers to trail along her cheek to the vulnerable nerve just below her jaw. "This is a public place!" she whispered hoarsely.

"Middle-class inhibitions never bothered me, darling," he laughed against her ear with incredible effect. "Besides, what's so outrageous about a kiss in the moonlight? Do you think the management expects its patrons to settle for a rousing game of Parcheesi?"

One of his hands was stroking the curve of her hip, sliding the weightless fabric of her dress over the thin nylon underneath, and she captured it with her own hand only to find herself pressing his touch to her like a burning brand.

"You're a rosebud, Fancey mine, an autumn rosebud, and I want to make you bloom," he murmured against her mouth. His tongue traced the line between her lips. "Will you let me?"

With his hands on her hips and her breast, his tongue caressing her mouth languorously, Frances was all but demented. She struggled to salvage the last few remnants of her sanity before it was too late, and she found herself agreeing willingly to whatever Cabel suggested. "Olivia...Doyle! Th...they'll be searching for us," she cried, frantically backing away from him.

Cabel made a rude suggestion, using a word Frances wasn't aware of being in use among staid financial advisors; then he sighed and let his hands drop to the cool roughness of the baluster. "It might be better if we left them to find their way home together."

Steadying her breath, Frances grasped at conversation as a barrier between them. "I was right, then? Olivia's getting too close for comfort?"

He grinned at her with the insouciance of the unregenerate rake. "The trouble is, Olivia's a determined little girl. She insists on wanting permanent board to go with her bed and I'm beginning to wonder if the game's worth the candle. You, on the other hand, are no danger to me. We know where we stand from the outset, so what do you say we leave those two to their own devices and slip away to the hills of Haw?"

A streak of some nameless anticipation robbed her of breath for just a moment, to be replaced by a sense of loss. But before she could form a reply, they were interrupted as Doyle hailed them from the French doors. "Hey, you two, the band's gone into overtime and Livvie's gone and left me to powder her cute little nose. What say we join forces for the rest of the evening?"

Against Frances's every instinct, they remained together for the next hour, and Doyle divided his time between dancing with Cabel's date and his own, and even when he was dancing with Frances, he was talking about Olivia.

In a way it was a relief; at least she didn't have to keep moving his hands back where they belonged any more, but she found her eyes following Cabel and Olivia as they danced slowly on the other side of the room, with Cabel every bit as attentive to the exquisite brunette as if he hadn't spent those few moments alone with Frances on the terrace.

Had it all been some sort of a joke on his part? Was he teasing her, carrying their half-serious, half-jesting battle one step further? But the red-tipped fingers that now sifted through that silver-tipped hair were no joke, and

Frances flinched at the shaft of pain that shot through her at the sight of Cabel's head thrown back in laughter. It occurred to her that her own head had been aching for some time, ever since Doyle had surprised them on the terrace.

On Monday Frances lost her job. Stunned, she leaned back in the corner of the office and listened while Howard Stinson tried to offer excuses.

Oh, there had been warnings—if she had had her wits about her instead of spending so darned much time thinking about her aggravating neighbor. It wasn't the recession; it wasn't just another small, underfinanced business going under. In the case of Orange Import, it was simply a matter of the small fish being swallowed up by the bigger fish. They had been bought up by a chain of import shops which had been cutting into their business deeper each year because of having a more advantageous buying position. But Frances mourned the fact that the cheaper, mass-produced merchandise would take over instead of the carefully selected, hand-crafted items she had taken such pride in handling.

"They're bringing in their own manager, my dear, because I'm to old to learn new tricks. I'll be the assistant, and... well, you see where that leaves you," he ended helplessly. "As it is, Myrtle will have to find a job to make ends meet. Of course, with all the kids in school, it won't be so bad, but good Lord, three sets of braces I'm paying for, and in a few years, three in college at one time. I'm telling you, Frances, it's almost more than a man my age can handle. Thank your lucky stars you're still young and unattached and can take your time looking around for something better."

Not so unattached, after all, Frances declined from telling him. She was very much attached to a mortgage and to utility bills and a heating contractor's expensive services. And besides that, she had developed a habit of eating three meals a day, a habit she hated to have to break.

Not that there was any need, but she worked out the week. It was as if the malaise they all felt flowed out the door and onto the sidewalk. The few customers who looked in merely glanced at the half-empty shelves and walked out again. Even on football Saturdays, with the town full of parents and visiting alumni, the sales were way down from last year.

On Saturday afternoon she cleared out her personal coffee mug, her small beveled mirror in the pewter-beaded frame, and her copy of *Diary Of An Edwardian Lady* and drove home an hour early. The heat had returned full blast for one last stand before Indian Summer gave way to hog-butchering weather. She opened her windows as she drove south on the Pittsboro Road, allowing the wind to have its way with her hair. Before leaving town she had picked up copies of the *Durham Herald*, the *Advocate* and even the little biweekly published in Bynum and now the wind whipped them about on her back seat.

There was no sign of a maroon Mercedes parked on the hill, thank goodness. At least she wouldn't have to put on a front to save her pride where Cabel was concerned, an almost impossible task at the best of times. She hadn't seen him since that night at the supper club and for that small blessing she offered heartfelt thanks. After a good deal of painful self-searching, she had decided after that night that the less she had to do with her all too charming neighbor, the better off she'd be. Something about him was decidedly bad for her self-imposed policy of noninvolvement, although she'd die before she'd ever let him know just how susceptible she was to his particular brand of charm.

Just a frustrated, inhibited, hormonal leftover, she chided herself in one of her more brutally frank moments. Maybe if I join a health club or go in for basketball, it'll pass.

The joblessness wasn't something that would pass, though, at least not without some hard looking on her part. The trouble with a college town was that there were too many lookers and not enough positions, and there was absolutely no industry in Orange County. Little enough anywhere within easy commuting distance from her home.

Her home. There was the rub. Ironic that her grand gesture of self-determination should prove to be the anchor, the albatross around her neck that kept her from going further afield in search of work. Commuting was too expensive, even with a moderate-sized car like hers, and she couldn't afford to trade it in on an even smaller one. Her savings account held enough for almost two mortgage payments plus the insurance, and almost enough left over to cover the taxes that would be coming due pretty soon. Her pantry revealed an awful lot of bare shelf, and Mama had already canned, frozen, and preserved everything in the garden and divided with Kay and Jean, who helped her with it all. Frances had not encouraged help of any sort in her stupid quest for independence, and now she was afraid she might regret her stiff-necked pride.

Pouring herself a tumbler full of inexpensive wine, she tucked the newspapers under her arm (after changing into a pair of white shorts and a rosecolored halter) and made her way down to the river. In the shade of a cluster of ragged field cedars she privately had designated as Daisy, Mort, and the kids, she settled herself, tucking her feet up under her knees, and proceeded to study the help-wanted columns. She had already decided that if she hadn't found anything by the middle of the week she'd go to one of the agencies that took an arm and a leg in return for pointing her to a job. So far, it looked as if she could choose between short order cook, night shift, and concessions at the Mobame Tobacco Market, none of which would pay her enough to live on.

Oh, blast! She took a deep draught of the wine and decided its quality wasn't up to deep draughts, only tentative sips, and then she took another one. A canoeist passed and saluted her with his paddle and then two more went by in close succession. She took another swallow of wine and tried to recall if it was an eight-percent or a twelve. In the heat of the somnolent September afternoon, it was acting more like twelve.

Draining the glass, she stood up impulsively and began to wade along the shallows, hopping from rock to rock for the most part and waving her arms wildly to regain her balance when one of them shifted under her feet.

"Fancey! Climb out of there, girl, before you drown yourself!" someone called out after her when she had all but rounded the curve and was out of sight of her house. She looked over her shoulder and almost lost her balance again in the process.

Cabel was rolling up his pant's legs and coming after her, and she giggled and hopped to another group of rocks, out of the rush of the mainstream current. By the time she had gone another fifty feet, he was right on her heels, cursing occasionally when he missed his footing and ordering her to wait for him.

A minute more and he caught her arm, practically jerking her off her feet before she could wriggle away. "What the hell is wrong with you, anyway? I find a pint-sized jelly glass reeking of cheap wine and see you waltzing across the damned river like Little Liza with the full pack on her heels. Have you lost what feeble mind you had? Don't you know you could break your silly neck this way?"

It dawned on her slowly that he was truly angry and she peered up at him uncertainly. "Would you care?" she asked lugubriously.

"Good Lord, you're drunk!"

"Oh no, I'm not. I'm just . . . mellow," she finished demurely.

"Mellow, hell, you're loaded! Come on, I'm getting you out of here before you dunk us both!" He pulled on her arm; she resisted, and they glared at each other. "Look, Frances, be a good girl, will you? It's been a damned tough week and I'm not in the mood to go chasing a sodden naiad down the river Haw. Come on home and tell ol' uncle Cabe what's wrong, won't you?"

"Let's go down to Pokeberry Creek," she countered contrarily.

With a sigh of exasperation he asked, "Where the hell is Pokeberry Creek?"

"It's not far," she replied eagerly. "Come on, Cabe, I'll show you. Please?" She took his hand and they hopscotched along the edge of the bank until they came to a place where a shallow creek some ten feet wide led back into the woods. Frances tugged at his hand. "C'mon, the dogwoods are turning and the sun sets through them if we're in just the right place. Please, Cabel, it's just a little way."

They climbed out onto a mossy bank and sank down. Frances was glad to be still for awhile, for her head was misbehaving. Her fingers caressed the stiff fronds of a fiddelhead fern, and suddenly she felt terribly shy in the intense silence of the woods with Cabel's watchful eyes on her.

Somewhere nearby, a quail called softly and was answered as the small covey gathered together for the night. "Well?" Cabel prompted quietly into the bush of the forest.

She sighed heavily. "I lost my job. Today was my last day," she admitted, still not looking at him. The seat of her shorts was stained with moss and red mud and leaf mold, and her halter gave scant protection from the branches that reached out to snare the careless. Already she was beginning to itch as perspiration found its way into her small scratches.

"So?"

"So! What do you mean, so? I lost my job, I tell you! What am I expected to do now, starve? Lose my house? End up in debtor's prison?"

"I think that's been discontinued, but as a matter of fact, I expect you to go out and get yourself another job. Or are your talents so limited that you can't get another one?"

"Quit mocking me, McCloud! I feel awful enough without your taking cheap shots!"

"All right, for starters, exactly what do you do at that emporium of the exotic where you work . . . worked?"

"Worked is right," she echoed dolefully. "Past tense. I kept up with the stock, but lately Mr. Stinson wouldn't reorder, and so there wasn't all that much to keep up with. I kept up with the correspondence with some of our suppliers . . . that was mostly on the art-type stuff because I knew more about that than Mr. Stinson did. He thought it... oh, sort of added something to the atmosphere to have a BA in art history talking shop with the small galleries and individual studios, so he did mostly the wholesale warehouse end and left me to the individual accounts. And we had a bookkeeper to do that end of it." She scratched her arm and watched an ant crawl around toward her elbow before brushing him off, her eyes straying everywhere but at the man who lounged close enough so that if she had wanted to, she could have reached out and touched him.

After awhile she continued, since Cabel didn't seem inclined to break the silence. "I waited on customers and Mr. Stinson kept promising me I'd get to go on buying trips, but I never did."

"Surely there are other retail outfits who could use your services," he reasoned.

"Try and find one. I searched three papers today and there wasn't a single thing that would keep me in commuting gas, much less room and board. I can't go all that far afield, remember, because I'm not free to just pick up and move."

"So in spite of all that prattle about independence, you're caught in a trap of your own making, hmmm? Possessed by your possessions." He leaned back, crossing his arms under his head, and gazed up at the arch of branches overhead. It was growing dim in the woods now, but the coolness was welcome after a day of near-ninety degrees.

"At least I'm not trapped by somebody who has me cleaning and cooking and sewing day and night," she said in exasperation.

"No? You mean you don't clean or cook or sew or do anything except have a good time?" The gleam in his lazy-lidded eyes glowed with disturbing fire in the shadowy greenness, and she stirred uneasily.

"Well, of course I do those things, but it's different."

"You mean, it's not work when it's done for love," he prompted.

"I don't know what you're getting at," Frances came back suspiciously, "but I'm in no mood for jokes."

"Nor am I, Frances," he said mildly. "I just assumed you loved your little house and didn't begrudge anything you did in its behalf, that's all. I know that love for a man is totally out of the question, as far as you're concerned."

"How did we get off on this subject?" she wailed, rolling over on her stomach and cutting a rebellious look at his bland face. "I might have known you couldn't help me... Uncle Cabel," she added mockingly.

"Whoa there, girl, don't jump to any conclusions. Who said I couldn't help you? I'm just getting ready to offer you my special of the day." He lay there, long legs crossed at the ankle, arms beneath his head, and grinned up into the yellow leaves of a poplar tree.

"What's that?" Frances asked grudgingly when it appeared that he had forgotten all about her.

"What about all the other options? Sure you've exhausted them?"

Her shoulders moved, a small motion that made her halter fall away from her body so that a heavenly current of cool air seemed to circulate between her breasts. "There don't seem to be all that many, so you may as well make your offer," she said with a singular lack of interest. The wine had seeped away, leaving behind a growing depression.

"Marriage."

Chapter Six

Silence throbbed around her as the dampness of the mossy earth chilled her bones. "Marriage?" she repeated incredulously when she could get her breath again.

Cabel nodded, without bothering to turn his head to look her way.

"But . . . but what purpose would that serve?" Before he could answer, she sat up and shook her head. "I knew it was a twelve-percent wine instead of just an eight." She turned to stare directly into Cabel's suddenly opaque eyes. "Now, what's all this malarkey about marriage. Who? And to whom?"

"You, and to me," he replied laconically, turning over onto his side to face her, one elbow still sticking comically in the air.

"Stop joking, Cabel. I need your help, not your warped idea of a joke."

"And it almost kills you to have to ask for anything, doesn't it? In fact, you couldn't do it without stiffening your spine with a jelly glass full of cheap wine." He sat up in one fluid motion. "Look, Frances, it makes a lot of sense whether or not you realize it. Think about it, girl! What's the one impregnable position from which our independence can't be shot down? How's the best way to have your cake and eat it, too?"

Her eyes, the color of the small, mossy pools in the depths of the woods, widened. "How?"

"Simple! We go through a marriage ceremony...oh, all very legal and all that, but purely a business arrangement. Then, you go on with your life and I go on with mine. We can go out with as many people as we want to...Olivia, Doyle...whoever strikes our fancy, and the minute things start getting sticky, we flash our wedding rings and we're home safe!"

The fumes of the wine had mostly dissipated now; all the same, Frances couldn't quite reach the same exalted plateau of sangfroid that Cabel had attained. "Are you sure?" was the best she could come up with. The logic of the solution somehow escaped her.

"Of course I'm sure! It's a natural! Here we are, two adults who have long since passed the age for any romantic foolishness. Well?" He looked at her expectantly. "Haven't we?"

"Oh, of course! Yes, certainly we have," Frances hurriedly assured him.

"Right. So as long as neither one of us is fool enough to fall in love, we've got it made. Then there's the property, too. You live in your house, maintain your own lifestyle and I live in mine, free to do to suit myself with no nagging, no one to have to account to for my time, and no role-playing. Cards on the table from the first."

"I...I think I'm beginning to see what you mean. But Cabe," she ventured uncertainly, unconsciously using the diminutive he had used earlier, "I still don't see how that gets me a job."

"Oh, didn't I explain the best part? Well, it works this way. I have a housekeeper three days a week. Dreadful woman! Drinks like a fish and I'm damned sure the silverware's walking out a spoon at a time. Also a few of my best pipes have turned up missing."

"I didn't know you smoked a pipe," she interrupted irrelevantly.

Cabel looked at her quizzically. "There's a lot you don't know about me. That's part of the beauty of the whole situation. No prying, no embarrassing intimacies. We could still be Mr. McCloud and Miss... well, make that Ms. Harris if you want to. How about it, would you like to keep your own name? No ego problem on my part." He looked pleased as pie for having come up with the idea but Frances shook her head in a small negative gesture, not knowing why, only knowing she was weakening to the whole idea and that if she took him up on it, she wanted to be Mrs. Cabel McCloud. In name only, of course, she added to herself in muddled confusion.

"No matter," he continued quickly. "The important thing is that you'll protect me from getting in over my head with irresistible females and if you need any help with overly amorous boyfriends, I'll be just a shout away, but back to Hazel..."

At her frown, he elaborated. "Housekeeper. Drinks, dips, and Lord knows what else. Got her from Olivia and that's the one thing that makes me keep her on. She's a good cook, though. And once I have someone to keep her in line, she'll work out all right. Livia swears by her. You'll get a regular salary for managing my household and when I'm entertaining... it'll be great to have some place to bring people for a change, restaurants just aren't the same. Anyway, you won't mind serving as hostess on those occasions, will you?"

"You could always find another housekeeper and Olivia would be more than glad to serve as your hostess," Frances objected doggedly.

With plausible earnestness, Cabel leaned forward, and she could see the fine lines radiating out from the corners of his eyes. His lashes, she noted to her distraction, were brush-thick and perfectly straight, with no hint of a curve, so that they could shutter his eyes as effectively as storm blinds, concealing any hint of expression. "But don't you see, Fancey, that's just what I'm trying to avoid. Lord, can you imagine what a conniving female would make of a chance like that? Give her an inch!"

"You didn't seem to think she was so conniving at the club."

His mouth twisted momentarily and then straightened again. "Honey, I'm no monk. I need a woman as much as any man, but when you allow a woman to insinuate herself into every aspect of your life, when you once let her think you have a weakness for her, then you're a goner. May as well just lay your head on the block and point your finger to the dotted line." He shook his head sorrowfully. "No, Fancey, as far as I'm concerned, a woman is made for enjoyment, and the minute she starts telling you what to do and when to do it, the fun's over."

In a small voice she asked him, "Aren't you afraid I might try to tell you?"

He looked at her askance. "You?" he snorted disbelievingly. "With your commitment to independence and single-blessedness? The only thing that could possibly make you try to take over my life would be if you fell in love with me." Then, as if the idea just occurred to him, "You haven't, have you?"

Tipping back her head to reveal the fine line of her jaw, Frances choked off a laugh. The hateful color she should have outgrown ten years ago arose to add sparkle to her eyes above high, flushed cheeks and she blurted out her negative answer. "Good Lord, no! I was born with better judgement than that!"

"You don't have to hurt my feelings," he protested.

"Then don't go talking such arrant nonsense," she rejoined, getting to her feet to dust off the seat of her shorts.

Cabel gazed up the long, tanned length of her smooth leg and said, "It's a deal, then?"

"No."

He came to his feet beside her without bothering to use his hands, she noticed disdainfully. Show-off! "You mean you won't marry me?" he asked disbelievingly.

Through some trick of the deceptively dim light in the woods, it almost seemed for a moment that the muscles in his face tightened. Surely it was just the greenish gloom that seemed to rob him of his tan.

She was being fanciful. "Well, I'm flattered and all that," she declared facetiously. "After all, it isn't every day of the week a girl gets proposed to on Pokeberry Creek in broad daylight."

The wide shoulders lifted and fell. "Saved by the bell. I must admit, I admire you one hell of a lot, Fancey Ann Harris. Damned few women of my acquaintance would pass up a chance to take control of a five-bedroom house, not to mention a six-figure income, but then you're a class act. Not even to keep the wolves from the door will you knuckle under to expedience."

They waded out toward the golden light that filtered in from the opening on the river. "As a matter of interest,

Cabe, why *did* you buy such a big place when you had no intention of...of populating all those bedrooms?"

He caught at her arm when she would have slipped on a mossy rock and released her immediately, even though she could have done with his support. "I didn't say I wasn't planning to populate them. I have no objection to overnight guests, although it doesn't usually take more than one bedroom...mine," he grinned. Then, as they turned to wade the river proper, his face sobered. "Matter of fact, I'm afraid I bought it on impulse. I came down here to North Carolina one day last February for a conference and it was sleeting like the very devil when I left O'Hare. Didn't think we'd get off the ground for awhile. Then I walked out of the airport here and you were having one of those spring preview days...looked like an Easter card. I liked the weather, I liked the people, and I liked the lay of the land. With no ties, I was free to move, and so I did. Nor have I regretted it."

"Didn't you have any family at all?" Frances was slogging along half a step behind him, the water chilling her feet now, and she saw the tightening of his jaw this time with no mistake.

"I have a mother. She's somewhere in Nassau with husband number four...or is it five?" He shrugged. "A stepmother in Madison, Ohio, and a stepsister living with her current lover in New York...current one being about the sixth in line, I believe. My father..." Here his voice changed, became noticeably warmer. "My father died two years ago. He was the first McCloud at McCloud, Inc. We worked together until he had his third and last heart attack."

She was silent while they climbed out onto the low bank, because she didn't know quite what to say to him. But then she saw that the familiar half-mocking expression was back on his face, and it was too late. She couldn't say she was sorry now, for the moment had passed, and so she mentioned the house again. "Well, I must say, you do your impulse-buying on a grander scale than I do. A pair of shoes or a double fudge sundae usually does it for me, but all those rooms! Do you suppose it will ever become known as the McCloud Place instead of the Cairington Place?"

"Who knows? One of these days it may belong to somebody else, if I get another impulse like I did that day in Combs's and Webster's office, the day you fell for me the first time."

"I didn't fall for you, Cabel, you tripped me!" Not even to herself would she admit the yawning emptiness that opened up inside her at the thought of no Cabel McCloud on the hill.

"Well, either way, no matter. Here, this place is slick," he murmured, helping her over a particularly mossy area. When he forgot to drop her hand, she didn't remind him.

By the time they reached her front porch the sun was well down, the air too chilly for her damp shorts and halter, and she shivered.

Immediately, Cabel threw a casual arm across her shoulders. "Sure you won't change your mind now, girl? Don't be embarrassed. I understand a gal's supposed to say no the first time she's asked... keeps her from seeming too eager. No, that's second servings, isn't it? Oh, well, maybe it applies to both."

She gurgled and her voice, when she told him he was ridiculous, reflected the fine tremor of her chill. When Cabel put the other arm around her and swung her easily up against the warmth of his body, she felt a return of the earlier wine-weakness in both her knees and her resolution, and she leaned her face against the earthy-smelling shirt he wore.

"Since I know we're both safe from any romantic nonsense with each other, how about a kiss to tide me over until I pick up my date tonight? I'm a man who needs a lot of demonstrative affection." Without waiting for her outraged reply, he lifted her chin and smiled warmly into her eyes even as his mouth came down on hers. She kept her lips clamped tightly together against his invasion and then, as she felt laughter shaking his whole frame, she jerked her head away in order to tell him just what she thought of him. He pounced, taking advantage of her momentary weakness to kiss her thoroughly and expertly until she was clinging helplessly to him.

His face lifted and his fine, clear eyes shone down on her as if lighted by some secret, inner amusement. "There now, you're not shivering any more, are you? Good deed for the day."

"Darn you, Cabel McCloud, I hate you!"

"What, for rising to your challenge? Or for trying to keep you from getting a chill?"

"I didn't challenge you and I was certainly in no danger of getting a chill. And you know it!"

One finger traced the line of her jaw, lifted proudly now on her long, graceful throat. "There's the challenge, love. Be careful how you lift that stubborn little chin of yours because one of these days, you're going to get what you're asking for."

He was gone before she could come up with an answer, striding up the hill as if he hadn't a care in the world, as if he hadn't proposed marriage and been rejected only a few minutes earlier. Well, of course, he hadn't a care! He hadn't wanted to marry her, anyway, and his job was secure. He could well afford to maintain a mansion for one man alone . . . or rather, one man and as many mistresses as he cared to install!

Oh, hell's bells! She let herself in, stomping heavily as she marched through the dark house to send a gush of hot water into the rust-stained bathtub. She had more important things to think about than any irritating man who had to keep on proving his macho appeal to every woman who crossed his path!

Doyle called to invite her to drive to Seagrove with him to see the pottery, and she declined with a thin excuse. He said, as if hoping to make her jealous, that he thought he'd ask Olivia. Frances replied sweetly that she hoped they both enjoyed it.

The next day, after a fruitless morning of job hunting, she got another call. "This is Sean Machlin. Your Aunt Helen's husband's nephew."

In a mood to plunge headlong into any activity that might keep her from thinking, she agreed to meet him at Crook's Corner instead of his driving all the way to Bynum, and they settled on a time. She dressed carefully, softening her usual hairstyle so that it haloed out to flatter her face. In consideration of the cooler evenings, and the fact that they'd probably be sitting on the terrace at Crook's, she wore a black midi-length skirt with a bold design in rust and gold and teamed it with an ivory silk blouse with a plunging neckline and flamboyant sleeves. A bit splashy, perhaps, but then, she felt rather like cutting a dash tonight with the unknown Sean Machlin.

Tilting her head at her reflection, she was reminded of Cabel's charge that she threw out a challenge every time she raised her chin; she ducked her head and tried looking demure instead, but it came off as a simper.

There was an exhibition opening at Morehead Planetarium, and they took it in between drinks and dinner. Sean wanted an introduction to a few of the local attractions, and Frances was determined to offer him a varied selection. For dinner they chose one of the newer restaurants along West Franklin Street. Frances found it exciting, for she was fascinated by different types of food, although she didn't think Sean really appreciated the plaki or the chickpea dip. He ordered Guinness Stout and when it came frosty cold, he drank it without demur and Frances, with the beginnings of disillusionment, wondered if he even knew better. Cabel would have sent it back quietly but firmly and asked for a bottle from supply, but then that was Cabel and this was Sean, and the two were as different as rocks and rainbows.

Oh, well, perhaps she was being unfair. Perhaps Sean was only trying to keep the peace. They went on to a party given by some people she knew fairly well and she wondered how he'd fare with them. In spite of all Aunt Helen's promising words, he was coming across as depressingly conventional, but she put on a broad smile and asked him if he liked homemade music, which was what the party was all about.

It was fortunate that he happened onto someone he knew there, for the two of them seemed far more interested in discussing football than in the music, which was mostly traditional folk with an occasional outburst of bluegrass. Frances circulated, nibbled the refreshments, some of them rather ambiguous, and sipped perhaps more of the spiced wine than she should, but she had a surprisingly good time, considering the fact that her date sat in a corner with another man and smiled at her from time to time as if he couldn't quite remember her name.

Sometime later Frances dropped Sean off at the house where he rented a room. He thanked her politely for showing him around town and she thanked him politely for her drinks and dinner. Rack up another frog, instead of the Prince Charming Aunt Helen had promised her. Not that she put any stock in her family's evaluation of men. It was a wonder her father, Uncle Jerrold, and her two brothers-in-law weren't total washouts, considering the Harris women's blind spots.

She had barely crossed the Chatham County line when her left front tire blew, with a noisy and frightening explosion that wobbled her over to the edge of the highway.

"Well, drat it all to pieces," she intoned exasperatedly. It was well after one in the morning and there wasn't a light anywhere to be seen, much less a phone booth where she could call for help. Her thoughts turned immediately to Cabel and she just as immediately rerouted them. He was probably curled up somewhere with Olivia about now, and the last thing he'd appreciate was being called out to change a tire by someone who had just turned down his marriage proposal.

Or by anyone else, she tacked on with all the fairness she could drum up. Damn! Face it, Frances, you've been staring at Sean Machlin and seeing Cabel McCloud all night long. What if she had said yes? Would she be here in the middle of nowhere with a crippled car on her hands right now? Would *he* be somewhere wrapped around that sultry blackheaded piranha?

She pried off the hubcap and then chased it into the weeds beside the highway, while she wondered if he had been serious or simply trying on another of his droll jests at her expense. Oh, drat, she had forgotten to take out the jack when she got the tire tool and the spare. Which came first, anyway, jacking it up or taking off the thingamabobs around the wheel, assuming she could get them loose?

For all her vaunted ability to look after herself, she had been singularly fortunate that the only other flat she had ever had was when one of her mother's lame ducks was with her. As a conversationalist, he was a washout, but when it came to changing a tire he was ranked among the best. She should have taken a few lessons while she had the chance, she thought wryly, wrinkling her nose at the smear of grease that streaked the back of her hand.

She tried to roll her sleeves up and ended up getting even more grease on her best ivory silk blouse. She let fly a few choice oaths of the milder variety as she wrestled with the machine-tightened lugnuts. A car passed by and kept on going and she swore again and then decided perhaps she didn't want any strangers stopping by to offer help anyway at...at...Good Lord, unless her watch was on the blink, it was close to two o'clock in the morning! The evening hadn't warranted the loss of sleep.

By the time she rolled up beside her house, she was dead tired, her finery wilted and showing lamentable signs of her recent struggle. Her hair was askew, thanks to a brush with a fender while she was trying to make the darned jack let go of her bumper. The chickpeas and spiced wine were having an argument with the barbecued spareribs.

Her hand had just closed around the doorknob when she heard someone leap up onto the porch behind her and she froze, her heart sinking into her shoes.

"This is a fine time to come cruising home," Cabel announced.

"What business is it of yours what time of night I choose to come home?" She fumbled with the key until he took it away from her and unlocked the door.

"I do feel a certain responsibility, although Lord knows why I should! Let's just say it's because I've met your mother and I know she'd be having a fit if she knew you were out doing God knows what until all hours, coming home looking like the tag end of a bad dream. Where's the boyfriend, or did you wear him out?"

She turned to face him, eyes blazing in an unnaturally pale face. "I don't know just what you think you're getting at, Cabel McCloud, but whatever it is, I don't care for your insinuations! You can just get out of here and don't come back! When I need your interference in my life, I'll send you a telegram!"

"You need more then my interference, you overaged brat! You need to be taken across somebody's knee and whaled good until you can't sit down! It's one thing to be independent; it's quite another to run wild all over the damned countryside until all hours without letting anyone know where you are! What if something had happened to you? Who'd have known, much less cared?"

"Don't tell me you'd have cared," she sneered, struggling to hold back tears of pure, unadulterated rage.

"I should be so foolish! A man would want his head examined to care for any such headstrong, stubborn, reckless..."

"Don't flatter me too much, Mr. McCloud. It might go to my poor senile head," Frances managed in a voice that hardly shook at all.

With an expression of stifled rage, he grabbed her, practically pulling her off her feet as he hauled her unceremoniously into his arms. "If this is what you're looking for, you don't have to go chasing all over the countryside to find it," he growled, bearing down on her frightened mouth with an exasperation that bruised her lips.

Muffled protests escaped her as she twisted futilely, pounding his shoulders with grease-streaked fists. "Mmmm, damn you, Cabel McCl...!" she choked as he repositioned his mouth to plunder the depths of her aroused emotions. His tongue fought against hers and won, and she felt her anger seep away to be replaced by other, far less welcome sensations. Then she didn't think any more, she only felt as his hands gentled and coerced her body into a helpless, clinging mass of raw nerve endings, nerves that clamored for something that hovered just beyond the fringes of her knowledge.

The blouse was ruined anyway; the thought drifted idly through her mesmerized mind, like a small cloud on a sunny day, as she felt the buttons go. When her bra was lowered and the small fullness of her breast lay in his hand, ripe and aching to be taken, she moved against him, whimpering small, longing protests. Her hands were threaded through his hair, loving the velvety thickness of it, the live, virile feel of him as he positioned her against him. But when he turned her in the direction of her bedroom without easing the hold on her body, she dug in her heels.

"No, Cabel," she reproached, burying her face in his throat. "I don't..."

"Don't give me that, Frances. You want me as much as I want you and I can tell you right now, that's pretty damned badly," he groaned.

"No! That's not true," she lied, panic strengthening her so that she was able to pull herself free of his arms. She braced herself against the contempt she saw in his heavy-lidded eyes. "What's the matter, did Olivia disappoint you tonight?"

"Olivia never disappoints me, darling," he sneered, "but when I saw you turn up here alone, it occurred to me that you might have had a dull sort of evening, and it seemed the neighborly thing to do to try and cheer you up."

Just for a moment, she couldn't speak for the pain, but she wouldn't let him have the last word! "There's just no end to your good will for your fellow man, is there? No sacrifice too great!" She had to get him out of here before she either killed him or burst into tears.

He raked her with glittering eyes, taking in the further deterioration of her already disheveled state. She was miserably conscious of her tumbled mop of hair and the filthy, grease-stained blouse, now held together only by her dirty, trembling hands. She had never felt so much at a disadvantage before in her life and never had she hated a man as much as she hated Cabel McCloud this minute!

"Cabel, I truly hate you," she declared, her voice no more than a hoarse whisper. "I've never hated a man so much in my life and if you don't get out of my sight, I'm going to..."

He didn't wait to hear out her threat, which was perhaps a good thing. Instead, he turned on his heel and slammed out the front door into the silent darkness, leaving her to think of all the things she'd like to do to him.

Chapter Seven

News of Frances's unemployment could not be kept a secret for long, and she began receiving calls from members of her family. Her mother called first with plans to clear out Frances's old room so that she could move back to Saxapahaw. Then, when she finally accepted the fact that there was no chance of that, she promised to call all her friends who might be able to use the services of a nice girl who had graduated from the university with excellent grades.

At the moment, Frances might wish those good grades had been in a subject more marketable than art history, but hindsight was no help now.

Helen called next with the suggestion that she try the job market in Durham, put her house up for rent, and move into the spare bedroom now that her cousin Waldo was at Annapolis. "Oh, and by the way, how did you and Sean get along?"

Frances fielded all such suggestions with admirable tact and assured her aunt that Sean was a perfect gentleman. She continued to study the ads and pester the agencies but it was through Margaret Shober, the bookkeeper at Orange Imports, who had lost her job at the same time Frances had, that the first really promising lead came.

Armed only with the information that a salesroom for Oriental art objects was opening in the Chapel Hill-Carrboro area, and that they were looking for a manager as well as sales personnel experienced in the field, Frances set up an appointment with the interviewer for the following morning at nine.

A Mrs. Gwinn was meeting applicants at a local inn and as early as Frances was, she discovered there were three women waiting and one in with Mrs. Gwinn when she arrived. Hardly a promising state of affairs, in spite of her experience and the special interest she had taken in Oriental art as an art history major. She eyed the others and saw that they were doing the same to her. One was hardly more than a girl and could have had little, if any, experience but the other two were somewhere between forty and fifty, both smart-looking and confident, none of which made Frances feel very optimistic.

Her turn came next. She stated her experience, elaborated on the special emphasis that might tip the scales in her favor, and went on to relate anything she thought might be of interest.

For her part, Mrs. Gwinn was frank, friendly, and seemed favorably inclined. Frances's spirits began to lift. The salary was better than she had expected and, of course, the responsibilities were increased commensurately, which only whetted her appetite.

"There's just one thing, Miss Harris, and I'm afraid I'm going to have to be perfectly frank about this. The owner of the business prefers either married women or those past middle age," she said apologetically.

"But why?" Frances exclaimed. She had been almost certain the job was hers.

"It's embarrassing for me to have to say this, and I'd hate for it to get back to Mrs. Macheris, but the plain truth is, Mr. Macheris presents a problem. They both travel for the company, and as often as not, one of them will be here while the other one is on the West Coast or at the Kowloon headquarters in Hong Kong. Which means that the manager will be working closely with Mr. Macheris part of the time, and this is what Mrs. Macheris has to guard against. To put it bluntly, Miss Harris, he's a chaser and I wouldn't be fair to you if I let you think your qualifications were lacking in any way. They happen to be exactly what we're looking for but I'm afraid..." her voice trailed off expressively and Frances's heart plummeted.

To have come so close to the job of a lifetime! One that could conceivably take her across the Pacific... Good Lord, she had never been west of the Mississippi! "Would a...a fiancé do?" she asked hopefully.

The well-tended grey hair swayed as Mrs. Gwinn shook her head. "Sorry, dear. Engagements are a dime a dozen, but a real live, on-the-scene husband can be a deterrent that Mrs. Macheris might be willing to take into consideration. After all, it's not as if you were a plain girl."

"Well, I suppose," began Frances slowly, carefully, "I suppose we could sort of hurry along our plans. What if we were to get married within the month? Would that help?" She was out of her mind and she knew it. There was no way she could come up with a husband in a month's time, in spite of Cabel and his ridiculous ideas. All the same, if it would buy her time...

She left the inn with Mrs. Gwinn's encouraging words ringing in her ears. Better even than a husband of long standing was a brand new bridegroom. Not even the most suspicious of women could suspect a new bride of playing fast and loose with her husband... or anyone else's.

During the whole drive out to Bynum, Frances pulled the idea back and forth through her mind, examining every facet of it. Almost every facet, that is. She preferred not to dwell on her own preferences in the matter. The fact that it was necessary, if she were to secure this position, was enough to be going on with, and even that was asking almost too much of her after the way Cabel had behaved the last time she had seen him.

No. She simply couldn't do it. After his insults she had sworn off his company for good, and the idea of marching up to his house to ask him to reconsider marrying her was out of the question.

On the other hand, he had been the one to bring up the possibility. Why? Because he needed her, that's why. She hadn't for a single minute been fool enough to think he had any other motive, and certainly not just as a means of putting a little money in her pocket. That much he could do with a loan; not that she'd accept one from him.

By the time she crunched up on the gravel drive beside her house she had made up her mind. Now all she had to do was make up her nerve!

She changed out of her successful-career-woman suit into a gathered skirt of deep turquoise, matching it with a lighter shell top and a pair of multicolor print espadrilles, then quickly changed into her jeans and her oldest shirt. And then she stood in front of her mirror and muttered aloud, "Be darned if I will!"

That night Sean called and asked if he could come out and see her, and in a weak moment she told him he could.

She spent the next day wondering why she had put herself in line for another night of boredom. They had very little in common. He was bored with art and she was not especially interested in computers. He wasn't interested in ethnic foods and music, and she couldn't abide beer and football. Besides that, he wore a bow tie!

Because she was thoroughly ashamed of her attitude, she put herself out to be entertaining, with the result that it was midnight when he left, in spite of her stifled yawns and her hints about an early morning. He stood on the porch talking while Frances wondered if she'd really sleep after he left. She hadn't been able to for several nights now, in spite of having nothing to keep her from it.

Contrary female, you're exactly what Cabel says you are: stubborn, cantankerous, and unreasonable. Over her thoughts ran Sean's monologue about fifty-yard-line seats and pregame rallies and she smiled sweetly as she wondered where Cabel was and what he was doing. In that state of absentmindedness, she was caught off guard when Sean pulled her into his arms and proceeded to kiss her with an eager, slightly off-center enthusiasm that brought to mind painfully the last time she had been kissed.

Oh, hell's bells, she thought sourly as she closed the door thankfully behind him and watched the red taillight wobble away over her uneven driveway. No way would I deliberately put myself in line for any more of Cabel's mocking derision, she thought.

It was as if Sean Machlin had never been at her house that evening as she envisioned a dark, silver-riddled head of cropped hair, a blade of a nose beneath a pair of wicked eyes and a fatal combination of sensuous mouth and implacable jaw. Damn the man, why couldn't he stay up on the hill where he belonged instead of haunting her house down on the river?

The next morning, Frances poured over the help wanted ads once more and made a call to the agency—all to no avail. There was nothing, absolutely *nothing* that she could find to do that would support her and make the house payments possible, and she'd be darned if she was going to knuckle under before the third payment was even due! The thought of moving out again was inconceivable and so she dressed quickly and backed out the drive, swooping up into Cabel's section to make a K turn. Then she headed out for the highway, throwing up a trail of gravel behind her.

Forty-five minutes later she left the bank with a bankbook reading of twenty-three dollars and thirty-seven cents. The house payment was made and the last installment on the furnace was out of the way. She picked up a few items from Fowler's while she was in town and then headed for Bynum again. No point in hanging around town in case she weakened and bought something. The way she was feeling at the moment, she couldn't even afford a friendly smile.

A few minutes after lunch, which had been a bite of chicken for her, the rest of it for Tripod, and an apple for Mollie, who didn't know any better, she got a call from Mrs. Gwinn saying the job was hers if she meant to go through with her wedding plans; otherwise, there was an older woman who had not the experience Frances had, but who had lived in the Far East for several years.

"I'll take it, Mrs. Gwinn," Frances announced without giving herself time to think. "We'll be getting married within the month."

Well, that settled it. Regardless of how distasteful it was, she was going to have to march up there and propose to that impossible man. Never had she thought to see the day when she'd be reduced to using a man as security, certainly not after all her fine prattling about equality and independence and standing on her own two feet. But there were some things she simply had not taken into consideration.

With her mind made up, she could hardly wait until he got home from work. To keep herself occupied, she baked a pie with the last of the apples her mother had sent her and then, in a spurt of nerves, she sat down and ate a quarter of it. She shook her wrist to be sure her watch was running properly and then took it off and strode out to the woods to bring back several armloads of kindling from the trees Cabel had cut for her. She had yet to build her first fire, and now that the weather called for heat of some sort—at least at night and in the early mornings—she found herself subject to all sorts of odd little worries about her chimney, the roof itself, and even the condition of the stove, which wasn't new by any means.

You *are* getting to be a clinging vine, Frances Harris! She dropped the load and went back for another. What if he didn't come home from work today? What if he had gone directly to pick up Olivia? Maybe he even had another girl by now. Lord knows, he probably had a dozen! Safety in numbers, and he made no bones about liking women, which made it even more puzzling that he didn't just ask one of them to marry him. Ah, but there was the rub, she concluded, forgetting completely that he had done just that...if he married one, then he automatically did himself out of the others and he was a man who liked variety. He'd be easily bored by one woman, as witness the fate of poor Terri Whatchamacallit.

While she stood there with an armload of hickory branches, staring absently at a chipmunk hole under her woodpile, she heard the Mercedes drive up the hill. She dropped the wood and fled into the house.

Twenty minutes later, breathless, still slightly damp around the edges from her quick shower, Frances strolled with feigned unconcern up the grassy slope to the yellow house. She rapped on the door before she lost her nerve, and when no one answered immediately, she turned and was halfway down the steps when the door opened behind her.

Framed in the doorway was the tall figure of Cabel McCloud, his ice-blue shirttail hanging out of the creased trousers of his summer suit and even as she watched, he unfastened the last button and tugged the already loosened tie from his neck. "Want me?" he asked easily.

With her eyes focused somewhere below the base of his throat, Frances opened her mouth to speak, cleared her throat, and made another effort. "Could... would it be possible to see you?"

"Any particular part, or just my chest?" he taunted, and her eyes flew up to reproach him as wild color stained her cheeks.

"Come on inside, Frances." He stepped back and held the door for her and she had to force her feet to obey her mind, for it was almost more than she could do, to squeeze past him and enter his foyer.

He knew it, too, and he wasn't going to make it any easier for her. It was almost as if he knew her purpose in coming and was determined to draw the last bit of satisfaction from her embarrassment. Leading her into the gracious room, he said, "You haven't seen my house, have you?"

"Yes, I have. You've forgotten."

He lifted a shoulder nonchalantly and continued to remove his thin gold watch, laying it carelessly on the mantle before turning to her expectantly. "Did you just drop in for a neighborly chat or had you something more specific in mind?"

"No. I mean yes. I mean..." Oh, Lord, how did one go about rescinding a rejection? She closed her eyes momentarily and breathed deeply while he waited with a pleasant, impersonal little smile on his face. "Look, Cabel, did you mean what you said the other day?"

"Which was that?"

"Oh, you know! About...about needing a housekeeper and a hostess."

"Oh, yes...my offer of employment. Well, I don't suppose it could be called employment in the strictest sense...maybe a supervisory capacity, but..."

"Damn it, Cabel, stop that! Either you will or you won't, and at the moment, I don't really care much which one, but don't play your childish little games with me! Just tell me yes or no!"

"I'd be delighted to oblige, Fancey, if I had any idea of what it was you were asking," he declared with mild exasperation.

Her fists balled in the pocket of her skirt and unconsciously she lifted her chin another two degrees. "Marry me."

Without looking directly at him, Frances had an impression of sudden stillness, and then he shifted so that his feet were braced apart, the powerful muscles of his thighs clearly evident under the lightweight stuff of his trousers. He extended an arm casually along the mantle and leveled his gaze at her. "All right."

She expelled the breath she wasn't even conscious of having held as her eyes flew to his face. "All right?" she repeated dazedly.

He nodded. "Sure. If that's what you want, I don't mind obliging you. As I mentioned the first time we discussed the matter, it will be convenient for me not to have to worry about the ordering of my household."

Oh, how romantic we are, she thought, biting her bottom lip against a sudden hysterical desire to laugh. "Fine, then," she gulped. "When?"

He glanced at his watch, as if expecting her to try and drag him off to a registrar's office before it closed for the day, and she tried for an offhand note when she replied that it didn't matter all that much. "It's only that there's this job," she explained.

"I didn't think it was my fatal charm," Cabel retorted dryly.

She went on as if she hadn't heard him. "I have the right qualifications and it's a marvelous position, only the husband . . . well, he chases, according to the woman who interviewed me for the owners. No single ladies under forty need apply, or words to that effect." She watched him closely, anxiously willing him to understand that there was absolutely nothing personal in it at all. "I told her within the month," she added timidly.

A square-tipped hand lifted to stroke the stubble on his chin and Frances watched the rhythmic movements with growing fascination. There was a flat, matted place on his hirsute wrist where his watch had been, and for some queer reason, it was all she could do not to reach out and touch it. Her fingernails bit into her palm as she waited for him to speak.

"One day next week will be soon enough, then? I'm afraid it's the best I can do. I'm taking Olivia to Roaring Gap for the weekend, and on Monday I'll probably be pretty well worn out...Tuesday, then. Shall we get started on the preliminaries on Tuesday?" He looked at her blandly, as if he were mentally shuffling through his engagement book, and she felt about three feet tall.

"Fine," she said through gritted teeth.

One hand tucked under his low-riding belt, Cabel lifted the other to stroke the back of his neck as he stifled a yawn. "Damn, I'm tired. Didn't get in until almost one last night, then up at the crack of dawn. Getting too old for that sort of foolishness." He looked at her with a disarming grin. "Maybe it'll settle me down, this business of marriage."

She resented the flash of white teeth, resented the handsome face, and resented being put in the position of an object of charity. "All right, then, Tuesday," she said grudgingly.

"Great. Call my secretary first thing and she'll tell you what time...No, on second thought, why don't we make it twelve-thirty. I can take time out to give you lunch and then we can sort out the red tape on the way back to the office. When do you start?"

"Start?" she echoed stupidly.

"Work. The new job."

"Oh. Next week, I guess. I forgot to ask."

He looked at her curiously and picked up his watch from the mantle. "Was there anything else?" he asked politely.

Flushing, she jumped to her feet. On her hasty way to the door his voice followed her, "It's only that I have a dinner date and as we're driving to Raleigh, I can't afford to be too late in starting off."

"Oh...!" She made her escape noisily, slamming the door behind her in an excess of childish bad manners. If only she could have thought of something devastatingly cutting to say to him, but he robbed her of even that satisfaction, his very calmness pushing her to the upper limits of rage. The man was absolutely the most infuriating, enraging, insufferable...!

The list carried her halfway down the hill and she decided adamantly that she wouldn't marry him if she were to be burned at the stake!

They were married in the office of a justice of the peace; oddly enough, it had been Cabel who had tried to talk her into having a church wedding with friends and family in attendance. All the time she was spouting her piece about business arrangements and the importance of maintaining an impersonal atmosphere, something inside her was drifting closer and closer to the surface of her consciousness. And because her every instinct of self-preservation forced her to ignore it, she insisted on the minimum of fuss.

Which was not to say that she didn't wear a dress of uncharacteristic frailty, an ivory georgette streetlength dress whose effectiveness was due to the fineness of fabric and cut instead of any frills. And when Cabel handed her a nosegay of Talisman rosebuds, it was all she could do to maintain her composure. With her chin tilted to an imperious degree, she accepted the tearful best wishes of her family and practically dragged Cabel from the waiting room, where everyone stood around talking about other weddings and happy brides and all the things she least wanted to think about.

They left the building with Cabel's fingers biting into her arm, and his increasingly grim countenance hovered somewhere between her nervous glance and the steady stream of downtown traffic. She waited impatiently for two cyclists to pass and then stepped off the curb in front of a van, only to be jerked back by Cabel's far from gentle strength.

"Damn it to hell, Frances, don't make me a widower before I'm even a bridegroom!" he snarled.

She stood trembling on the edge of the sidewalk, oblivious to passersby, and he stared down into her bleached face with a baffled sort of anger. Then, as if defeated by something he saw there, he propelled her to where his car waited.

By the time they had left the fringes of Chapel Hill, she was able to breathe more freely and the feeling of faintness had left her. What on earth was the matter with her? She usually managed to dodge in and out of traffic with all the ease of a practiced jaywalker, so why now, with only the normal Friday afternoon traffic, did she seem bent on self-destruction?

"Feeling better?" he asked curtly, tilting a vent to deflect a stream of air into her face.

"I guess I ought to thank you," she conceded.

"Don't overdo it."

She twisted in her seat, conscious of the buttery soft leather beneath her lightweight coat. "I'm sorry, Cabel. I don't know what's wrong with me. I'm not usually so dense, believe it or not."

He slanted her a closed sort of look as he directed the heavy car with the same skill he brought to everything he did. "Traditional wedding jitters?" he asked laconically.

"That's hardly applicable in this case, is it?"

Beneath the custom fit of his medium gray suit, a shoulder moved disparagingly. "You tell me," he invited in an offhand voice.

She bit her lip. "Well, after all, it's not as if we were really married," she began, when he interrupted her to demand softly just what she thought the ceremony meant.

"Oh . . . it means . . . it means you can use me as an excuse whenever one of your girl friends gets a little too demanding," she said with commendable lightness. "I understand from a tax standpoint we'll both suffer, but maybe I can save you enough on your housekeeping bills to make up the difference."

The car veered suddenly into the muddy entrance of a sloping pasture, and with numbed anticipation, Frances watched as a dozen or so Herefords lifted white faces to stare benignly at them. "Listen here to me, Fancey, you're my wife!" Cabel ground out, "With all the rights and privileges that term entails, and if . . ."

"No!"

"What do you mean, no?" A dangerously silky note had entered Cabel's deep voice.

"I mean . . . no rights, no privileges. You know that, Cabel," she pleaded, suddenly abandoning her spurious defenses. "Look, we both agreed that we wanted to stay . . . well, unattached, unentangled, and have all the . . . the benefits of marriage with none of the hazards."

"Perhaps you'd care to enlighten me on which is which?" he asked mildly. Somewhere along the line he had picked up her wrist and now his thumb was playing games with the sensitive skin over her throbbing pulse.

"I . . . I'll take charge of Hazel for you, and hostess any business dinners and you . . ." Her eyes flew up to meet his mocking glance and it was as if his eyes were challenging her, provoking her into what, she couldn't say. She rushed into speech, "And you'll be perfectly free to...to carry on as usual. I...I won't ask anything of you but the use of your name." Her glance dropped to her third finger, left hand, where, to her continued amazement, a hand-wrought gold and jade ring nestled beside the plain wedding band.

"That's big of you, Fancey Ann McCloud," he allowed softly, turning her hand in his and bringing it up to his lips.

While she hung there, suspended by the burning power of his eyes, he deliberately touched the center of her palm with the tip of his tongue, caressing a nerve that seemed to have a direct line to the center of her body. Her head fell back slightly as her eyelids drooped and she whispered unsteadily, "Cabel, don't do that."

"Do what?"

"You know very well what. We're...we're both experienced adults and we both know very well where this sort of thing can lead." Her voice could have been drifting in through the open window like the sound of cicadas on the earthy-sweet pungence of the pasture, so ephemeral was it. She hoped to God he hadn't any real idea just how limited her own experience was. He could wipe her out, totally annihilate her without half trying if she allowed it to happen, and then walk away without a backward glance.

Abruptly, he started the car. He didn't speak the rest of the way home and when, instead of dropping her off at her own house he continued on up the hill, she didn't protest.

"I thought you might want to familiarize yourself with the house, since Hazel comes tomorrow. The bedrooms and baths upstairs, linen closets, storerooms, and all the places you women like to spend endless hours talking about,'' Cabel mentioned, ushering her inside and closing the door against the increasing coolness as the sun settled down behind the wooded hills.

''You've a flattering opinion of my conversation, haven't you?''

''Nothing personal, Frances. Just thought you ought to check the place out if you've nothing else planned for the next few minutes.'' He was tugging loose his crisp silk tie and unbuttoning the neck of his shirt as he spoke, and he took the stairs two at a time, calling over his shoulder, ''I'll be in the first room on the right if you need me for anything.''

She was on the bottom step when Cabel reached the top and he turned to stare down at her, his foreshortened body looking even more threateningly masculine from her vantage point below him. She stood poised there, one slender foot in a bone calf T-strap resting uncertainly on the second step as she raised her face to him. In a split-second vision, one of those subliminal flashes that sometimes occur, she saw herself dressed in the mode of a previous century, looking up those same graceful stairs to where her husband stood, legs braced apart in frock coat, waistcoat, and dark, fitted pantaloons, his virile physique a magnet for her eyes as she asked in a strained voice, *Will you be long?*

''Will you be long?'' she asked now, in the same strained tone. She blinked to dispel the disturbing effect of déjà vu, never losing contact with those curiously shuttered brown eyes.

''You mean now? I'm only going to change clothes, why?''

"Oh, no reason." She dropped back to the polished floor, still more shaken than she cared to reveal. "I just wondered. I...I'll look around downstairs first and then I think I'd better run along home. Tripod needs feeding. She's been neglected since I gave away her babies."

He nodded and shrugged out of his shirt, his hand going to his belt buckle. "Right. Well, I probably won't see you again before I leave, then, so how about locking up for me if you're still here when I go. I'll be late getting home, I expect."

She took it like a stiff blow to the solar plexus, only glad he had already turned away. He was saying good-night to her! He had no plans to spend so much as an unnecessary minute with her on their own wedding night! She winced as she turned to hurry away to the back of the house, her eyes burning as she stared unseeingly at the bank of wooden-buttoned cabinets that lined the hallway leading to the large, old-fashioned kitchen.

Blast! Oh, just blast the hateful creature to smithereens! she heard the sound of his footsteps over-head, brisk, sure and firm; and when they clattered downstairs, she hurried over and yanked open one of the cabinet doors, staring intently at the rows of canned goods and unmarked cannisters when she felt his presence behind her.

With every cell in her body alert while she stood rigidly in position, she was still unprepared when his hand descended to her shoulder.

"I think on today, at least, I might claim this much," he said, giving her no chance to protest as his mouth came down on hers.

She resisted, her mouth clamped tightly shut as he teased the line between her lips with the tip of his tongue. His hands curled over her shoulders to tuck into the intimate warmth under her arms and he brushed his lips softly over hers, taunting her, making fun of her adamancy until she could have cried out in wretched frustration. There was no hiding her trembling from him, and his arms slipped across her back to draw her more closely to him, still without force, still without more than the most teasing hint of passion. But it was too much for her unsheathed nerves, and she ducked her face into the soft collar of his black knit shirt, burrowing into the clean scented firm flesh of his throat.

Neither of them spoke, nor did they move for unreckoned moments, and then, slowly, she became aware that Cabel's palm was smoothing the thin fabric of her skirt over her hips and tucking under the roundedness to bring her into closer proximity to his own stirring body. Against his throat, her lips opened and her tongue dared taste the faint sweet-saltiness of his flesh. Then he came fully alive, the length of his whole frame registering arousal as he lifted her chin and sought her eager mouth with his.

The kitchen. Why was it they always seemed to make love in the kitchen, she wondered fleetingly, and then all rational thought was swept from her mind as Cabel lifted her in his arms and strode through to the living room, to lower her onto one of the two long, quilted, feather-cushioned sofas. He positioned himself beside her, making her a prisoner with his body, and then he grinned down into her face, his eyes looking almost black as the pupils reflected her flushed, tousled appearance just before he kissed her again.

Buttons magically found themselves unbuttoned, her side zipper was released, and her skirt had somehow crept up over the satin of her slip. She laughed and whispered shakily, "I thought you were going out."

"I lied," he replied with engaging smugness as he released the catch of her lacy wisp of bra and then frowned comically down at the confusion of straps and sleeves about her shoulders. "Hmmm . . . there's got to be a better way to handle this."

"And you're the big lady's man," she chided audaciously.

"Ah, but you're no lady; you're my wife," he shot back triumphantly as he succeeded in baring her to the waist. His face went quite still as his eyes played over her body. "Oh, Lord, you're so very lovely, Frances," he breathed feelingly, and then he bent to capture the shy-proud peak of her breast between his lips, caressing it with his tongue until her head was writhing helplessly against the pillow.

"I can't take much more of this, love," he managed in a voice completely unlike his usual assured tones. "Let's go to bed before you push me quietly over the edge of sanity." He got up and took a deep breath. "I'll lock up, darling, because we may not be downstairs before Monday morning," he warned, extending a hand to help her to her feet.

"You look enchanting, Mrs. McCloud, with your hair falling all over your naked shoulders, but your untidy dress . . . tsk, tsk, tsk!" He shook his head with playful sternness as he allowed his hands the freedom of her body, covering her breasts, and then trailing a finger down to where her narrow gold belt still held the drapery of satin and georgette gathered about her hips. "Shocking, darling . . . positively indecent! Wait for me, hmmm?"

He turned and strode away and Frances stared after him with bemused eyes. Was this the man she had married? This tender, mocking playmate whom she could affect so marvelously with her body? Perhaps there was a chance for their union, after all. Even as hope arose like a newly sprouted seed just breaking through the earth's darkness to see the light of the sun, the phone beside her rang and, still in a state of euphoria, she lifted it unconsciously and spoke.

"Let me speak to Cabel! Who is this, anyway?"

Blighted hope withered away and turned inward again. "This is Frances Harris, Miss Dawson," she said in a flat voice.

"Well, give me Cabel. He was supposed to pick me up over half an hour ago!"

Frances's coat was still where she had dropped it, on the chair beside the double doors and she lifted it and draped it over her bare body, clutching it around her with numb fingers. She could hear Cabel slam and check the back door and she waited until he had reached the hallway before she spoke. "The phone's for you, Cabel. I'll see you around."

Her hand was already opening the door, and Cabel's startled pause gave her time to escape. She heard him call after her, heard the door behind her open, and as she ran down the hill, gravity aiding her flight, she heard him call after her, "Frances, damn it, come back here! Frances!"

The rest of the weekend passed like a bad dream, leaving Frances with an unpleasant feeling of disappointment and hopelessness that was as foreign to her nature as the regime she put herself through to avoid him until she could come to terms with herself.

She threw a few things into a bag, called and made arrangements to drop off Tripod with Margaret Shober. Next she called her old college roommate, whom she saw infrequently, although the two of them kept in contact with calls and cards, and then she drove to Winston-Salem.

It was almost eleven when she pulled into Racine's apartment complex and by that time, she had her story pretty well intact. Her rings were removed, the jade ring worn on her right hand and the gold band tucked into a corner of her satin jewel pouch, and she dropped her overnighter on Racine's yellow shag carpet and announced that she was in need of two full days of rest and relaxation, with no questions asked.

She got it. She toured Old Salem, the restored Moravian settlement where she bought tinware, pottery, and Moravian sugar cake; then she spent the afternoon going through an enormous, impressive tobacco manufacturing plant where she grew accustomed to the sweet pungent smell as she followed an attractive guide across the acres of polished hardwood floors that supported row upon row of immensely sophisticated machinery. She managed to smile and nod and look suitably impressed at the handsome, comfortable-looking facilities for the workers.

Afterward, she remembered practically nothing of what she had seen or heard, but she was totally exhausted, and after a swim in the apartment pool, Racine went out for barbecue sandwiches, and they watched television until Frances's eyes began to close.

No questions. Racine was a nurse now, and if she read anything in Frances's pale face and shadowy eyes, she kept her own counsel.

"Look, Fan, I've got to go on duty at three, so why don't we have a late breakfast and walk through Reynolds Gardens? None of the shops will be open, but the gallery opens at two, and then you can stay on as long as you want while I scram on over to the hospital?"

They more or less followed that plan, with both of them driving, since it was just after twelve by the time they finished a swim and brunch. Racine refrained from questioning her friend, although when she caught Frances's glance on a couple of uninhibited Wake Forest students who paused in a secluded section of the handsome gardens for a long kiss, she sighed rather heavily.

"Honey, anytime you need to get away, I'm here. Old See-No, Hear-No, Speak-No-Racine. But if you want to talk, then I'm available, too, and—count on it—it won't be anything I haven't heard before. Nurses come in for some confidences that would make a soap opera pale in comparison.

With masterfully poor timing, she found herself heading home on an autumn Sunday afternoon alone with everyone else who had been to Lake Norman or perhaps the Blue Ridge Parkway, only an hour away and at its loveliest. At least the traffic kept her mind occupied on the hour-and-a-half drive back to Bynum.

Never one for self-searching, Frances nevertheless was forced to come to terms with herself during the few days immediately following her hollow mockery of a wedding ceremony. And what she discovered came as no real surprise to her. Rather, it was almost a relief, as if the doctor had confirmed the suspected presence of a chronic disease, and now all she had to do was learn to live with the knowledge instead of the aching, nameless dread that had nibbled away her inner resources.

She had to come to terms with the knowledge that she was irrevocably in love with Cabel; then she had to put that knowledge on the shelf, where she might allow herself to glance at it once or twice as she went about the business of reconstructing her life.

Unfortunately, what worked in theory didn't hold up so well in actual practice. When Cabel dropped by Frances's house after work on her second day at the Bronze P'ou, she was unable to keep herself from devouring him with her eyes. She had been home long enough to change into a soft, full-length jersey caftan of cinnamon, black, and gold print that doubled as a bathrobe, but Cabel was still in his fine herringbone three-piece suit, the waistcoat unbuttoned and his tie twisted awry so that he could open the top buttons of his creamy shirt.

He sprawled in her one comfortable chair, legs extended before him and shoved a hand through the fitted cap of dark hair. "What a day! There are more schemes for breaking Wall Street than Las Vegas ever dreamed of, and every single instant-expert walked through my doors today. Legalities, morals, ethics—they all fly out the window when one of the have-nots thinks he sees a way to become a have."

"What about when one of the haves wants to become a have-more?"

He slanted her a quizzical look. "Not you, too! You think the world of Oriental art is inscrutable...try the wonderful world of high finance sometime and see if you can find your way out of the maze."

"Would you care for a drink?" Frances offered.

"Hmmm. Tempting, but what I'd really like is a needle-sharp shower and then twelve solid hours of sleep. Meanwhile, how are things going for you?"

"Just fine, if you mean the Bronze P'ou. It's marvelous to be surrounded by netsukes and Shiwan Ware and jades and ivories. It even smells exotic, and there's so much I didn't know, even after a minor in Oriental Art." She told him about the consignment of antique blue pottery from Jaipur she had unpacked just that day, and then, noticing the droop of his eyelids, she grinned unselfconsciously and allowed her voice to taper off.

The click of the furnace cutting in seemed to rouse him, and he sat up straighter, flexing his shoulders so that she wished she had the nerve to lay her hands on those tired muscles and work them loose again. "Hope you haven't made any plans for tomorrow night," he said, looking around at her extremely limited space with what almost looked like longing.

"Nothing I can think of. Why?"

"Good. Client of mine... nice fellow, you'll like him; coming into Raleigh-Durham Airport at seven tomorrow evening and I want to bring them...his wife's along, too... out here for a solid dose of Southern hospitality. Think you and Hazel can manage between you?"

Startled, she asked, "Just what did you have in mind?"

"Oh, nothing splashy. Just a comfortable, quiet, family-type affair that will help persuade him to move down here where, incidentally, he'll probably decide to locate a multimillion dollar plant he's planning to build. The choice lies between Piedmont, North Carolina and West Virginia, and another of my clients has an option on some property that might be just what he's looking for."

"All that reeks of...well, something or other," Frances accused doubtfully, pressing her back against the intricate scrolls of the bentwood rocker.

"Now that's a peculiar choice of words," Cabel snorted, wrenching himself upright in the upholstered chair. "The fact is, the sale of the property will enable the owner to invest in a small company he owns that's in danger of going out of business and taking some two hundred jobs down the drain with it, plus the fact that the plant, if it's built here, will employ a hell of a lot of local labor in the building stage and then provide even more jobs once it's finished, none of which strikes me as being particularly reprehensible! If there's a profit to be made along the way, it will no doubt be invested in still more expansion, which will provide more jobs."

"And you, just incidentally, will take a commission on it all," she retorted, wondering why she was baiting him this way.

One hand went to stroke the back of his neck. "Look, Frances, I'm not about to defend myself to you. I deal in a variety of investments. It's not a dirty word, believe it or not, and either you trust in my integrity or you don't. If you don't..." He shrugged and she wanted above all to take back her snide remark, wanted even more to be able to see the expression on his averted face.

"I'm sorry, Cabel. I do trust you. I couldn't..." She was about to say she couldn't have fallen in love with him without that trust, but she changed in the middle of the sentence. "I couldn't begin to understand the intricacies of high finance."

The smile he gave her was twisted, offering a wary acceptance of her apology. "You might call me a tour guide, then. Not too many people do understand even the simple fundamentals of investing." He stood and walked over to her front window to stare down at the restless river. The trees now were mostly blackened skeletons, a few wearing patches of lurid scarlet or yellow, having been stripped of their finery prematurely by a severe wind and rain the day before. "For your information," he remarked to the window pane as Frances followed the lines of his body with her eyes, "I'll get a modest commission on the land if it's sold; nothing at all on the plant, if it's built. Now...about tomorrow night?"

"How long will they be here and what do you want me to do?"

Chapter Eight

As to the first, I expect they'll be staying about three or four days. I thought we'd have a quiet dinner at home the first night and then plan something a little more ambitious the next. Ed's fed up with the social round, and I'd like to show him that we can be just as social with none of the pressure he's accustomed to in the circles he moves in. Perhaps you'd invite your family for the dinner party."

"My family?"

"Might be a good way to follow up those few minutes after the ceremony. Reassure them that little Fancey's all set so that they can stop worrying. After all, we haven't seen them lately."

"It's been all of what...? Four days? They'd naturally expect us to be honeymooning," Frances snapped, irritated by his bland composure.

"Hmmm. There is that aspect, I suppose. By the way, Mrs. McCloud, where'd you go on your honeymoon?"

She studied him, trying to fathom his mood and could discern nothing beneath the surface pleasantness. "I went to Winston-Salem," she told him.

"Which one of your team of Irishmen enjoyed your company, the traveling salesman or the bow tie?"

Bristling, she retorted, "Have I asked you which one of your mistresses you honeymooned with? But then, I don't have to... Miss Dawson was the lucky winner, I believe!" She would have given anything to have remained calm and aloof, but the pain swamped her all over again and it was all she could do to remain seated in the same room with him.

"About that call, Frances," Cabel began, but she cut him off.

"Forget it! We laid out the ground rules before we ever drew up the contract for this partnership, and I'm certainly not complaining. Now...my first duty will be this dinner tomorrow night...nothing fancy, you said, just a quiet relaxing evening. What about the next day? What will Mrs...?"

"Moultrie. Ed and Miriam Moultrie," Cabel filled in.

"Right. I assume he'll be with you, but what about his wife? I'll be at work, so I can't look after her."

"We'll work something out, never mind. I haven't met the lady so I haven't a clue what will suit her. And about the next night, how about inviting your sisters and their husbands, your mother, of course, and the aunt and uncle from Durham and...let's see...we'll need another man to make up numbers so...why not invite your two Irishmen and I'll invite Olivia to fill out the table. Suit you?"

She could have strangled him! This was going to be difficult enough without having every move she made examined by those ice-blue Dawson eyes. And for that matter, she could do without Sean and Doyle in attendance. "The menu," she mentioned, forcing herself to go beyond the problems presented by the company alone. "Will you want Beef Wellington and buttered artichokes or...?"

"Make it one of those delectable, high cholesterol Southern specialties...maybe roast pork, country ham, red-eye gravy and grits, and biscuits with butterbeans and...oh...you know the drill."

She had to smile. "Sounds as if you know it pretty well, too," she allowed.

"I'm a quick study," he said modestly, rising and stretching his shoulders tiredly. Frances wondered briefly, painfully, just how much of his tiredness came from his work, but she stood briskly and saw him to the door.

"I just hope Hazel is up to all this, because I'll be at work all day," she said.

"I'll arrange for her to be here full time as long as the Moultries are here," Cabel murmured as he reached for the door. "That way, you can set her a course before you leave in the mornings and check her on it later on, hmmm? I'm sure Olivia won't mind giving her to me for the duration."

I'm sure Olivia wouldn't mind giving you anything you asked for, Frances thought uncharitably, but she kept it to herself. Better not make waves now, of all times. "Good night, Cabel."

"Good night, Mrs. McCloud," he whispered, and before she could step back, he leaned over and laid a sweet, soft kiss on her startled mouth and let himself out.

Before leaving for the airport the next evening, Cabel called in at Frances's house, finding her in the kitchen where she had gone to feed Tripod as soon as she got in from work. The three-legged cat practically inhaled the dish of smelly fishmeal and then flopped an awkward rear end against Frances's leg, tail aquiver as it purred in appreciation.

"Look, it occurs to me that there might be a few awkward questions if my wife hops up after coffee, says good night, all, and takes off. How about bringing over a few things while I'm gone and staying for the duration?"

Nonplussed, she could only stare at him. That aspect of the situation hadn't occurred to her, oddly enough. He hadn't seemed to mind that the housekeeper knew they weren't sharing a house, much less a room, and that, of course, meant that Olivia was aware of the fact, as well.

"There won't be any real problem, will there?" he asked as if impatient to settle the matter and be on his way. "You can run back and forth to look after your cat and then, once the houseparty's over, you're free to take up residence here again."

She didn't know whether to laugh or cry. When an utterly ridiculous situation! His housekeeper knew the truth, his mistress knew the truth, so how on earth had he thought a mere marriage certificate would make a difference? Silly to pretend for a couple of business associates, but if that was what he wanted... "If you think it's important," she shrugged. "Does it matter which room? Oh, and where shall I put the Moultries? I thought the room across from yours. It has the best view of the river and the bath's convenient."

"Fine, then you can move into the one next to mine and we'll share my bath. May as well make it look good in case there's any suspicion. I expect your mother will want to get you off into a corner for a little female heart-to-heart, so we'll leave the connecting door open and make her romantic heart flutter a little faster, shall we?"

His grin was easy, a friendly thing with no overtones at all and he left without giving Frances a chance to disagree.

If he only knew, she thought, watching his lean, rangey figure slide in under the wheel of his car. Patsy would be hard pressed to understand a marriage that didn't center around a big double bed where all arguments were settled, all problems talked over and the news of the day capped off before a good-night kiss. Frances had heard her parents' voices mumbling through their bedroom door for years, whenever her father, who had been a tobacco auctioneer with a circuit to travel, was home.

By the time Cabel returned with the Moultries, Frances and Hazel between them had contrived a creditable meal and Frances had put fresh flowers in the main rooms. She had ordered them earlier in bulk and arranged them herself while Hazel put the finishing touches in the dining room.

In spite of all her efforts to be pleasant to the slatternly housekeeper, the atmosphere between the two of them was uncomfortable. Frances's position was undermined by the fact that Hazel knew very well she had not lived with her husband since their marriage, and if the woman was capable of any loyalty at all, it was to Olivia Dawson. Her attitude toward Frances was one of ill-concealed contempt, and there wasn't a thing Frances could do about it. Cabel hadn't married her to disrupt his household arrangements, but to improve them, and as things were, that simply didn't seem possible.

Meanwhile, there was tonight to get through. She had put her things in the room that adjoined Cabel's, noticing with more wistfulness than amusement the open door between them, and changed into something she considered suitable for a quiet evening at home with a middle-aged couple. The Thail-silk print of blue, lavender, and jade brought a warmth to her face, and she repeated the lavender very subtly in her eye shadow, glancing unconsciously at the jade ring as if to assure herself it was really there. It had been a total surprise, the ring, and she had protested Cabel's spending so much money on her in the circumstances, but he had cut off her argument with a freezing look.

"All I can say is, it ain't no time to go eatin' supper. Eight thirty, nine o'clock! I won't be here to wash no dishes an' I can tell you right now, I don't like comin' into no dirty kitchen first thing in the mornin'," Hazel announced as Frances made one last trip to the kitchen before going to the front door to greet the arrivals.

"You won't have to, Hazel," she told the disgruntled housekeeper quietly. "I'll see that everything's cleared away tonight before I go to bed."

"Hmmmph!" The woman cast her a knowing look from dull, colorless eyes and flounced into the dining room to bring back a heavy cut-glass water pitcher for filling.

There was no time to set her straight . . . nothing to set straight, anyway. Perhaps once this visit was over, she might look around for someone else, and Olivia be damned. If Cabel expected her to oversee his household, he'd have to allow her a certain amount of freedom, especially as he couldn't give her any amount of authority as his wife, at least where Hazel and Olivia Dawson were concerned.

The Moultries were a surprise. At least the distaff side was, for Miriam Moultrie was at least twenty years younger than her tired-looking husband. When the three of them entered the foyer, with Frances to greet them and

Hazel to take their bags, the tall, slender platinum blond cast a measuring look around her before she returned Frances's greeting with a perfunctory one of her own—minus the smile.

Ed Moultrie made up for his wife's lack of friendliness by his genuine interest in the house, the area, and the food, which was plain fried chicken and garden vegetables. The okra intrigued him, and Frances hoped his obvious appreciation would make up for his wife's derisive comments as she pushed around the small servings and made do with several glasses of the excellent wine Cabel had selected. Hazel was getting ready to leave when Frances went to the kitchen for the coffee and the older woman announced flatly, and in an embarrassingly loud voice, "That man done ate like a horse, he did, and she didn't do no more than mess her plate up."

"Yes, well, it was delicious, Hazel. Mrs. Moultrie evidently had something on the flight so that she wasn't really all that hungry."

The housekeeper slammed out the back door, mumbling something about going back to them that liked her ways, and Frances wished heartily that she'd make good her threat.

Shortly after they had coffee, Ed Moultrie said goodnight and Frances expected his wife to accompany him. But instead, Miriam looked at Cabel, a speculative light in her light gray eyes, and announced that she needed some exercise after the flight to put her in a mood to sleep.

There was nothing Cabel could do, Frances told herself as she watched him escort the lovely blond out the front door, except offer to accompany her on a walk down to the river. The fact that the moon would be rising within half an hour or so was an added inducement, and Frances began clearing away the dining room with an impatience that only partly disguised the hurt she was feeling. Miriam tonight, Olivia tomorrow night...if it was variety Cabel wanted, then he had arranged his affairs perfectly, only Frances wouldn't be part of that variety.

She blew an escaping wisp of hair off her forehead and plunged the last pan into the tired suds half an hour later. Cabel and Miriam were still out there somewhere, with Cabel no doubt exercising that exasperating, fascinating charm of his on the all too willing blond. It looked as if business took second place as far as he was concerned, for surely he didn't expect Ed Moultrie to be too happy about the situation.

There was satisfaction to be gained from scouring the crust from the frying pan, and long after the surface was scrubbed clean, Frances glowered at the steamy window over the sink and rubbed the copper bottom in vigorous time with her angry thoughts. It would serve him right if she walked out flat and left him to explain her absence as best he could. Nice family affair, my foot! Cabel's idea of a family affair was an affair with someone else's family! Namely, his client's wife! If she hadn't already invited her own family for dinner tomorrow night, she'd walk out right now, but that would take more explaining than she was capable of. Still, it might be amusing to watch them...Olivia and Miriam, Cabel and Doyle, with poor old Sean left to entertain her, no doubt!

"May I ask what you're mumbling about?" Cabel asked from behind her. She hadn't even heard him come in and now she whirled around, looking past him to the empty hallway.

"What happened to your guest, or did you put her back under her rock?" she asked, and then could have bit off her tongue.

"My, we're awfully testy tonight, aren't we? Are you already dissatisfied with your working conditions? Ready to renegotiate your contract?" It was as though he wanted her to flare up, as if he were taunting her deliberately. Contrarily, she refused to be baited.

"Not at all," she replied calmly. "Perhaps Mrs. Moultrie would like me to run her her bath for her... unless you've already offered," she added with saccharine sweetness.

"Now what can Miriam Moultrie have done to put you in this interesting frame of mind, I wonder," Cabel mused. "You sound almost as if you were jealous, but that's too farfetched, I suppose." He slanted her a querying look as he leaned back against the counter and fondled a cold pipe in his hand.

"Don't be ridiculous! I'm going up to bed," Frances announced, flinging the damp dish towel across the rack impatiently. Cabel's words had struck home and she didn't like dealing with herself in this mood.

"Sounds like a good idea," he replied with a benign smile.

"Alone!"

He levered himself away from the cabinet, switching off the light, and followed her across the broad gleaming expanse of polished pine floors, "Sorry you had to clean up all this mess. Maybe I should have asked Hazel to sleep over."

"Don't bother! I'd rather wash up after a regiment than put up with any more of her snide remarks."

"That bad, hmm?" He took her arm and steered her into the living room, and the teasing look was gone from his face as he seated her on the down-cushioned sofa. The coals of an earlier fire still glowed on the hearth and the room seemed warm and welcoming as the tiredness of the long, difficult day suddenly caught up with her.

Wordlessly, she stared back at him, too weary to care any more. It was as if the comfortable cushions drained her of the dregs of anger, jealousy, and hopelessness, leaving behind only an emptiness, waiting to be filled.

Cabel knocked his pipe out on the tile-faced fireplace and left it on the mantel before joining her on the sofa. Even then, he didn't touch her. Over the subtle scent of the apple wood that had taken the chill off the evening, she was aware of his cologne, a light, mossy fragrance that was almost not there, coupled with the odor of good woolens and aromatic tobacco. She stiffened herself against the imperceptible spell he could cast without even trying.

"Now," he said, turning to face her, "What's the trouble? All of it."

"In alphabetical order?" she quipped, trying for lightness and failing.

"Try starting with Hazel."

"All right, I will. She's dreadful! She knows very well I don't... I mean, we don't... and, well, she makes remarks."

"I take it you're referring to our rather unorthodox marriage arrangements. Hmmmm. Well, unless you're willing to really get into the part... for Hazel's benefit, that is, I don't see what I can do about it."

Getting wound up by now, Frances continued, leaning forward in order to press on him the seriousness of her charges. "And you know very well that what Hazel knows, Olivia knows," she pointed out, "so where's the value of our marriage? I might just as well have stayed home!"

"Except for the Moultries."

"Not that a little thing like a wife kept that woman from throwing herself at you," she charged sulkily. "And you standing there with a catcher's mitt on! What do you suppose poor Ed thought?"

Unexpectedly, he grinned. "If it's of any comfort to you, wife, she struck out, thanks to you. I'm afraid Miriam's the sort to get up to mischief whenever possible and I let her know in the kindest sort of way that my hands were full with my new bride."

"You didn't!" Frances crowed, suddenly feeling quite revived.

With a modest, if somewhat smug smile, Cabel nodded. "I'm not about to endanger the whole deal before it ever gets off the ground, so I thought I'd better get things straight in the beginning. What better way than to walk in the moonlight with one woman while I sing the praises of another?"

"Cabel! Did you really?"

"Scout's honor. You wouldn't have recognized yourself, Fancey, by the time I got through spreading it on."

The smile faded from her face. "Thanks for the vote of confidence," she jeered.

He gave her a measuring look that puzzled her and she reluctantly lowered a tucked-up foot to the floor and made as if to rise. With one hand, he stayed her. "What's the matter, Frances? The cards-on-the-table approach beginning to pall?" It was an easy matter to tip her back against the cushions, and he followed the action with a finger on her lip, a finger that pressed insinuatingly as his eyes began to speak.

Frances moved abruptly. The spell of the firelight, the almost overwhelming silence in the large old house, and the nearness of this man were confusing her, beguiling her, and she could ill-afford to be beguiled. His every word, every look, was open to misinterpretation in her present state of mind, and she tried for matter-of-factness when she suggested that he lean the fire screen up against the fireplace before he came upstairs.

"Frances?" he persisted softly, ignoring her words. "We could make things more convincing to the Moultries...to Hazel, too, if it matters."

In the face of her dismayed confusion, he persisted. "Why not?" He traced a line from her nose to her lips, her chin, and down her throat, meandering slowly into the shadowy valley between her breasts. "You can't deny you're attracted to me, and I haven't any objection to...shall we say, normalizing the situation between us?"

His smile was whimsical, a flashing of that lopsided dimple, a showing of strong white teeth, but his eyes were in shadow, unreadable in the dim light of the lamp behind them. Frances drew back and stared at him strickenly. If he had deliberately set out to prevent any such thing from happening, he couldn't have gone about it any more efficiently. She hid the bitter medicine of her disappointment with a brittle facade. "Careful, there. You might be getting in over your head. For all you know, I could take you up on it and then you'd be in trouble." She managed a parody of a smile and was thankful for the dimness of the lighting. "We agreed...no pretense between us, remember?"

With a lightninglike change of moods, Cabel withdrew, clamping his hands on his widespread, muscular thighs. "What the hell do you think I'm pretending?

Can't you accept the fact that I'd like to sleep with my own wife, for God's sake?"

"No, as a matter of fact, I can't! Oh, I'm not saying it might not be the truth, but let's get something straight, Cabel; you can do your... your womanizing somewhere else. I'm not interested in adding my scalp to your collection, and now if you'll excuse me, I have a big day tomorrow."

She twisted herself to a standing position, her head lifted high enough to disguise the beginning of tears as she stared down at him. Lord, was ever a man worth all the pain? She hated him, hated him for making her love him and even now, knowing he was simply passing time with her, she was tempted!

"All things considered, Frances, I think I've been pretty patient with you," he gritted out. She thought fleetingly that he looked... baffled, somehow. "Anytime you're ready to face facts and straighten out this stupid state of affairs between us, I'll be waiting, but you'll have to come to me. I can't fight your defenses any longer," he finished tiredly.

Taking a deep, steadying breath, she said, "In the first place, there is no affair to be straightened out between us, nor will there be. In the second place, the basic ground rules have been spelled out so that even a dimwit like myself can read them; and in the third place, Cabel McCloud, after this Moultrie debacle, I think it's about time we started working on our annulment! I'll hostess this one thing for you, but as for taking on your household, I can't work with your mistress's housekeeper! I'd advise you to take on the pair of them! Between them, they'll set you up in fine shape, but from now on, leave me out of it!" She whirled to go and he caught her at the base of the stairs.

"All right, you dried-up shrew, you've had your say, and now you're going to listen while I have mine! I married you when you needed a husband. Wait!" He held up a silencing hand when she would have flung his charge back at him. "Let me finish and then you can complain all you want to, I won't be here to hear it! I gave you my name and secured your job for you so that you could keep that squatter's shanty you call a home, and you think I'd trade off my freedom for one dinner party? Lady, I don't come that cheap!"

The glitter in his eyes was like nothing she had even seen before, and she drew back, unable to break away completely from the raw, unleashed power of him. Somewhere in the back of her mind there flickered a thought about his need for a wife to stand between him and the more importunate of his female friends, but his hard-driving voice chased all other thoughts from her mind as he continued speaking.

"There'll be two more things I'll require of you before I turn you loose and then you can go to the devil for all I care! The Moultries leave day after tomorrow. The next day is Friday and you can make plans to go with me to Nassau for the weekend."

She opened her mouth to protest, but he ignored her, washing over her puny resistance like a tidal wave. "We're meeting someone there and you're going to turn in an award-winning performance as a devoted wife or I'll make you know what being a real wife means! And what's more," his eyes narrowed as he raked her from head to toe, "you know exactly what I mean, don't you?"

A wheezy old clock struck eleven-thirty, and still they glared at each other. Frances's hands were clutching her stomach as if the pain that shafted through her body had an actual physical source. But Cabel's hands remained at his sides, his fingers curled into his palms so tightly that his knuckles showed white, as if he were fighting a desire to strike her.

Without another word, Frances turned and made her way up the stairs, each step measured and leaden as she moved like an unfeeling automaton toward the scant security of her room.

The next day finally passed after what seemed thirty-six hours. Not even the exquisite consignment of jadeite carvings that came in could lift her spirits, and Frances stood by the window of the Bronze P'ou and rubbed a pendant absently, while her mind drifted back to the house on the hill.

Her eyes felt dry and gritty from lack of sleep, but sleep had been impossible after she closed the door behind her. The communicating door had stood mockingly open, for one thing, and thanks to the aged, sloping floors, the only way she had been able to secure it had been to place a chair under the knob. There had been a slight satisfaction in hearing him striding about as he got ready for bed, slamming drawers with no consideration for the guests just across the hall, much less the wife on the other side of the paneled door. At least he wasn't indifferent to her, whatever else he wasn't.

With the dinner party irrevocably scheduled for seven tonight, Frances wasn't allowed the privilege of temperament. She had gone directly to the kitchen this morning as soon as she heard Hazel's noisy attendance, and given her orders for the day, ignoring the smug, malicious looks. Then she crossed the hall for her coat, intent on escaping before Cabel came downstairs.

But her plan was thwarted. He appeared at the bottom of the stairs to tell her that Miriam had agreed to join him and Ed for the morning. "I'll turn her over to my secretary and then, after lunch, we'll make some arrangements for shopping, or whatever you women do to pass time in a strange town. Pity you're tied up."

"Yes, isn't it?" she remarked coolly, sliding her arm into her lightweight beige topper. She was thinking, I didn't even know he had a secretary, although only an idiot would suppose otherwise.

"Will you be able to manage tonight?" he asked politely and she said, "Yes, thank you," just as politely.

They stared at each other for several long seconds and then Cabel shook himself and turned away toward the dining room. Frances closed the front door behind her. He hadn't even asked her if she'd had breakfast... which she hadn't. He hadn't asked if she'd slept well, either...which she hadn't, and from the looks of the gray lines beside his implacable mouth, neither had he.

Oh, God, she cried silently as she ground the starter unmercifully before shooting off down the hill, why can't I just let it flow? Why do I have to freeze up whenever he's around? On paper it looked as if we might have a chance, but we both seem to go crazy whenever we're together for more than five minutes!

That had been this morning. The afternoon had been little better, although she had sold a nineteenth-century Korean rice chest of Zelkovia wood to a collector from Southern Pines who promised to return with his wife, who collected snuff bottles. That had made it easier to ask for Friday off. And when she reminded Mrs. Macheris that she and her husband had never had a proper honeymoon, she was told to take Monday as well, if she wanted it.

She dreaded the party all the way home, but her thoughts about the upcoming weekend trip all but crowded the worries out, and she admitted to herself reluctantly that she was looking forward to being with Cabel somewhere away from all past ties. Perhaps it still wasn't too late. If she had only a hint that his feelings for her went deeper than convenience and a momentary lust, she might find the courage to tell him how she felt.

Chapter Nine

Only the fact that Miriam Moultrie was on hand to watch her performance allowed Frances to get through the time between leaving the Bronze P'ou and greeting the first arrivals. She was dead on her feet, as much from pure tension as from lack of sleep, and the thirty-minute soak as she sipped a glass of Madeira helped less than she had hoped.

Cabel, home early for once, was free to entertain their guests and thus allow her time enough to pull herself together. She paid extraordinary attention to the details of her dress, choosing a plain white silk jersey dinner dress and wearing only her wedding band, her jade ring, and a pair of plain gold earrings. She made up her face carefully in order to disguise the shadows that hollowed her cheekbones and enlarged her eyes, but nothing could hide a strange look of wistfulness. She hoped, as she added a final whiff of Odalesque, that it would be taken as worldly sophistication instead of the vulnerability it actually was. Her shell felt terribly fragile tonight.

Doyle brought Olivia and they and Patsy arrived in a group a few minutes before the others. She was chagrined to see a long white skirt under Olivia's velvet wrap and she couldn't help but glance down at her own dress.

"Honey, you look awful," Patsy announced in ringing tones as she wriggled out of her tweed and squeezed Cabel's arm. It wasn't Cabel she was addressing, however, and Frances brought off a creditable laugh as Doyle mentioned the newlywed state and Olivia glared coldly at her.

Either barrage might have been her undoing had not Cabel taken each woman on an arm and guided them into the living room, leaving Frances to show Doyle where to hang his topcoat.

"Hmm, bloody swank you landed in, Frances. No wonder you didn't have time for a struggling salesman."

"Don't be silly, Doyle. As I remember it, you ditched me as soon as you laid eyes on Olivia Dawson, so don't go crying any crocodile tears. Come on, I'll give you a drink." She suddenly felt on top of the situation. It would be all right, at least as long as her garrulous relatives were reasonably discreet.

From then on, the evening moved forward with a momentum of its own. Her sisters and their husbands arrived with Aunt Helen and Uncle Jerrold and Sean and Jerrold talked of Duke's team while Jean, Kay, and Aunt Helen went over the affairs of the younger generation. Both Kay and Jean had one child each under five, and while Frances adored them both, she could do without hearing about each bite they took and every word they spoke.

Patsy and Ed Moultrie found things to discuss while Cabel stood talking to Olivia. Frances's eyes were drawn again and again to the pair of them as they stood before the fireplace. Cabel looked unusually handsome without half trying, wearing a dark lounge suit and a modestly tucked shirt with a sober tie. The cufflinks he wore were equally sober, but the more elegant for it and from there, Frances moved on to study the sparkling brunette who was holding his attention.

Olivia Dawson would hold any man's attention, she admitted reluctantly. The white dress she wore put Frances's own modest creation in the shade, and the necklace that adorned it was stunning. It had to be real, for the depth of light in those tones could only come from diamonds and the blue central stone, only a few shades darker than Olivia's light blue eyes, was unusual in itself, and set in an intriguing design.

It wasn't until they were seated at the dinner table that Frances began to relax. The Madeira she had sipped in her bath, plus the drink Cabel had handed her when she came downstairs, helped, as did the familiar chatter of her own family, who were oblivious to any undertones.

The dining room gleamed softly, its high ceiling muting the mingled voices, as if filing them away with the residue of the past century or so. The table was long and made of walnut, as were the chairs, and though of no particular style, they were handsome and to Frances's way of thinking, distinctive. She was proud, for Cabel's sake, of the gracious overall effect of the traditional china, silver, and crystal in the dove gray room, and it occurred to her to wonder, not for the first time, how he had come by such possessions.

Not that he couldn't afford them. They had not discussed his financial standing, but it was evident that he was secure enough in his position to enjoy quality without ostentation. Most other moneyed bachelors of her acquaintance would have gone in for an indoor pool, or tennis courts and a sauna, or at the very least, a conference-sized hot tub.

"Hmmmm?" She returned to her surroundings to answer Sean's question and then, as she began to lapse back into her own soft-focused world, she became aware of someone's staring at her. Glancing around, she saw Olivia's marblelike eyes slide away as a secret little smile curled her lips.

Several times during the remainder of the meal, she caught the smug expression, the malicious gleam in eyes that refused to lock with hers, and by the time they rose from the table to have coffee in the living room, Frances was seething again.

The dozen people arranged themselves in small groups and from her vantage point in front of the heavy Georgian coffee service, Frances was able to let her mind flow into the different conversations, satisfying herself that all was well. Milo, Kay's husband, was telling Cabel about the distinctive breed of English setter that had taken all the field trial honors in the early sixties, insisting that Mollie had the right coloring, size, and conformation, and promising to look around for a dog of the same strain if he could have first choice of the pups.

Patsy was proclaiming the advantages of mulching to Ed Moultrie, who probably didn't do all that much gardening in Chicago, and Helen was telling Sean about the daughter of one of Jerrold's teaching friends. Olivia leaned back in the high-backed Queen Anne chair and gazed openly at Cabel, her eyes moving down the length of him and then back again at a slow simmer. Frances sat her cup down firmly. Determined to try and be civil, she crossed to take the matching chair.

"Miss Dawson, I couldn't help but admire your necklace. It looks handwrought, and I was wondering if the stones were from North Carolina? My father was a rock hound and he found some marvelous blue tourmaline that I've always wanted to have something done with."

Olivia's flawless white hand fluttered up to touch the gleaming arrangement of stones set in what appeared to be free-form cast gold. She leaned forward and said in a low, husky voice brimming with laughter, "I'm sure I don't know where they came from, darling. It was a gift." Her eyes cut to where Cabel stood, engrossed in a conversation with Ed Moultrie, Milo, and Jean's husband, Shelby. "We considered the jade...in fact, I think...well, of course, that's water over the dam now, isn't it?" Her eyes went meaningfully to Frances's ring. "I love these, though, and of course, they're sapphires, not tourmalines. He wouldn't think of giving me one of the lesser stones."

Somehow, Frances managed to get through the rest of the evening. She must have said all the right things, for Patsy took her aside as she was leaving to compliment her on finally growing up. "You were perfect for this place, Fancey Ann, and I'm not surprised that a man like Cabel saw it right off the bat. I couldn't have done better for you if I'd tried."

The Moultries went upstairs together for a change, and Frances waited until she heard Cabel let himself out the back door for Mollie's last run before making her way to her own room. She leaned against the coolness of the white paneled door and closed her eyes while the pain washed over her in waves.

So what else is new? You knew Olivia's position in his life when you married him. A man doesn't marry his mistress, but that's not to say he doesn't also need a wife in the background. But to bring her here, to flaunt her before Patsy and Kay and Jean...! And that necklace! Had they deliberated together, buying jade and sapphire both? Had Cabel then offered Frances, herself, the left-overs?

She tugged the ring from her finger and threw it across the room. She hadn't asked for an engagement ring in the first place, and to be offered one that another woman had refused was just too much to bear.

She was asleep when he finally came upstairs. Pure exhaustion had taken its toll, and if she roused on hearing a door open quietly, if she stirred restlessly as someone touched her shoulder, it was all forgotten in the morning, like the mist that rose over the river to be dispelled by the warming sun.

There were exactly forty-seven minutes between seeing the Moultries off for Chicago and boarding a plane for Miami and from there to Nassau. Frances had flown before and she had visited several of the low-lying islands along the Carolinas and Georgia, but she had never seen water as intensely blue as that she flew out over of Miami. When the water closer to the gemlike islands shaded into a jade that matched her ring, she rubbed the bare gold band on her left hand unconsciously.

She had brought the jade along with her, for just as she couldn't bear to wear it, she also couldn't leave it behind. There had been little or no time to discuss the matter with Cabel, not that she had any idea what to say to him on the matter, for he had buried himself in a brief-case full of papers when they left Raleigh-Durham and come up for air only when they touched down in Atlanta. He asked her then about the clothes she had brought along. She answered briefly and then they both stared away from each other while tension shimmered between them like a living presence.

Just as Cabel had secured them reservations on connecting flights at a moment's notice, so he whisked them through customs and immigration. Then they were ushered into one of the numerous waiting taxis, leaving Frances with a kaleidoscopic impression of bright, wide smiles, melodious, uninhibited voices, loud shirts and straw hats...and the sunshine. Surely the same sun didn't beam down on this ocean island that shone on Chatham Country, North Carolina?

After an initial reaction in which she ducked against Cabel to his amusement, Frances discovered that their taxi driver was no more suicidal than any other, that traffic could flow just as freely and safely on the left-hand as on the more familiar right. Cabel's indulgence was the first sign of anything other than mere politeness between them and against all logic, Frances treasured it. When his arm crossed her shoulder casually as he pointed out a particular view along the narrow, dusty road, she allowed it to remain.

"I'm glad this will be your first taste of the Bahamas," he murmured as they careened along beside a limestone wall, with dusty sage scrub and fluid palms flashing past. "I prefer something more off the beaten track when there's time, but my mother's been here for over a month now and she's anxious to meet you."

"Your mother!" she blurted out, pulling away from that bare arm draped so carelessly over her shoulder. "Why didn't you tell me?"

A grimace flickered across his face and disappeared almost before she recognized it for what it was: Cabel was ill at ease! Somehow, the idea that this enigmatic, often exasperating man she had married in such haste could be anything less than in command of a situation disarmed her completely, and she remained silent during the drive to their tall, blindingly white hotel. She had come along with the full intention of telling him what she thought of any man who would flaunt his mistress under the noses of his wife and in-laws, but somehow, there was a sense of unreality about the past few days—about everything that had happened between them so far, in fact. Reality failed to stretch across the hundreds of miles they had traveled, leaving her encapsulated within a fragile, impossibly colorful bubble with this man whose nearness was beginning to have an effect on her breathing.

"We'll talk about it after we check in and loosen the kinks with something tall, cool, and rum-filled. I'd have preferred one of the out islands, at least, but bear with me . . . it'll only be for a weekend."

"Look, Cabel, I'm no blasé world traveler. Frankly, I'm still trying to get over Miami International, so a taste of typical tourist fare won't bore me at all. Is your mother at this hotel?"

"Lord, no!" he paid the fare and handed their bags to a beaming porter whom they followed into the gleaming coolness of the lobby. "Mother's over on Paradise Island. We came to see her, but I have no intention of living in her pocket while we're here. You'll see what I mean when you meet her."

A touch of grimness entered his voice again and Frances slanted a curious look up at him. But when Cabel said later, he meant later, and she followed him meekly to the desk and then to the handsome, impersonal suite he had booked them into.

The flowers were nice. They took away some of that mass-produced, sanitized feeling common to so many chain hotels. But if it were a chain, it was an exclusive chain and Frances wandered about, opening doors and looking out of windows, delighting in the small balcony that was theirs alone. There was one bedroom, with two double beds, but she assumed Cabel would be sleeping on the sofa in the attractive sitting room. Either that, or she would!

"I've had drinks sent up, if you'd like to shower and change into something first. Mother'll be here for dinner...her current spouse, as well, I'm afraid. I haven't met this one, so I can't guarantee anything, but...well, go and shower. We'll talk over rum punches."

They did. Frances had changed into a summery yellow gauze and she waited, enchanted with the abundance of flowers and glossy green shrubbery around the base of the hotel. Further out was a travel-poster view of the sea, looking like a mosaic of gemstones as it traced the curving beaches of cream-colored sand.

Cabel came through the sliding louvered doors, drops of water glinting on his cap of dark hair. He had changed into white duck pants and a black knit shirt and he dropped down beside her and reached for his drink. "Mother," he said in a baffling tone. He pursed his lips and lifted expressive brows. "Well, in case I haven't filled you in, my mother left us when I was about five. I didn't see her again until I was ready for prep school, and after that, probably no more than half a dozen times in all. Oh, we kept up with each other. When Dad died, Mother wanted to come, but she was in Mexico getting a divorce and...well," he shrugged, "it just didn't work out. This will be the first time I've seen her in about four years."

"But Cabel, how did she know about me?" Frances asked, puzzled over more than just his attitude toward his mother.

"I called to tell her we were getting married...not to invite her, you understand." A sardonic twist of his mouth appeared as he gazed out over the coral-tinted sky. "Lord, I can see it now, Mother and Patsy exchanging views on the holy state of matrimony."

Frances stiffened, suspecting a slight to her own family, but Cabel quickly put her straight on that score. "I wouldn't have subjected Patsy to my mother for the world, Frances. Nor you, either, until I had time to prepare you."

"But why now?" she asked, meaning why now that our marriage is already grinding to a halt?

Again that lift of a shoulder. "You had to meet her sooner or later, I suppose. May as well get it over with. Besides, I owe the woman something. She gave me my first taste of what marriage could be like, seeing her and my father together when I was too young to realize what was going on, and then seeing my father trying his damndest to recover from what she did to him."

A fragrant breeze lifted the hair from her neck, and she heard sounds of laughter, traffic and music. She felt as if she were someone else; not the Frances who had tramped the red hills of home, collecting dried weeds from the edges of fields of millet, corn, and tobacco not long ago.

"What are you thinking?" Cabel asked unexpectedly.

She told him, adding that she was afraid she was a dyed-in-the-wool provincial. "I'll embarrass you, just you wait. I want to stare at everything and then taste it, touch it, or smell it to be sure it isn't plastic. Imagine flowers that size growing this time of the year! It's...it's indecent!"

He laughed and some of the tension seemed to ease from his face, making her aware for the first time that it had been there, under the seemingly casual description of his relationship with his mother. He might think he wasn't still affected by her, but Frances had a new insight into this man she had married, and it brought with it certain doubts. Lord knows, she couldn't afford to start looking beneath his deceptively attractive surface now, not when she had made up her mind to leave him as soon as they reached home again.

For that matter, he had as good as told her he had had enough, which made it all the more puzzling, this meeting with his estranged mother.

"It'll be another hour and a half before we meet for dinner, if you'd like a nap," he offered.

"Hmmmm, I don't know. I think I'll just sit out here and watch the sun splash down, if that's all right."

"Suit yourself. I have some calls to make, so if you'll excuse me . . . ?"

There was a perfectly good telephone in the suite, but Cabel chose to go elsewhere to make his calls, leaving Frances to wonder if he was trying to prepare his mother to meet her. In the end, she did lie down on one of the beds and managed to doze until he roused her to dress for dinner.

It was a little tricky, getting bathed and dressed with the one bedroom and bath between them and Frances bit back a remark about the accommodations. No doubt, Cabel was expecting his mother to visit their rooms sooner or later, and he was only trying to prevent any embarrassing questions.

In spite of a feeling of distaste for it, Frances wore the white jersey again, for her selection of resort wear was limited. She was fastening on her gold earrings when Cabel wandered out into the bedroom, looking unfairly handsome in his white linen, and Frances wondered when, if ever, she could learn to remain unaffected by him.

"Where's your ring?" he demanded, suddenly coming to a halt just behind her.

She stared at his reflection in consternation. This was no time to go into the matter of her engagement ring, not when they were expected downstairs in a matter of minutes. "I . . . it's in my dressing case."

"Why aren't you wearing it?"

There was no escaping the compulsion of his eyes and she found herself mumbling something about the fit, but he ordered her to get the ring.

"Really, Cabel, I think I can manage to select my jewelry without your help," she declared, fumbling with the backs of the nugget-shaped earrings.

"Here, let me do that," he said gruffly, taking the tiny part from her and pushing her head down at an angle.

His touch was electric, especially in the sensitive area just below her ear, and when he secured the backing onto the post and let his fingers trail across her exposed nape, she shuddered involuntarily.

"Why aren't you wearing it, Frances?" he asked gravely.

There was nothing to do but answer him. When she told him that she refused to wear a ring he had initially purchased for another woman, his fingers bit into her shoulders with a force that would leave marks for days to come.

"God! You don't pull your punches, do you?" he demanded fiercely.

"Cabel, you're hurting me!"

"I ought to strangle you!" he threatened, but his grasp eased, all the same. "What the hell gave you the idea that I bought that ring with anyone but you in mind?"

"Well, you might say I got it straight from the horse's mouth!" She attempted a brittleness that would mask the bitterness she felt, but when Cabel turned her to him roughly, glaring down into her face as if he intended to rip the truth from her, no matter what, she told him frankly. "Your...friend, Olivia, said that the two of you considered both the jade and the sapphires you gave her before discarding the jade. I suppose you thought it was a shame to waste it, after she decided she liked the necklace better, but really, Cabel, I'd have been happier with just the band. I'd have been happier with nothing at all, if you want the plain truth!" she finished angrily, as her voice betrayed her by its uneveness.

Pushing an unsteady hand through his hair, Cabel turned away from her, his shoulders lifting and falling as he expelled an exasperated breath. "Oh boy, what timing. We really manage to stage these things beautifully, don't we?" he jeered softly, turning to her with a look she found impossible to interpret. "Look, Frances, if it matters to you, I..."

"But it doesn't!" she interrupted brightly, swallowing against a painful lump that had arisen in her throat. "It doesn't matter at all, so why make a federal case out of it? If you think I look like a poor relation without any more jewelry, then pick me a flower. I'll wear it over my ear! Let's see," she raced on feverishly, turning away to hide the sudden brilliance that shimmered in her eyes, "which is the proper ear for a married woman? But then, that wouldn't do either, would it?"

He exploded. "Frances, shut up! Come here to..."

"Oh, you finally lost an argument to me, didn't you?" she taunted. "Remember what you said about...?"

"I remember what I said, all right," he growled, "only I never said enough! Well, maybe now's the time to set the record straight, Frances McCloud." He reached for her and she evaded him, anger trembling away into something far more dangerous.

"There's no time to argue with you, but there's time enough for this!" he promised, as he captured her by the wrist and swung her into his arms.

No sign of gentleness now, nothing but hard, frustrated anger as he forced her head back and took his fill of her stubbornly closed lips. "Open your mouth, Frances. You'll not deny me this time if you know what's good for you."

"Oh, we're resorting to threats now, are we? Well, you made another threat when you ordered me to come on this trip with you, Cabel and if you think you're going to get away with treating me like... like you would one of your... your women, then you can think again!" His arms were crushing her against him, making her stunningly aware of the masculine force of him, inflaming her against all her resistance, and she could have wept at the weakness of her pitiful defenses.

Magically, his voice poured over her trembling senses, like melted chocolate over gravel, and she became aware of a change in the way he was holding her. "I don't want to treat you like one of my women, Fancey. I want to treat you like my wife," he whispered, while his hands stroked the silken lines of her body. He lowered his mouth to hers again, slowly this time, as his glowing eyes dared her to refuse him.

Her mouth met his like a flower meets the sun, opening and coming to a fullness that was inevitable. The pure mastery of his hold on her was irresistible and she gave in to the demands of her own body, accommodating herself to him as he shaped her closer to his blatant masculine strength.

His fingers were in her hair, her ears, touching her breasts and running sinuously down her flanks to cup under the roundness of her hips. When the phone shrilled against the shimmering emotional tension that held them suspended in time and space, she crumpled against him with a small whimper.

"Oh God," he groaned, holding her away from him with trembling hands. There was a curious vulnerability about him that struck to the core of her as she watched him struggle for control. When he crossed the room to bark into the receiver, she leaned her weight on the dresser, her head falling onto her chest as she willed her heart to behave.

Quit crying for the moon, she pleaded silently. What he offers is not enough and you'd be better off without ever knowing what it is you'll be aching for all the rest of your life. A simple kiss can play havoc enough with your common sense; Lord knows what it would do to you to have him make love to you in the fullest sense!

Katherine McCloud Beal came as a complete surprise. Frances wondered if she even remembered all those names in between, as she touched the heavily veined, perfectly manicured hand that was extended and quickly withdrawn.

They had met in the lobby and gone on to a nearby restaurant instead of stopping in the hotel dining room, and on the short ride, Frances had had plenty of time to study her as she kept up a line of stiff inconsequential chatter with her son.

About fifty-five, Frances concluded, although that would have made her awfully young when her son was born. She looked both older and younger than her probable age, and Frances concluded that it was due to expert cosmetic surgery that gave her face that masklike look, as well as the most expensive salon treatments available. The pale mink she wore despite the balmy weather matched her hair perfectly. And her clothes, even to Frances's relatively unschooled eyes, were definitely top-drawer designer, one-of-a-kind, and they fit her tiny, fragile figure with a kindness that disguised the lack of any feminine curves.

Much later, she learned that Katherine had fought a recurring battle with alcohol that had left her little more than a husk, but a glamorous husk it was, and Frances was more than a little in awe of the woman that first night.

Tony Beal was somewhere in his late forties, she surmised, and addicted to drink, rich food, and probably a few other things. He admitted to having spent the past eight nights at a casino and added facetiously, with an overdone wink at Frances, that he was glad he had been coerced into coming along to meet his new family.

Cabel's distaste for the man was barely disguised, and it increased over the next few hours, as Tony grew more and more familiar with his new daughter-in-law several times removed. It was impossible to judge Katherine's reaction to her husband's philandering, for her jaded eyes, so like Cabel's in color, if in nothing else, seemed to be permanently and bitterly amused at the world in general.

They finished the peppery conch chowder, and the grilled grouper. By the time Frances sampled the tiny sugar bananas Cabel insisted she try while the Beals had still another drink, she was ready to leave. More than ready, for she had met Katherine and that was the main purpose of the trip, and the meeting had left her feeling terribly sorry for both Cabel and his mother. Katherine Beal was one of the most unhappy people she had ever met, and Cabel... well, any unhappiness Cabel had felt at the desertion by his mother had gradually sunk deeply into his innermost self, and was long since covered by layers of urbanity, each a little more polished than the last, all serving to leave him impervious to the hurt a women could inflict on a man.

The compulsive rhythm of drums and electric guitars followed them out into the incredibly soft night air, mingling with other music from other sources. And when Tony offered to show Frances the straw market, the shopping arcade, and the casinos while Cabel and Katherine visited together the next day, she declined quickly, without even waiting for Cabel's opinion.

They said good-night and Cabel invited her to walk along the beach before turning in.

Wary of the witchery of the island, she hesitated. "Perhaps we'd better save it for tomorrow," she stalled.

He took her hand and led her to where a darkfaced Bahamian waited smilingly beside his taxi. "You may be able to sleep after a meal like that, but I'd have nightmares from the chowder alone. The stuff was the color of gunpowder."

Allowing herself to be drawn along, she laughed shakily. "It was pretty well-seasoned, but I enjoyed it. Have you ever had clam chowder at Hatteras? It's got almost as much pepper...they leave out the milk and use mostly clam juice with onions, potatoes, and fried bits of salt pork...and the clams, of course."

They discussed the food, but Frances's mind was not on what they had dined on, and she had a strong idea Cabel was no more interested in the comparative cuisine than she was. His fingers threaded through hers as the driver accepted payment from him and bade them good-night in a melodious Bahamian accent. Frances told herself she was imagining that knowing lilt in his voice.

They didn't mention Katherine at all. They didn't speak until they both stood barefooted at the edge of the surf, with the stored warmth of the sun seeping into their bones like an insidious invitation to stretch out on the soft sands. "Look at me, Frances," Cabel murmured against the whisper of the water.

Compulsively, she obeyed him, tilting her head up so that the fullness of the moon shone on her face. If he had eyes to see, he could read her heart there, for she was beyond dissembling; far beyond anything at this moment. The night, the island, the seductive perfume of exotic flowers—all combined to rob her of any defence against his overwhelming attraction for her, and she stared up at him, willing him to kiss her.

When he didn't move, but continued to search her features for something, some elusive answer she would have given him willingly had she but known what he asked of her, she deliberately broke the spell. "Maybe...maybe we'd better be getting back to the hotel," she whispered in a parody of her usual assured tones.

"Maybe you're right," he agreed huskily, his eyes still moving relentlessly over her hair, her lips, her body. "Yes, let's go now, before I..."

To her acute disappointment, he turned her in the direction they had come and all too soon, with only one yearning, backward glance at the spectacle of moonlight on a tranquil sea, she allowed herself to be ushered into another taxi.

There was a message at the desk that there had been two calls for Mr. McCloud, and Frances wondered sinkingly if perhaps Katherine wanted to see him again tonight.

Don't let it be that, she prayed silently. Don't let him leave me now, not now that the practical, independent Frances has finally surrendered to this island magic. It had been inevitable once they began this trip; she knew that, only it had been hard to accept the fact that, come what may, tonight she was going to become Mrs. Cabel McCloud in fact as well as in name.

With no thought for the ashes of tomorrow she allowed the flame to leap up the moment Cabel closed the door behind them. He touched her cheek...only touched it lightly, but it was enough to set off the conflagration that had been smouldering for so long. His kiss was a tender coercion of her drunken senses, and then it deepened, as if he were setting his brand on her for all time. He lifted his head and smiled at her response, his eyes heavy-lidded and unnaturally dark, and when he led her to the bedroom and began unfastening the hook and eye at the back of her neck, sliding the long zipper down to slip his hands in along her sides, she leaned back against him, tremulously aware of his aroused state.

Somehow, in a slow, sensuous sequence that never seemed quite real, they managed to move to the bed, with her gown falling to the floor, followed by Cabel's white linen suit and blue silk shirt. He drew her down beside him, his eyes lit from within with a passion that licked at her nerves like raw, greedy flames.

"Reach the light, darling," she whispered, captive under the weight of him.

"I want to see you while I'm making love to you. I want to watch those jade-green eyes of yours melt when I touch you...here and here." He followed his words with small kisses, lighting butterfly soft on her body as she trembled helplessly. "Touch me, darling," he groaned, taking her hands and moving them to his chest.

Her fingers tangled in the crisp hair and followed it as it swirled down the flat of his abdomen. He groaned in pleasure. Instinct guided her—pure, wanton instinct born of loving the man until she was well-nigh distraught with it.

"God, how did you learn to please a man like that?" he ground out, his eyes glowing with a metallic hardness as the tendons of his neck held his head away from her. "It kills me to think about it," he groaned.

She was in no fit condition to think, much less talk, but as the meaning of his words gradually seeped into her mind, Frances grew still. Her eyes were enormous troubled pools as reason struggled with pure animal passion. She whispered almost inaudibly, "But I never learned, Cabel...I...I only *know*."

As if the sound of her voice ripped away the last shred of his control, he moved over her, guiding her pliant body to accept him and then his sudden look of shock, her soft cry, like a wounded bird—all were caught up in the maelstrom of irreversible passion. If there was a new gentleness in the way he held her, they were both beyond knowing it, beyond knowing anything but the spinning free-fall through space that left them both half-unconscious in each other's arms.

Hours later, it was the intrusion of the phone that brought her awake. She moved and felt an aching awareness of her body, and beside her Cabel stirred.

"Mmmm, darling?" he murmured, reaching for her, but then came the shrill summons again and he turned with a muffled oath and lifted the receiver.

Frances, her eyes devouring him hungrily, saw the sudden stiffness in his shoulders, and then the shutters that came down over his eyes hid his feelings from her completely. His voice, though, when he spoke roughly into the phone, made her know he was shocked.

"How did you know...No! I can't see you now... Alright, then...yes. Half an hour."

She waited. It was all too new to her and she couldn't break through the barrier he had erected to ask what was wrong, but she willed him to tell her, not to shut her out...not after last night.

"I have to go out," he said tersely, throwing aside the sheet to stride across the floor.

He was naked and the sight of his powerful, beautiful body brought a weakness to the center of her body. "Alone?" she asked tentatively.

"Yes."

While he showered Frances curled up into a defensive ball and tried to hold onto a fragment of the magic of her wedding night, but it was no use. Cabel had closed her out as effectively as if she had been back in her little house on the river, instead of on this bewitching island with him.

She pretended to be asleep when he emerged from the bathroom and whether or not he was convinced, it obviously suited him to go along with the deception. He closed the door softly behind him. She felt herself collapse and realized she had been holding herself in a frozen attitude for so long she could barely move.

The whole time she was soaking in her bath, she was wondering if Katherine had summoned him for some personal reason of her own. Someone *had* to see him...immediately. Could it be Tony? Had marriage number four—or was it five?—dissolved right under their very noses?

There was no point in second-guessing. Cabel was no stranger here in the Bahamas and it could be anyone. He had made several calls earlier, and come to think of it, there were those two calls last night while they were out. Perhaps it was business.

Yes, that was it! It was business and Cabel didn't want to allow business to interfere with their newly established intimacy. She had not imagined the tenderness last night when he had discovered that she wasn't as experienced as she had led him to believe. At the time, there had been no turning back, not for either of them. But in retrospect, she saw again that sudden stunned expression, felt again the almost cradling tenderness that had immediately been swept away on waves of white-hot flames.

She had dressed in a sleeveless green linen and was considering ordering herself something to eat when there came a soft tap on her door. She answered it, opening it to see Katherine Beal standing there in a flawlessly designed steel-gray silk that could have only come from Paris.

"Where's Cabel?" his mother asked, glancing into the suite.

Confused, Frances stood back to allow her to enter. "Why...I thought he might be with you," she said.

"Not since last night, but that's better still." The older woman seemed to have made up her mind about something. She turned to Frances and said, "Frances, I need to talk to you...alone. Can we go somewhere where we won't be disturbed?"

Chapter Ten

There was plenty of time on the long, lonely flight home to dwell on the few hours after she had opened the door to the sad, embittered woman. Katherine had come in and paced like a small, highly strung animal until Frances asked her if she'd care for some coffee.

She had turned about at that, and asked point-blank, "Frances, do you love my son?"

Subterfuge was out of the question. There had been such a world of feeling behind the half-dozen words that Frances could only nod slowly. "Yes. For my sins, I'm afraid I do."

The floodgates were down then. Katherine had not minced words in telling Frances about the almost unbearably happy days of her marriage, when she had been all of eighteen. "Mac...Cabe's father, was almost twenty years older than I was, already well-established. He had just moved into a big house on Park Ridge with all his family's things... My own people had nothing, you understand. There were his offices in the Loop, all his friends and business acquaintances who had known him long before I had."

She broke off to light a cigarette and Frances remained silent, sensing her need to unburden herself.

"I was just too damned young and ignorant to know what was good for me!" she cried in a voice that was stripped of everything but pain. "I loved that man more than anything on earth, more than I did my own child, but I didn't have sense enough to realize it until it was too late."

After the brittle silence had stretched too far, Frances prompted softly, "What happened?"

Blinking as if she had just returned from a long trip back in time, Katherine had spelled out an all too common tale of a busy husband and a bored wife, tied to a home and a child too soon, afraid she was missing out on all the more glamorous things life could offer. "God, what did I care that the wretched china was museum quality, that the family predated the Revolution? Along came a beautiful, fast-talking actor with an eye to the main chance and I ran off without one backward look—all set to live a glamorous life in Beverly Hills!"

Only the glamorous life had never materialized, and poor Katherine had gone from disillusion to disillusion, ending with the present husband who had married her for the money Cabel's father had settled on her when they had been married. It had been skillfully invested and now paid her a more than generous allowance, but it had not brought happiness.

"Frances, all I ask is that you love my son with every beat of your heart. Don't do to him what I did to his father, or I don't think I can stand it." Those tragic eyes, so like Cabel's, had bored into Frances's very soul; even now, she couldn't forget them, nor the careless words a few moments later that had shattered any chance for her own marriage.

"Are you expecting Cabe back soon?" Katherine had asked, stubbing out another cigarette in the overflowing ashtray.

"I really don't know. He got a call and had to go out. Business, I suppose."

"Oh, that would be the Dawson woman," Katherine had said carelessly. "She called me after I got in last night, said Cabe's secretary had given her my phone number. I told her where he was staying. Just like his father; business twenty-four hours a day, seven days a week."

By the time Frances reached Atlanta, things began to take on a grayness that matched her mood. There was little to do but think, for the elderly man beside her slept the whole way, snoring occasionally, then rousing to shuffle his feet, smack his lips, and doze off again.

At Raleigh-Durham, she was faced with a dilemma; they had come in Cabel's car and he had the keys. But she called Helen Aurther who came and fetched her and, after one long, measuring look, began chattering about a grad student, female, who was going to move into Milo's room for the term.

"You're sure you don't want me to come in with you?" Helen pressed on the porch of the small house by the river. "I could call Jerrold and tell him where I am."

"Thanks, Aunt Helen, but it's really not necessary. It's been so long since I've had a minute to relax. I'm going to heat some soup, make a pot of coffee, and sleep until Tuesday morning."

"And Cabel?"

"He'll be along tomorrow night. We went to see his mother, you know, and he decided to stay on for another day." She had thought it all out, the excuses that would prevent any questioning until things were settled and the split was irrevocably made.

After only two days the house had that unused feeling, but of course there had also been the two days she'd stayed at Cabel's house before she left. Shrugging off her coat, she reached for the thermostat and then decided that she needed the psychological boost of a blazing fire tonight. So she put a match to the logs that had been laid in the wood stove over a month before.

Under her beige coat, she was still wearing the green linen dress she had put on first thing this morning...Was it only this morning? Lord, it seemed two lifetimes ago! Funny how a mind refused to stretch over long distances sometimes. In Nassau, Bynum hadn't seemed quite real; and now here in Bynum, Nassau was a figment of her imagination.

But would a figment of her imagination cause such a very real pain in her heart? Would the dull ache in her mind, the persistent refusal to dredge up certain memories result from a figment of her imagination?

Turning her face away from the answer, she put on a pot of coffee and set a pan of canned soup on the wood stove to heat, adding another log to the fat blaze inside the chubby little iron stove before running herself a bath. Outside, the rain drummed down on her tin roof as though it would never end.

Before going to bed, she sat huddled up in her comfortable chair, snug in a long-sleeved, highnecked nightgown of rose-sprigged flannel, and stared at the untouched cup of coffee in her hands. The soup had been inedible, cooked down on the roaring fire to a thick, ambiguous concentrate under a shiny skin that sagged over the top. She put it aside for Tripod.

Must remember to pick her up tomorrow...or the next day. Or the next. She sniffed and hoped she wasn't coming down with a cold. Her unfocused thoughts picked up the homey smell of soup, coffee, and rich pine wood that had replaced the empty-house atmosphere. This was her home, after all. This was the real world, the autumn rain that flailed the stoic pines and cedars and whipped the bare branches of the ailanthus and the redbud. Outside, the red hills were washing down to thicken the river, and the red and yellow leaves that had hung on until now would be plastering her white Aspen tomorrow when the sun came out again. If the sun came out again.

Oh, Lord, I'm getting maudlin! She got up and stirred herself to heat a cup of milk, pouring the coffee down the drain in disgust. One thing she didn't need was another sleepless night, and on the heels of that thought came another: there'd be nobody to keep her awake tonight, at least.

Her bed was a lonely place, which was ridiculous, considering that she had slept alone all her life but for that one night. Finally, the rain on the roof took effect, and she surrendered to an emotional exhaustion that even surpassed her physical tiredness.

The rain had let up to a dispirited drizzle when she opened her eyes to the darkness again. For several minutes she lay there, half-asleep, and wondered what had aroused her. Then it came to her.

"Oh, my Lord, no!" she whispered, sliding her feet out of bed and feeling her way to the door.

The smoke in the living room was thick enough to gag her. She stepped back into her bedroom and slammed the door, stunned with a sense of disbelief. It couldn't be happening. It simply couldn't! Hard on the heels of her discovery, she was galvanized into action by the sound of something falling overhead, and she opened the door and peered out to see the terrifying glow that grew brighter even as she watched. With no thought except to get out, she threw open the window and leaned out. It wasn't more than six feet. The rain beat on her head and in a moment of pure, blind panic, she dashed back across the room and snatched the watercolor off her wall and then grabbed her purse, thinking not of her money, but of the jade ring she had tucked into the handkerchief in one compartment before leaving Nassau.

Once on the ground, she backed off, wide-eyed and dazed, and saw the first flicker of flames lick up her chimney. She turned with a small, inarticulate cry and ran up the hill to the dark house that loomed against the darker trees. She still had the key in her purse, not that she had even thought of that until she actually stood at the door, but she let herself inside with trembling hands and hurried to the phone to summon the fire department.

The firemen had gone, having come too late to do more than watch the roof settle into the foundation. Frances had stood outside and watched, in spite of all the efforts to make her go back inside Cabel's house. Now she waited for Patsy to come and get her. She was wet and her gown flapped disconsolately about her legs, but she wasn't even aware of the fact that she was gray with soot and smoke, that she was shivering with a fine tremor that had as much to do with nerves as with the fact that she had been standing outside in her sodden nightgown for more than an hour. Now she sat alone in the hallway of Cabel's house, unaware of the chill of the rooms, oblivious to anything except relief that Tripod wasn't there when the fire started.

The watercolor she had rescued was propped outdoors in the rain against the walnut tree that had stood halfway between the two houses...only now there was only the one.

Shock absorbed the worst of the pain, leaving only numbness behind it. When she saw the sweep of headlights strike the front door, shattering rainbows as it crossed the beveled edges of the decorative glass panels, she lifted her head and waited patiently. Only the sound of the slamming car door and the feet that pounded up the stairs roused her out of her protective shell of apathy, and she jumped up with a small cry and ran forward to throw herself into Patsy's comforting arms.

Only it wasn't Patsy who stood there, blocking out the gray curtain of rain, filling the doorway and filling her heart to overflowing. Momentum had carried her forward, checking her only when it was too late, and Cabel wrapped her in his arms with a crippling strength, wringing her to him as he repeated her name over and over.

It didn't occur to her to wonder how he knew; she simply let him hold her, let him lift her in his arms and climb the stairs with her to lower her onto his bed and wrap her in a down-filled comforter.

"Cabel," she whispered hoarsely, holding up a grimy wrist to twist it slowly before her bewildered eyes, "I'm dirty. I'm filthy, Cabel. You shouldn't get your nice clean bed all wet and dirty."

"Shut up, precious," he growled, stepping into the hallway long enough to turn on the furnace in the basement. He peeled off the light raincoat he wore and tossed it aside, returning to study her face with grave concern. "I'm going to run you a hot bath and bring you something to drink. Don't move from here until I get back, do you understand?"

She blinked at him from the thick pillow. "You don't need to do that, Cabel. Mama's coming for me. She'll take care of everything." Her voice was small, but very calm and it held an almost dreamlike quality that brought a quick expression of pain to the man's narrowed eyes.

"Stay here," he repeated tersely, disappearing into the large, old-fashioned bathroom with its enormous porcelain and golden oak bathtub. He left the room and she heard his feet take the stairs two at a time. Then she allowed her mind to drift again, unwilling to reach for reality until she had someone to hold onto.

Cabel was back almost immediately with the brandy. He poured her a stiff dose and then watched while she forced it down, not protesting, but choking slightly. He took the glass from her unresisting fingers, then lifted her, and began stripping off the ruined gown. "God, you're like ice!" he muttered, his voice hardly recognizable as he stood her naked on her feet and then swept her up and carried her the few feet to lower her into the steamy water.

"Ouch! That's hot," she wailed, rousing slightly for the first time as something from the outside world impinged on her inner haven.

"Good! It's going to take more than hot water to get you clean again. You look like a chimney sweep!" He soaped the cloth and went to work and suddenly, it was as if her vision cleared and she sat up and snatched the washcloth from his hand.

"Get out of here! You have no business in here while I'm bathing!" she protested angrily, sliding down under the water that was already beginning to look slightly gray.

By the time she had run two tubs of water and scoured herself until her skin was an angry red, she heard sounds coming from the adjoining room that announced Patsy's arrival. She climbed out, wrinkling her nose at the messy ring she was leaving and patted herself dry with one of Cabel's enormous wraparound towels, tucking another over her hair. Then, seeing that there was nothing else to wear, she let herself out of the steamy atmosphere into the comparative chill of the bedroom and there her mother greeted her with a small cry.

"Mama, it's all right," she crooned over and over to the weeping woman. Cabel leaned against the bedroom fireplace, cold and dark, she saw thankfully, and watched as she brought her mother to a state of acceptance. "Look, the house was insured and I certainly didn't have all that much tied up in furnishings. My cat was with Margaret, so I haven't really lost anything that can't be replaced." She forced a small, brittle laugh as Patsy backed away, fumbling for a handkerchief. "Besides, the kitchen was impossible. I'd never have been able to fit a decent cabinet in there. This way I can plan everything the way I want it. After all," she concluded, "the land's still mine."

"Well, all right, Fancey, but I'm sure I don't know how you can take everything so calmly. If it were me, I'd be all to pieces!"

"Don't worry about Fancey, Mrs. Harris," Cabel broke in, moving forward with a purposeful air now. He picked up Patsy's coat and held it for her and she had no choice but to slide her plump arms into the sleeves.

"Oh, but..." she began twisting to cast a questioning look up at Cabel.

"I'll just see you out, Patsy," he told her firmly. "I think Fancey needs an early night...good Lord, it's broad daylight, isn't it?" He left with an arm over the older woman's shoulder, and Frances stared at the door he had closed deliberately behind him. It was as if he had spoken the words aloud: Stay here. I'm not finished with you.

She stayed because there was little else she could do, other than run after Patsy and insist on going with her. She knew her days as her mother's daughter were at an end in that sense. It didn't bear dwelling on, the options still open to her, and she could only wait, her mind drifting off into that self-protective cocoon again, until she heard her husband's firm, relentless tread coming back to her.

Instead of coming to her immediately, he crossed to the walnut highboy—one that must have been in his family for generations, she now realized—and lifted out a navy blue silk pajama shirt that looked as if it had never been worn, which was no less than the truth.

"Put it on," he ordered evenly.

She turned her back and let the towel slip while she eased her arms into the luxurious comfort. Lord knows, there was little need for modesty now, not after he had dumped her into the tub and scrubbed her filthy body. Nevertheless, she buttoned the last button before turning to him again, to wait expectantly for whatever was to come next. Whether it was to be recriminations for running out on him, or explanations for the breakup of their marriage, or simply condolences on the loss of her house, she was prepared to face it. Time and distance had taught her that she could turn away from truths too painful to accept. It didn't cure anything, but it bought time for the healing process to begin.

"Well?" he prompted, throwing her into a state of minor confusion. The ball was in his court, or at least she had tossed it there when she walked out on him, whether he picked it up or not.

"Well?" she echoed numbly. She was seated on the edge of the bed, her shoulders held rigidly and her hands clasped in her lap. Outside, the watery sun was beginning to reveal the devastation of the night, but she didn't look to the window. She kept her eyes focused on the tall, grim-faced man who stood leaning against the mantle, not sparing her with his raking scrutiny.

"All right, I'll go first, but in that case, you're not to speak until I give you permission," he said implacably.

Her chin lifted as some of the sparkle returned to her shadowed eyes. "Now, just a minute, there, McCloud, I..."

"Quiet!"

She subsided, clenching her fingers until her broken nails bit into her palms. Then she lowered her chin again and closed her eyes. He began to speak and then he stopped abruptly.

Her eyes flew open and as she stared at him in consternation, taking in the lined grayness of his face, the stubble on his aggressive jaw, she saw his eyes grow suspiciously bright and with an oath that was torn from him roughly, he crossed to where she sat meekly and gathered her up into his arms.

"Oh, Frances, you don't know what you're doing to me!" he groaned into her damp hair. His hands were biting into her flesh, holding her so closely that she could feel the hardness of his chest, the edge of his rib cage bruising the softness of her tender breasts.

"Cabel," she protested, trying frantically to prevent herself from simply accepting his comforting sympathy as a substitute for what she could never have.

He lifted his head slightly to stare down at her, and she thought wonderingly that from the expression in his eyes, her loss had hurt him even more than it had her. She reached up and traced the deeply chiseled line from his nose to the corner of his mouth with an unsteady finger.

"Cabel?" she whispered. "It's all right. I can rebuild after awhile, or...or even let you buy my land, if you want to clear it off, and I'll relocate somewhere else." She looked at him hopefully, not allowing herself to think of the coming separation. She had grown skilled at separating her feelings from her mind lately, through trying to spare herself unbearable pain.

Space between them widened, allowing the coolness of the morning air to flow between them and he turned away from her, leaning his arms on his thighs as he stared at the faded rug beneath his feet.

Clearing her throat of the miserable lump that seemed to have lodged there permanently, Frances asked, "Is that what you want, Cabel?"

"What I want!" The gray face that turned to stare with a twisted grimace bore little resemblance to the sardonic, sophisticated man she had married. "Shall I tell you what I want then, Frances? Shall I hand you a laugh? You could use one about now." His biting words cut through her sensitivity like a serrated blade. "I *want*...you, Frances. Not to run my household, not to play hostess to some unimportant business connection, but to be a part of my life, a part of *me*...the part that was missing all my life, only I was too damned stupid to know it.'' He continued to stare at her as if expecting her to join him in the joke, but she could no more laugh than she could fly!

Defenses were flung up helter-skelter as she silently warned herself not to walk blindly into another trap.

''Frances? Don't you see the joke? It's funny, girl...it's hilarious. It only started sinking in when I discovered you were gone, but I had plenty of time on the way home to enjoy the fine irony of it.''

He was torturing himself and it was tearing her apart. She laid a hand on his arm and he flinched as if her touch were electric. ''Cabel,'' she insisted, reaching for him again and grasping one of the fists that rested on his taut, muscular thigh. ''Cabel, I don't know what you're getting at exactly, but if it makes it any easier, I want you to know that...that...'' Here came the hard part. ''I love you.''

She might just as well have struck him, for the response she got. He stared at her with dark, glittering eyes, his mouth even harder than before. ''Is this your idea of a punch line? As much as I admire your sense of humor, girl, I...''

''Cabel, damn it, I love you!'' she shouted, shaking his fist in both her hands. ''If you're going to be so pigheaded about it, I'll just...''

She got no further, nor did she know what she would have done if he hadn't flung her back on the bed and made further words impossible. He was kissing her as if kissing were a language that extended beyond the realm of mere words. She discovered that it was just that as his searching, seeking tongue, his hands and his lips and every part of his body told her of an aching need that went far beyond all reason.

Somewhere along the way, his shirt, the black knit that still smelled of the islands and of Cabel, himself, had come off, and the outsized pajama top she wore fell by the wayside as he made love to her with all the tenderness imaginable. When the rest of his clothes followed the shirt, he led her into another world, a world of the senses where he proved himself a knowledgeable guide and she could only cling to him and trust him to bring her back safely to earth.

It was a long, long way down, but eventually they lay satiated in each other's arms. "Fancey?" he whispered, his voice still unsteady as the surging of his heart slowly subsided. "Say it again."

"I love you, Cabel." She was beyond being coy, beyond pretending, even though she was still uncertain just how the miracle had come about.

"Always?"

"And beyond that, darling. Always is too specific for the love I have for you. It spells out limits and there are none."

With his lips traveling along the line of her still damp hair, he began to tell her of his feelings. "I guess you're never so vulnerable as when you think you know it all. I knew all about women when I met you. Knew exactly what I wanted from them and how to get that and nothing more...how to be a real bastard, I suppose."

She was silent, knowing that the basis of his feelings went back a long way.

"When you came along...in a manner that couldn't be overlooked, I might add, I told myself you were a new challenge. At that time, I honestly don't know what I wanted from you. I enjoyed our fights. Like pepper in the chowder," he grinned down at her, touching one of her eyelids with the tip of his tongue. "But then I began to be bored with all the others. Not only that, you imp of the devil, but I found my...ah...prowess as a lover suffering drastically. When the setting was right, the mood, the timing, everything perfect, I'd see your impudent eyes flashing green fire at me and hear your crusty remarks, as if you were standing there in the background passing judgment. I can tell you, you played hell with my love life!"

"Oh, Cabe, I didn't," she gurgled, her imagination filling in the delightfully amusing details. "But you kept on...I mean, Olivia kept on..."

"Hush, darling. I don't want that conniving female to cause us any more trouble, so let me just say that Olivia's...uh...charms had begun to pale shortly after I met you, but I couldn't just drop all my social life and sit up here on the hill while you went prancing out with those Irishmen. In fact, if you want the whole truth, I wasn't above trying to make you jealous," he admitted, "hoping I could make a dent in that cast-iron armor plate you wore."

"Oh, you made a dent all right! I could have crowned you with a king-sized chunk of it more than once," she teased, allowing her fingers to play through the crisp curls on his chest. "Did you actually offer that woman my jade ring before you..."

"Listen, and get this straight! I never offered any woman more than a first-class dinner and a good time. I bought that ring because you told me about your interest in the Orient and because it's the color of your eyes just before you laugh aloud...oh, yes, they change color and I'm well aware of every single shade. Want to know what my favorite is?" He grinned down at her audaciously.

"I'm afraid to ask," she ventured, discovering new delights as she allowed her hands to grow bolder.

"When they begin to grow darker and darker as the pupil swallows up all but a tiny rim of green...the way they're beginning to do right now," he growled, turning over to press her against the mattress. "Shall I make the last bit of green disappear?"

She held off the inevitable with one slender hand as she persisted, "Then you didn't give Olivia that sapphire necklace?"

"Give her...Good Lord, Frances, do I look like that sort of a fool? Olivia sells the stuff. She works at one of the better jewelry stores and no, for your information, my precious little porcupine, I did not buy your ring from Olivia. Now, will you shut up and allow me to get on with the rest of our life?"

* * * * *

Books by Dixie Browning

Silhouette Romance

Unreasonable Summer #12
Tumbled Wall #38
Chance Tomorrow #53
Wren of Paradise #73
East of Today #93
Winter Blossom #113
Renegade Player #142
Island on the Hill #164
Logic of the Heart #172
Loving Rescue #191
A Secret Valentine #203
Practical Dreamer #221
Visible Heart #275
Journey to Quiet Waters #292
The Love Thing #305
First Things Last #323
Something for Herself #381
Reluctant Dreamer #460
A Matter of Timing #527
The Homing Instinct #747

Silhouette Special Edition

Finders Keepers #50
Reach Out to Cherish #110
Just Deserts #181
Time and Tide #205
By Any Other Name #228
The Security Man #314
Belonging #414

Silhouette Desire

Shadow of Yesterday #68
Image of Love #91
The Hawk and the Honey #111
Late Rising Moon #121
Stormwatch #169
The Tender Barbarian #188
Matchmaker's Moon #212
A Bird in Hand #234
In the Palm of Her Hand #264
A Winter Woman #324
There Once Was a Lover #337
Fate Takes a Holiday #403
Along Came Jones #427
Thin Ice #474
Beginner's Luck #517
Ships in the Night #541
Twice in a Blue Moon #588

Silhouette Books

Silhouette Christmas Stories 1987
"Henry the Ninth"